Early Papers on Diffraction of X-rays by Crystals

Early Papers

on

Diffraction of X-rays by Crystals

Edited by

J. M. Bijvoet, W. G. Burgers and G. Hägg

1969

Published for the International Union of Crystallography

by A. Oosthoek's Uitgeversmaatschappij N.V., Utrecht

In January 1965, the Commission on Crystallographic Teaching of the International Union of Crystallography recommended the Union's Executive Committee to: '... *consider the publication of a monograph, or series of monographs, containing reprints of significant early papers in X-ray Crystallography*'. The proposed book was intended '... *not only to serve as a pedagogic aid, but also to make the student aware of the history of his science*'. Because of the breadth of the subject matter, it was clear that more than one volume could easily be filled. It was, therefore, suggested that for an initial step *one* volume only be considered. If this met with success, companion volumes could be undertaken.

During the Seventh General Assembly of the Union in Moscow in July 1966, the Commission reported further, and a short time later Professors J. M. Bijvoet (Netherlands), W. G. Burgers (Netherlands) and G. Hägg (Sweden) agreed to serve as Editors for the book.

The Editors decided to 'condense' the material that would be used, rather than simply reprint the historic papers. The drastic reduction so achieved still corresponded to some 800 pages of print. So it was decided to publish part of the total manuscript first—the present volume—and to print the rest of the manuscript as a second part as soon as the interest shown by crystallographers warranted the taking of a further financial risk.

The Editors further decided to use the authors' own words—and, therefore, also the languages in which the original papers were published—rather than to translate the texts into English. It was suggested that an English translation of the French and German texts should be added, but the consequent increase in price led to a decision not to do so at present.

Many thanks are due to the authors and to the publishers of journals and books who have kindly given the Union permission to reproduce excerpts from the original historic papers. Great efforts on the part of the Union have been taken to try to find the addresses of all the authors (or of their next-of-kin). Unfortunately, it proved to be impossible to find all addresses. Nonetheless, the production of the book has been undertaken because the Editors and the Union felt confident that those authors who could not be reached would have given their consent.

The Union is very much indebted to the Editors, especially to Prof. Bijvoet, for their great efforts in producing this book; the task of firstly selecting the papers to be used and secondly editing or 'condensing' those papers can hardly be overestimated.

For the preparation of the manuscript a contract was signed between Unesco and the Union for a generous grant under the Unesco Pilot Project on the Teaching of Crystallography in relation to the Physics and Chemistry of Solids. The Union wishes to express its gratitude to Unesco for this financial assistance.

The Technische Hogeschool Delft (Netherlands) has also helped with the production of the manuscript, mainly by supplying photo copies of the original papers. These photo copies have been shaped—by the judgement of the Editors, a pair of scissors and glue—into the final manuscript.

June, 1969   THE INTERNATIONAL UNION OF CRYSTALLOGRAPHY

Preface

In preparing this book consisting of parts of early papers on diffraction of X-rays by crystals, we have been guided by the objective proposed by Prof. A. Guinier (France), then Chairman of the Commission on Crystallographic Teaching of the International Union of Crystallography: '*Il ne s'agit pas seulement d'honorer ceux qui ont fait oeuvre original, mais aussi nous voudrions que le livre soit utile pour la formation et la culture des jeunes cristallographes*'. We, therefore, had in mind a book similar to a text book on the fundamentals of X-ray diffraction in the original authors' own words—restricted to the period up to and inclusive of Patterson's (second) paper (1935) on his famous synthesis.

We were of the opinion that a large number of papers, rather than only a few key papers, would serve that purpose best. It was obviously impossible to reproduce a large number of papers in full, and we decided to use excerpts frequently. Sometimes, only a few sentences have been quoted. In particular many specialized mathematical derivations have been omitted. We wish to apologize to the authors for those cases where the included parts of their papers do not reflect the papers' essence. Apart from a few instances, where a lack of continuity was caused, we have not indicated in the text, where material has been omitted. For any critical study it is evidently advisable to consult the original papers.

The sequence of papers selected led to a rather coherent text with little need for introductions or text links. Because of the existence of Ewald's *Fifty Years of X-ray Diffraction* *, in which an unsurpassable account of the early period can be found, we thought it best to confine ourselves to a simple compilation without any commentary. Minor adaptions and additions made by us are placed between square brackets.

The collection is not restricted to papers dealing with ideas which are still valid. Particularly in the very beginning of our science several different points of view were brought forward. Although later abandoned, these remind us of the struggle to reach the understanding which is now so easily taken for granted in the directness of a text book.

Lists of papers to be considered for inclusion reached us, by the initiative

---

* *Fifty Years of X-ray Diffraction* by P. P. Ewald and numerous crystallographers. Published for the International Union of Crystallography by A. Oosthoek's Uitgeversmaatschappij, Utrecht 1962.

of the Commission on Crystallographic Teaching, from several National Committees for Crystallography, a fact which we gratefully acknowledge. The proposed papers often differed widely, both as to period as well as to content, and many of these papers could not therefore be included. On the other hand, we have included many papers not suggested by others. Special thanks are due to Dame Kathleen Lonsdale for valuable suggestions, and to Dr Helen Megaw for her active interest in the project.

We have restricted ourselves, for reasons of lack of space, to the diffraction of X-rays by crystals (thus there is no mention of electron diffraction, and diffraction by gases and liquids). Even within this subject we had to omit several aspects. For instance no spectroscopy has been included; even Moseley's famous paper *The High Frequency Spectra of the Elements* (1913) (on the relation between the frequency of the K-lines and the atomic number) is absent.

This volume, apart from containing the very first papers, deals with the intensity of X-ray diffraction in the kinematical and the dynamical theory. The development of X-ray Crystallography in the 'trial-and-error' period and the (re-)birth of the Fourier method are planned to form a second volume.

The papers are arranged in chapters according to subject. Whilst within each chapter the historical line is obvious, there is also a rough historical order in the sequence of the chapters. In case any reader wishes to get a first introduction to X-ray diffraction from this book, we would suggest he reads, besides pages 1 and 5, the following selection of papers: numbers 1, 9, 11, 15, 16, 17, 22, 24, 25, 26*a*, 27, 28, 32, 34, 35, 38, 40, 43, 47, 50, 51, 52, 56, 60, 63, 64, 70, 75, 76, 82. The major part of these papers was written by W. H. and W. L. Bragg, a fact which will not surprise any crystallographer.

The Editors wish to express their sincere thanks to the General Secretary of our Union, Dr G. Boom, for his keen interest in the book and for his invaluable part in converting the manuscript into publication.

June 1969   J. M. Bijvoet
                                                    W. G. Burgers
                                                    G. Hägg

Contents

CHAPTER V

The f-Factor Continued, Extinction, Anomalous Scattering

THE INTENSITY OF REFLECTION BY ROCK-SALT

CALCULATION OF THE ATOMIC SCATTERING FACTOR

The discovery of X-ray diffraction ranks as one of the epoch-making discoveries in the history of science. It has extended the power of observing minute structure ten thousand times beyond that given us by the microscope. The number and the range of the published papers which deal with the methods and results of the new X-ray analysis are in themselves an indication of its power. Yet its importance is more correctly assessed when it is realised that in almost any investigation dealing with the structure and properties of matter, the findings of X-ray analysis, and of its recent derivative analysis by electron diffraction, are used as a foundation. In physics, chemistry, bio-chemistry, metallurgy, mineralogy and other sciences new points of view have been adopted as a result of this more intimate knowledge of the ultimate structure of matter.

W. H. BRAGG and W. L. BRAGG
Current Sci. 1937, p. 9

1

CHAPTER I

The Discovery of X-ray Diffraction by Crystals

Interpretation

Some of the First Structure Determinations

Um dem Leser ein möglichst anschauliches Bild der Auffindung der Röntgenstrahlinterferenzen zu geben, sei es mir gestattet, die Verhältnisse in München zur Zeit der Laueschen Entdeckung zu skizzieren.

Die Anwesenheit W. C. Röntgens *selbst als Vertreter der Experimentalphysik brachte es mit sich, daß im physikalischen Institut viel über Röntgenstrahlen gearbeitet wurde. Es mögen hier nur die schönen Arbeiten v.* Angerers *über die Energiemessung und die* Baßlers *über die Polarisation der Röntgenstrahlen erwähnt werden. Mich selbst hatten die Röntgenstrahlen, mit denen ich mich schon während meiner Gymnasialzeit beschäftigt hatte, an die Wirkungsstätte ihres Entdeckers gezogen, und ich hatte das Glück, mit einer Arbeit über die azimutale Intensitätsverteilung der Röntgenstrahlen, die gleichfalls als Stütze der Wellentheorie herangezogen wurde, promovieren zu können.*

Als Vertreter der theoretischen Physik wirkte schon damals A. Sommerfeld *als Nachfolger* Boltzmanns *in München, dessen mannigfaltige Arbeiten über die Theorie der Röntgenstrahlen und ihrer Beugung bekannt sind. Gerade in die Zeit vor der Laueschen Entdeckung fallen auch seine Arbeiten über eine Hypothese, die er zur Vervollständigung der Impulstheorie ge-*

macht hatte, daß nämlich der Bremsvorgang des Kathoden-
strahlelektrons durch das Plancksche Wirkungsquantum regu-
liert werden sollte.

Die Optik hatte ihren berufensten Vertreter in M. v. Laue.
Wie er selbst in seiner Nobelvorlesung sagt, bestand bei ihm
die Vorliebe für die Optik, im besonderen die Interferenz-
erscheinungen von Jugend auf, und er bezeichnet es als ein
glückliches Moment, daß er zur Zeit der Entdeckung mit der
Niederschrift des Encyklopädieartikels der mathematischen
Wissenschaften über Wellenoptik beschäftigt war.

Von nicht zu unterschätzender Bedeutung für die Geschichte
der Entdeckung der Röntgenstrahlinterferenzen war fernerhin
die Anwesenheit des Altmeisters der Kristallographie P. v.
Groth. *Die außerordentlich interessanten Vorlesungen* Groths
über den Bau der Kristalle und über Kristalloptik wurden gern
besucht, und in Verbindung mit der Vorliebe Röntgens *für*
Kristalle und Kristallphysik bedingten sie eine eingehende Kennt-
nis dieses Forschungsgebietes bei den Münchener Physikern.

So war denn der Boden für die Lauesche Entdeckung in der
glücklichsten Weise wie wohl nirgends wo anders vorbereitet.

Den äußeren Anlaß zu dem glänzenden, so außerordentlich
fruchtbaren Gedanken Laues, *daß beim Durchgang von Rönt-*
genstrahlen durch Kristalle Interferenzerscheinungen ähnlicher
Art, wie beim Durchgang des Lichtes durch ein Beugungsgitter,
auftreten müssen, bildete die Arbeit P. P. Ewalds *über das*
Verhalten langer elektromagnetischer Wellen in einem Raum-
gitter, die dieser auf Veranlassung Sommerfelds *begonnen*
hatte und später als Doktorarbeit herausgegeben hat. Wie wir
von Laue *wissen, kam er bei einer Besprechung dieses Problems*
mit Ewald *auf den Gedanken, nach dem Verhalten von Wellen*
zu fragen, welche gegen die Gitterkonstanten des Raumgitters
klein sind. Hier sagte ihm sein optisches Gefühl sogleich, um
mit ihm zu sprechen, dann müssen die Gitterspektren auftreten.
Die Größenordnung der Gitterkonstante eines Kristalles von
10^{-8} *cm war aus der Dichte, dem Molekulargewicht und der*
Masse des Wasserstoffatomes bekannt. Die aus den Walter-
und Pohlschen Beugungsversuchen sowie aus den theoretischen
Überlegungen von Wien *und* Sommerfeld *zu erwartende*
Größenordnung der Wellenlänge der Röntgenstrahlen betrug
10^{-9} *cm. Demnach waren die Bedingungen für das Zustande-*
kommen von Interferenzerscheinungen beim Durchgang von
Röntgenstrahlen durch Kristalle außerordentlich günstig, und
Laue *sprach auch sogleich* Ewald *gegenüber seine Vermutung*
aus.

W. FRIEDRICH,
Die Geschichte der Auffindung der
Röntgenstrahlinterferenzen,
Die Naturwiss. **10** (1922) 363

1. INTERFERENZ-ERSCHEINUNGEN BEI RÖNTGENSTRAHLEN

von

W. Friedrich, P. Knipping und M. Laue

Vorgelegt von A. Sommerfeld in der Sitzung am 8. Juni 1912

THEORETISCHER TEIL
von M. Laue

Einleitung

Barklas[1] Untersuchungen in den letzten Jahren haben gezeigt, daß die Röntgenstrahlen in der Materie eine Zerstreuung erfahren, ganz entsprechend der Zerstreuung des Lichtes in trüben Medien, daß sie aber noch daneben im allgemeinen die Atome des Körpers zur Aussendung einer spektral homogenen Eigenstrahlung (Fluoreszenzstrahlung) anregen, welche ausschließlich für den Körper charakteristisch ist.

Andererseits ist schon seit 1850 durch Bravais in die Kristallographie die Theorie eingeführt, daß die Atome in den Kristallen nach Raumgittern angeordnet sind. Wenn die Röntgenstrahlen wirklich in elektromagnetischen Wellen bestehen, so war zu vermuten, daß die Raumgitterstruktur bei einer Anregung der Atome zu freien oder erzwungenen Schwingungen zu Interferenzerscheinungen Anlaß gibt; und zwar zu Interferenzerscheinungen derselben Natur wie die in der Optik bekannten Gitterspektren. Die Konstanten dieser Gitter lassen sich aus dem Molekulargewicht der kristallisierten Verbindung, ihrer Dichte und der Zahl der Moleküle pro Grammolekül, sowie den kristallographischen Daten leicht berechnen. Man findet für sie stets die Größenordnung 10^{-8} cm, während die Wellenlänge der Röntgenstrahlen nach den Beugungsversuchen von Walter und Pohl[2] und nach den Arbeiten von Sommerfeld und Koch[3] von der Größenordnung 10^{-9} cm sind. Eine erhebliche Komplikation freilich bedeutet es, daß bei den Raumgittern eine dreifache Periodizität vorliegt, während man

---

[1] C. G. Barkla, *Phil. Mag.*, z.B. **22** (1911) 396.
[2] B. Walter und R. Pohl, *Ann. d. Phys.* **25** (1908) 715; **29** (1908) 331.
[3] A. Sommerfeld, *Ann. d. Phys.* **38** (1912) 473; P. P. Koch, *Ann. d. Phys.* **38** (1912) 507.

7

bei den optischen Gittern nur in einer Richtung, höchstens (bei den Kreuz-
gittern) in zwei Richtungen periodische Wiederholungen hat.

Die Herren Friedrich und Knipping haben auf meine Anregung diese
Vermutung experimentell geprüft. Über die Versuche und ihr Ergebnis
berichten sie selbst im zweiten Teil der Veröffentlichung.

Die Theorie und ihr qualitativer Vergleich mit der Erfahrung

Wir wollen den oben angedeuteten Gedanken mathematisch zu fassen
suchen. Den Ort der Mittelpunkte der Atome bestimmen wir durch die
rechtwinkligen Koordinaten x, y, z, deren Achsenkreuz seinen Ursprung
im Mittelpunkt eines beliebigen Atoms im durchstrahlten Teil des Kristalles hat. Das Raumgitter gehöre dem allgemeinsten, d.h. dem triklinen
Typus an; die Kanten seiner Elementarparallelepipede mögen also beliebige Längen haben und beliebige Winkel miteinander einschließen. Durch
spezielle Wahl dieser Längen und Winkel kann man immer zu Raumgittern
anderer Typen übergehen. Stellen wir diese Kanten nach Länge und Rich-
tung durch die Vektoren $\mathfrak{a}_1$, $\mathfrak{a}_2$, $\mathfrak{a}_3$ dar, so liegen die Mittelpunkte eines
Atoms an einem Ort

$$x = m\mathfrak{a}_{1x} + n\mathfrak{a}_{2x} + p\mathfrak{a}_{3x}$$
$$y = m\mathfrak{a}_{1y} + n\mathfrak{a}_{2y} + p\mathfrak{a}_{3y} \tag{1}$$
$$z = m\mathfrak{a}_{1z} + n\mathfrak{a}_{2z} + p\mathfrak{a}_{3z},$$

wobei m, n, p positive oder negative, das Atom numerierende ganze Zahlen
(einschließlich der Null) sind.

Für die Schwingung eines einzelnen Atoms wollen wir zunächst einmal
die Annahme machen, daß sie rein sinusförmig verläuft. Dies kann hier
natürlich ebensowenig wie in der Optik streng richtig sein. Aber ebenso wie
in der Optik kann man spektral inhomogene Strahlung durch Fouriersche
Zerlegung auf Sinusschwingungen zurückführen. Die von einem Atom ausgehende Welle können wir dann in großer Entfernung vom Atom darstellen
durch den Ausdruck

$$\Psi \frac{e^{-ikr}}{r}, \tag{2}$$

wo r den Betrag des Radiusvektors vom Atom zum Aufpunkt bedeutet,
Ψ eine Funktion seiner Richtung und $k = 2\pi/\lambda$ ist, wo λ die Wellenlänge
der später interferierenden Röntgenstrahlen darstellt. Wäre, wie man es in
der Optik gewohnt ist, das Atom klein gegen die Wellenlänge, so wäre Ψ

eine Konstante[1]. Hier aber muß man mit der Möglichkeit rechnen, und die Versuchsergebnisse legen die Vermutung nahe, daß infolge der mit der Wellenlänge vergleichbaren Abmessung des Atoms Richtungsunterschiede auftreten. Berücksichtigt man ferner noch, daß die anregende Schwingung in (als eben vorausgesetzten) Wellen mit Lichtgeschwindigkeit fortschreitet, so sieht man, daß man noch den Faktor $\exp\{-ik(x\alpha_0 + y\beta_0 + z\gamma_0)\}$ hinzufügen muß, wenn $\alpha_0, \beta_0, \gamma_0$ die Richtungskosinus der einfallenden primären Röntgenstrahlen sind. Über Einzelheiten des Anregungsvorganges brauchen wir dabei keine weitere Voraussetzung zu machen, als daß er bei allen Atomen gleich erfolgt. Insbesondere ist es für den weiteren Verlauf des Vorganges vollkommen dasselbe, ob die Schwingungen im Atom durch Schwingungen gleicher Frequenz in der primären Strahlung erzwungen oder ob es durch die primäre Strahlung einmal angeregte, sonst aber freie Eigenschwingungen sind. Stets finden wir als Superpositionseffekt aller Elementarwellen

$$\sum \Psi \frac{e^{-ik(r+x\alpha_0+y\beta_0+z\gamma_0)}}{r}. \tag{3}$$

Wir berechnen diese Summe nur für Aufpunkte, deren Abstand sehr groß ist gegen die Abmessungen des durchleuchteten Kristallstücks, und benutzen die auch sonst in der Gittertheorie übliche Näherung, d.h. wir setzen für das r im Nenner den Betrag R des Radiusvektors vom Nullpunkt des Achsenkreuzes zum Aufpunkt und geben der Richtungsfunktion Ψ den Wert, welcher dessen Richtung (α, β, γ) entspricht. Für das r im Exponenten setzen wir aber den Näherungswert:

$$r = R - (x\alpha + y\beta + z\gamma).$$

Unter Berücksichtigung von (1) geht somit die Summe (3) über in:

$$\Psi(\alpha, \beta) \frac{e^{-ikR}}{R} \sum e^{ik[x(\alpha-\alpha_0)+y(\beta-\beta_0)+z(\gamma-\gamma_0)]}$$
$$= \Psi(\alpha, \beta) \frac{e^{-ikR}}{R} \sum m \sum n \sum p\, e^{i(mA+nB+pC)}, \tag{4}$$

---

[1] Vgl. H. v. Helmholtz, *Abh. I*, p. 331.

Gehen von beliebig vielen, in einem endlichen Bereich liegenden Strahlungsquellen Kugelwellen aus, so ist die Erregung in einem Punkte, für welchen der Radiusvektor vom Mittelpunkte des Bereiches den gegen dessen Abmessungen großen Betrag r und die Richtungskosinus α, β, γ hat:

$$\sum_n \frac{e^{-i(kr_n-\theta_n)}}{r_n} = \frac{e^{-ikr}}{r} \sum_n e^{ik(x_n\alpha+y_n\beta+z_n\gamma)+i\theta_n}$$

Diese Summe ist im allgemeinen einen Funktion von α and β. Sind aber alle x_n, y_n, z_n klein gegen λ, so wird sie konstant.

wo zur Abkürzung

$$A = k[\mathfrak{a}_{1x}(\alpha - \alpha_0) + \mathfrak{a}_{1y}(\beta - \beta_0) + \mathfrak{a}_{1z}(\gamma - \gamma_0)]$$

$$B = k[\mathfrak{a}_{2x}(\alpha - \alpha_0) + \mathfrak{a}_{2y}(\beta - \beta_0) + \mathfrak{a}_{2z}(\gamma - \gamma_0)] \tag{5}$$

$$C = k[\mathfrak{a}_{3x}(\alpha - \alpha_0) + \mathfrak{a}_{3y}(\beta - \beta_0) + \mathfrak{a}_{3z}(\gamma - \gamma_0)]$$

gezetzt ist. Denken wir uns den durchstrahlten Teil von Ebenen begrenzt, welche zu den Seiten eines Elementarparallelepipedes parallel sind, so ist die Summation nach m von einer Zahl $- M$ bis zu $+ M$, nach n von $- N$ bis $+ N$, nach p von $- P$ bis $+ P$ auszuführen. Die Lage der Intensitäts-maxima ist von derartigen Annahmen nicht abhängig[1]. Die Intensität der Schwingung (4) wird dann:

$$\frac{|\Psi(\alpha, \beta)|^2}{R^2} \; \frac{\sin^2 M A}{\sin^2 \frac{1}{2}A} \; \frac{\sin^2 N B}{\sin^2 \frac{1}{2}B} \; \frac{\sin^2 P C}{\sin^2 \frac{1}{2}C} . \tag{6}$$

Jeder dieser Sinusquotienten erreicht sein Maximum bekanntlich, wenn sein Nenner verschwindet. Die Bedingungen für die Maxima lauten also:

$$A = 2h_1\pi \text{ d.h. } \mathfrak{a}_{1x}\alpha + \mathfrak{a}_{2y}\beta + \mathfrak{a}_{1z}\gamma = h_1\lambda + \mathfrak{a}_{1x}\alpha_0 + \mathfrak{a}_{1y}\beta_0 + \mathfrak{a}_{1z}\gamma_0$$

$$B = 2h_2\pi \;\; ,, \;\; \mathfrak{a}_{2x}\alpha + \mathfrak{a}_{2y}\beta + \mathfrak{a}_{2z}\gamma = h_2\lambda + \mathfrak{a}_{2x}\alpha_0 + \mathfrak{a}_{2y}\beta_0 + \mathfrak{a}_{1z}\gamma_0 \tag{7}$$

$$C = 2h_3\pi \;\; ,, \;\; \mathfrak{a}_{3x}\alpha + \mathfrak{a}_{3y}\beta + \mathfrak{a}_{3z}\gamma = h_3\lambda + \mathfrak{a}_{3x}\alpha_0 + \mathfrak{a}_{3y}\beta_0 + \mathfrak{a}_{1z}\gamma_0.$$

Die links stehenden Summen sind gleich der Länge je einer Kante multipliziert mit dem Kosinus des Winkels zwischen ihr und der Richtung α, β, γ. Jede der Gleichungen (7) stellt somit eine Schar von Kreiskegeln dar, deren Achse mit der Richtung einer der Kanten $\mathfrak{a}_1, \mathfrak{a}_2, \mathfrak{a}_3$ zusammenfällt[2]. Nun wird es freilich nur in Ausnahmefällen vorkommen, daß eine Richtung allen drei Bedingungen gleichzeitig genügt. Darin liegt die Komplikation gegenüber dem einfachen oder dem Kreuzgitter. Dennoch ist ein sichtbares Intensitätsmaximum zu erwarten, wenn die Schnittlinie zweier Kegel der ersten beiden Scharen einem Kegel der dritten Schar nahe liegt. Wir wollen diese Verhältnisse etwas näher betrachten für den in Fig. 5, Tafel II abgebildeten Fall, in welchem ein regulärer Kristall in Richtung einer der Kanten $\mathfrak{a}_1, \mathfrak{a}_2, \mathfrak{a}_3$ durchstrahlt wird.

---

[1] Damit stimmt die Beobachtung überein. S. [this Vol. p. 18, last paragraph].

[2] Man macht sich, wie in der Gittertheorie, leicht an der elementaren geometrischen Konstruktion des Gangunterschiedes zwischen zwei parallelen, von benachbarten Teilchen ausgehenden Strahlen klar, daß dieser Gangunterschied auf den genannten Kegeln konstant ist.

In diesem Falle erhalten die drei Kanten die gleiche Länge a und stehen senkrecht aufeinander, so daß wir in ihre Richtungen die Koordinatenachsen legen können. Da dann

$$a_{1y} = a_{1z} = a_{2x} = a_{2z} = a_{3x} = a_{3y} = 0, \quad a_{1x} = a_{2y} = a_{3z} = a,$$

ferner

$$\alpha_0 = 0, \quad \beta_0 = 0, \quad \gamma_0 = 1$$

wird, so gehen die Gleichungen (7) über in:

$$\alpha = h_1 \lambda/a, \quad \beta = h_2 \lambda/a, \quad 1 - \gamma = h_3 \lambda/a. \tag{8}$$

Auf einer zum einfallenden Strahl senkrechten photographischen Platte sind die Kurven α = const. und β = const. Hyperbeln, deren Mittelpunkt im Durchstoßpunkt des primären Strahles liegt und deren Achsen aufeinander senkrecht stehen. Wären nur die beiden ersten Bedingungen in (8) zu erfüllen, so sähe man das bekannte Kreuzgitterspektrum, bei dem an jedem Schnittpunkte zweier Hyperbeln ein Intensitätsmaximum liegt. So aber wählen die Kreise γ = const., deren Mittelpunkt ebenfalls im Durchstoßpunkt des primären Strahles liegt, aus diesen Kreuzgitterspektren diejenigen aus, welche einem von ihnen hinreichend nahe liegen, d.h. man wird auf der Platte diese Kreise nicht ganz, sondern nur in einzelnen Punkten vertreten sehen. Dies ist aber in der Tat der Eindruck, welchen die Figur macht. Die Kreise

$$1 - \gamma = h_3 \lambda/a, \tag{9}$$

welche der Periodizität in der Strahlrichtung ihre Entstehung verdanken, haben in der Optik ein schon seit Newton bekanntes Analogon in den sogenannten Queteletschen Ringen[1]; diese treten bei Bestäubung einer ebenen, auf der Rückseite stark reflektierenden Glasplatte im Fraunhoferschen Beugungsbild auf. Es interferieren nämlich die von einem und demselben Staubteilchen aus dem einfallenden und aus dem gespiegelten Licht abgebeugten Wellen miteinander. Bei senkrechter Incidenz liegen die Maxima auf den durch Gleichung (9) angegebenen Kreisen, sind aber viel flacher als in unserem Falle, weil nur zwei Wellen interferieren. Ließen sich die Staubteilchen zum regelmäßigen Kreuzgitter anordnen, so ließe sich die Analogie zu den obigen Interferenzen an Kristallen zweifellos noch weiter treiben.

Es muß beachtet werden, daß bei gegebenem Raumgitter die Einteilung in Elementarparallelepipede keine eindeutige ist, sondern auf unendlich viele Arten vorgenommen werden kann. Beim regulären Raumgitter z.B. kann man statt in Würfel in solche Parallelepipede zerlegen, deren eine Seite die

[1] Vgl. z.B. A. Winkelmann, *Handbuch der Physik* VI, Leipzig 1906, p. 1083.

Diagonale einer Würfelfläche ist und somit die Richtung einer zweizähligen Symmetrieachse hat. Die Intensitätsmaxima müssen sich nach dem obigen auch zu durchbrochenen Kegelschnitten um solche Achsen zusammenfassen lassen, wie überhaupt zu jeder derartigen Einteilung eine Art, die Maxima zusammenzufassen, gehört. Auch in den komplizierteren Figuren hat man stets den Eindruck, daß sich die Intensitätsmaxima zu durchbrochenen Kegelschnitten verbinden lassen. Soviel bisher zu sehen ist, läßt sich die Theorie unter der Annahme mehrerer Wellenlängen von $0,038a$ bis $0,15a$ gut der vierzählig symmetrischen Aufnahme (Fig. 5, Tafel II) anpassen. Da a für Zinksulfid gleich $3,38.10^{-8}$ cm ist, würden sich daraus die Wellenlängen in dem Intervall von $1,3.10^{-9}$ bis $5,2.10^{-9}$ cm ergeben.

Trotz dieser Übereinstimmung darf nicht verschwiegen werden, daß unsere Theorie auf jeden Fall weitgehender Verbesserung bedarf. Die Wärmebewegung bei den Molekülen verrückt diese nämlich schon bei Zimmertemperatur um einen erheblichen Bruchteil der Gitterkonstanten und infolgedessen um ein Vielfaches der Wellenlänge, ein Umstand, der durchaus der Berücksichtigung bedarf. Deshalb wäre es auch voreilig, wenn man aus dem Ausdruck (6) Schlüsse auf die Schärfe der Interferenzmaxima schließen wollte.

Daß von allen bisher untersuchten Kristallen mit Ausnahme des Diamants die Intensitätsmaxima auf einen spitzen Winkel gegen die Richtung des primären Strahles beschränkt sind, statt nach allen Richtungen auszugehen, wie man zunächst nach Gleichung (6) erwarten könnte, wird man wohl auf die Richtungsfunktion Ψ zurückführen müssen; doch ist es auch denkbar, daß die Wärmebewegung zur Erklärung herangezogen werden muß.

Allgemeine Folgerungen

Diskutieren wir zum Schluß noch ohne allen Bezug auf die Formel die Frage, inwiefern diese Versuche für die Wellennatur der Röntgenstrahlen sprechen.

Daß die vom Kristall ausgehende Strahlung Wellencharakter trägt, ist wohl durch die Schärfe der Intensitätsmaxima bewiesen, welche als Interferenzphänomen leicht, auf Grund korpuskularer Vorstellungen aber wohl kaum verständlich ist; daneben auch durch ihre große Durchdringungsfähigkeit, welche von allen bekannten Korpuskularstrahlen nur die schnellsten β-Strahlen erreichen. Dennoch könnte man aber vielleicht die Wellennatur der primären Strahlen bezweifeln. Denken wir nun einmal, die Atome des Kristalls würden im Fall von Fig. 5, Tafel II durch eine Korpuskularstrahlung angeregt. (Die von manchen Forschern angenommene Lichtquantenstruktur der Röntgenstrahlen kann hier unter der Bezeichnung korpuskulare Strahlung mit einbegriffen werden.) Zu kohärenten Schwingungen könnten dabei nur solche Reihen von Atomen kommen, welche von demselben Korpuskel getroffen werden, d.h. Reihen, welche zur z-Richtung parallel sind. Atome, welche in der x- oder y-Richtung einen gewissen Abstand voneinander haben, würden von verschiedenen Korpuskeln angeregt; eine bestimmte Phasendifferenz zwischen ihren Schwingungen könnte nicht auftreten. Infolgedessen würde von dem Intensitätsausdruck (6) nur ein Sinusquotient übrig bleiben; wir erhielten nur eine Bedingung für ein Intensitätsmaximum und diese wäre, wie schon aus Symmetriegründen einleuchtet, auf Kreisen um den Durchstoßpunkt des primären Strahles erfüllt. Die Durchbrechung dieser Kreise, die doch tatsächlich auftritt, wäre danach unverständlich. Zudem aber sind die primären und die vom Kristall ausgehenden Strahlen allem Anschein nach so gleichartig, daß man von der Wellennatur der letzteren wohl ziemlich sicher auf die Wellennatur der ersteren schließen kann. Ein Unterschied freilich bleibt bestehen: Die vom Kristalle ausgehende Strahlung hat sicher eine erhebliche spektrale Homogenität, d.h. eine gewisse Periodizität. Die primäre Strahlung hingegen wird man nach Sommerfelds Vorstellungen wohl, soweit sie 'Bremsstrahlung' ist, als aus durchaus unperiodischen Impulswellen bestehend annehmen müssen; die im folgenden mitgeteilten Versuche sind jedenfalls mit dieser Annahme verträglich. Unentschieden bleibe vorläufig, ob die periodische Strahlung erst im Kristall durch Fluoreszenz entsteht oder ob sie neben den Impulsen schon in der primären Strahlung vorhanden ist und durch den Kristall nur ausgesondert wird[1]. Doch scheint uns durch den Kristall nur Hoffnung zu bestehen, daß weitere Versuche bald darüber Aufschluß geben werden.

EXPERIMENTELLER TEIL

von W. Friedrich und P. Knipping

Zur experimentellen Prüfung der im vorhergehenden Teil beschriebenen Überlegungen wurde nach einigen Vorversuchen mit einem provisorischen Apparat folgende definitive Versuchsanordnung verwandt, die in Fig. 1 schematisch abgebildet ist. Von den von der Antikathode A einer Röntgenröhre ausgehenden Röntgenstrahlen wird ein schmales Bündel von ca. 1 mm Durchmesser durch die Blenden B_1 bis B_4 ausgeblendet. Dieses Bündel

---

[1] Vgl. auch [this Vol. p. 21].

durchsetzt den Kristall *Kr*, der in einem Goniometer *G* aufgestellt ist. Um den Kristall waren in verschiedenen Richtungen und Abständen photographische Platten *P* angebracht, auf denen sich die Intensitätsverteilung der vom Kristall ausgehenden Sekundärstrahlen registrierte. Gegen nicht gewollte Strahlen war die Anordnung durch einen großen Bleischirm *S* sowie durch den Bleikasten *K* in genügender Weise geschützt. Die Größe der wichtigen Teile der Versuchsanordnung lassen sich aus der Fig. 1 entnehmen, die im Maßstab 1 : 10 gezeichnet ist.

Die Einstellung der gesamten Versuchsanordnung wurde auf optischem Wege bewerkstelligt. Ein Kathetometer, dessen Fernrohr mit einem Fadenkreuz versehen war, hatten wir ein für allemal unverrückbar aufgestellt. Der Reihe nach wurden Brennfleck der Antikathode, Blenden und Goniometerachse in die optische Achse des Fernrohrs gebracht. Auf diese Weise konnten wir die recht umständliche Einstellung mit Röntgenstrahlen durch die viel bequemere optische ersetzen. Kontrollversuche mit Röntgenstrahlen selbst erwiesen auch, daß diese Justierung auf optischem Wege völlig ausreichend war. Die Blenden B_1 bis B_3 schirmten hauptsächlich die Sekundärstrahlen der Röhrenwände ab, während die eigentliche Begrenzung für das auf den Kristall auffallende Röntgenstrahlenbündel die Blende B_4 bildete. Diese hatte gewöhnlich 0,75 mm Durchmesser, war in eine 10 mm dicke Bleischeibe gebohrt und konnte vermittelst dreier Stellschrauben (nicht gezeichnet) so justiert werden, daß die Achse des Loches genau mit der Fernrohrachse resp. Achse des Strahlenbündels zusammenfiel. Hierdurch wurde erreicht, daß ein Strahlenbündel von kreisrundem Querschnitt auf den Kristall fiel; ferner wurde hierdurch das Maß der von der Wand jener Blende B_4 ausgehenden Sekundärstrahlen auf ein Minimum reduziert, was nötig war, um den Plattenschleier möglichst zu unterdrücken. Um diese Einstellung auch während der Aufnahme kontrollieren zu können, photographierten wir das Primärbündel, nachdem es den Schutzkasten durch ein langes Ansatzrohr *R* verlassen hatte, zu welchem Zwecke eine eigene Kassette am Ende dieses Rohres angebracht war (nicht mitgezeichnet). Das Rohr *R* diente sonst dazu, die Sekundärstrahlen, die bei dem Auftreffen der Primärstrahlen auf die hintere Kastenwand entstehen würden, möglichst zu vermeiden.

Nach diesen Justierungen, deren Güte wir vor jeder Aufnahme kontrollierten, wurde die Goniometerachse auf dem üblichen Wege senkrecht zum Strahlengang gerichtet. In gleicher Weise waren die verschiedenen Plattenhalter so justiert, daß die Primärstrahlen die aufgestellten Films resp. Platten senkrecht durchsetzten resp. parallel zu ihnen verliefen. Wenn der Apparat soweit orientiert war, wurde der zu bestrahlende Kristall, der mit einer Spur Klebwachs am Goniometertisch befestigt war, eingestellt und zwar wieder

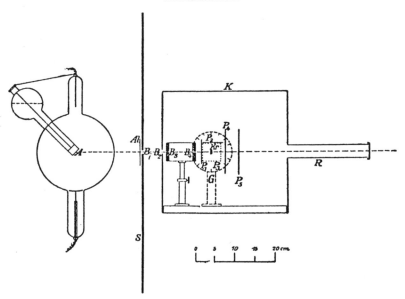

Fig. 1.

Abstand Antikathode-Kristall. . . . . 350 mm
„ Kristall-P_1 resp. P_2 resp. P_3 . 25 „
„ Kristall-P_4 . . . . 35 „
„ Kristall-P_5 . . . . 70 „

mit Hilfe des schon genannten Fernrohres in der bekannten Weise unter Benutzung eines 'Signales'. Diese—wie sich später zeigen wird—sehr wesentliche Justierung konnte von uns bis auf eine Minute genau vorgenommen werden. Als Aufnahmematerial benutzten wir, nachdem wir einige andere Sorten als nicht so geeignet befunden hatten, Schleußner-Röntgen-Films, die mit Jodinal (1 : 15) entwickelt die besten Resultate lieferten.

Die Überschlagsrechnungen nach den bisherigen Erfahrungen über Sekundärstrahlen zeigten, daß recht beträchtliche Expositionszeiten notwendig waren. Die Belichtungszeiten bewegten sich bei 2–10 Milli-Ampère Belastung (je nach der 6–12 Wehnelt betragenden Härte der Röhre)[1] zwischen 1–20 Stunden. Als Röntgenröhren kamen teils Intensivröhren von Gundelach, teils Rapidröhren mit Wasserkühlung von Müller zur Verwendung, die von einem 50 cm Klingelfuß-Induktor betrieben wurden. Als Unterbrecher gelangten teils ein Wehnelt-, teils ein mechanischer Unterbrecher zur Verwendung. Vor die Röntgenröhre wurden passende Ventilröhren zur

---

[1] Zwei Härtemesser waren uns in dankenswerter Weise von der Firma Reiniger, Gebbert & Schall zur Verfügung gestellt.

Vermeidung von Schließungslicht geschaltet. Es wurde mit Pausen exponiert, um die Röhre nicht allzusehr zu erhitzen. Für die bisher ausgeführten Versuche erwies sich eine Härte von 8–10 Wehnelt als geeignet.

Vorversuche mit dem provisorischen Apparat[1]

Da wir anfangs glaubten, es mit einer Fluoreszenzstrahlung zu tun zu haben, mußte ein Kristall verwendet werden, der Metall von beträchtlichem Atomgewicht als Bestandteil enthielt, um möglichst intensive und zugleich homogene Sekundärstrahlen zu erhalten, die für die Versuche am geeignetsten zu sein schienen. Nach Barkla kamen in erster Linie die Metalle vom Atomgewicht 50–100 in Betracht. Da wir vorderhand keinen guten Kristall, der derartige Metalle enthielt, zur Verfügung hatten, benutzten wir zu den Vorversuchen einen leidlich ausgebildeten Kupfervitriolkristall. Dieser wurde ziemlich willkürlich in den Apparat eingesetzt, und zwar fielen die Röntgenstrahlen ungefähr senkrecht auf eine Pinakoidfläche 3. Art (110) auf. Im Abstand von 40 mm von ihm waren zwei photographische Platten—entsprechend P_2 und P_4 in Fig. 1—aufgestellt. Nach der Exposition war die obere Platte schwach, aber gleichmäßig geschwärzt, P_4 wies außer dem Durchstoßungspunkt der Primärstrahlen eine Reihe von anscheinend geordneten Flecken auf (siehe Tafel I, Fig. 1).

Um sicher zu sein, daß diese Flecken durch die Kristallstruktur des Kupfervitriols bedingt waren, wurden Kupfervitriolkristalle grob pulverisiert, in ein kleines Papierschächtelchen eingeschlossen und der vorhergehende Versuch bei sonst gleichen Bedingungen wiederholt. Die Platte P_2 zeigte keine Änderung, dagegen waren die großen geordneten Flecken auf P_4 verschwunden; statt dessen erschien der Durchstoßungsfleck mit einem Saum von vielen kleinen, unregelmäßig angeordneten Pünktchen umgeben. Die Vermutung, daß bei ganz fein pulverisiertem Material der Rest der Flecken verschwinden würde, fand seine Bestätigung durch den nächsten Versuch. Ein weiterer Versuch mit herausgenommenem Kristall bei sonst identischen Bedingungen zeigte, wie wohl zu erwarten war, daß die Platten bis auf den Durchstoßungspunkt der Primärstrahlen ungeschwärzt blieben.

Es folgten noch zwei Aufnahmen mit dem zuerst genannten Kupfervitriolkristall. Bei der einen wurde bei gleicher Orientierung der Kristall parallel zu sich verschoben, so daß eine andere Stelle des Kristalles durchstrahlt wurde; bei der zweiten der Kristall um einige Grade gegen die Röhre ge-

---

[1] Dieser war im Prinzip wie der spätere, nur einfacher gehalten und ohne genaue Einstellungsmöglichkeit. Die Blendöffnungen betrugen hierbei 3 mm.

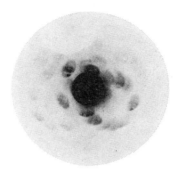

Fig. 1.

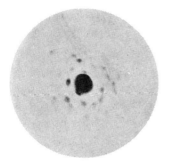

Fig. 3.

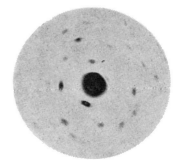

Fig. 4.

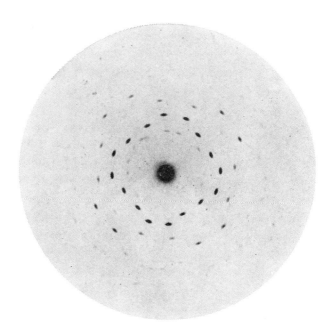

Fig. 5.

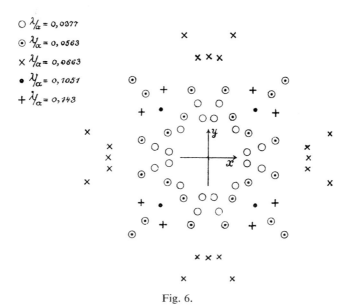

○ $\lambda/_\alpha = 0,0377$
⊙ $\lambda/_\alpha = 0,0563$
× $\lambda/_\alpha = 0,0663$
● $\lambda/_\alpha = 0,1051$
+ $\lambda/_\alpha = 0,143$

Fig. 6.

Tafel III

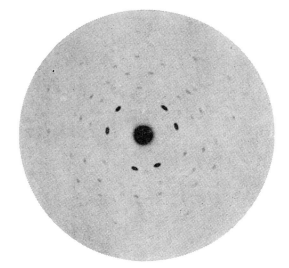

Fig. 7.

Tafel V

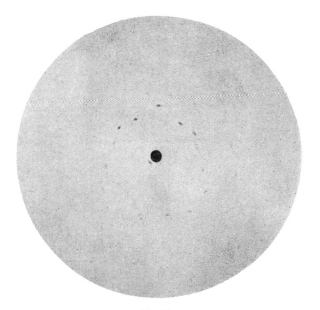

Fig. 11.

neigt. Jene Aufnahme ist identisch mit Fig. 1, Tafel I, die Erscheinung ist unabhängig vom Ort der Durchstrahlung. Die andere Aufnahme zeigt, daß die Lage der sekundären Flecken von der Orientierung des Kristalles gegen die Einfallrichtung der Primärstrahlen abhängig ist.

Da die eben beschriebenen Versuche erwiesen hatten, daß die obigen Überlegungen experimentell verifizierbar sind, ließen wir den vorhin beschriebenen besseren Apparat bauen, stellten aber inzwischen weitere Versuche mit Zinkblende, Steinsalz und Bleiglanz (Spaltstücke) an. Diese ergaben ganz ähnliche Resultate wie bei Kupfervitriol. Wir werden jedoch von einer Beschreibung derselben Abstand nehmen, weil, wie sich zeigen wird, eine genaue Orientierung der Kristalle notwendig war, um einen tieferen Einblick in die Erscheinungen zu gewinnen.

Versuche mit genauer Orientierung des Kristalles zur Richtung der Primärstrahlen

Mit dem definitiven Apparat wurde zunächst die auf Fig. 1, Tafel I abgebildete Aufnahme wiederholt, und zwar wurden sämtliche in Fig. 1 angegebenen Platten aufgestellt[1]. Die Orientierung des Kupfervitrioles war möglichst dieselbe wie vorher. P_2 und P_3 zeigten gleichmäßige Schwärzung; P_1 wies bloß den Durchstoßungspunkt der Primärstrahlen auf. Auf P_4 und P_5 war eine ähnliche Figur wie bei Aufnahme 1 zu sehen; indessen waren jetzt entsprechend der kleineren Blendenöffnung die sekundären Flecken zusammengeschrumpft (siehe Tafel I, Fig. 3 und 4). Bemerkenswert ist, daß sich die Abstände (Kristall–P_4) zu (Kristall–P_5) verhalten wie die Größe der Figuren auf P_4 resp. P_5, wodurch erwiesen wurde, daß die Strahlung gradlinig vom Kristall ausgeht. Ferner ist zu beachten, daß die Größe der einzelnen Sekundärflecken trotz des größeren Abstandes der Platte P_5 vom Kristall dieselbe geblieben ist. Dies dürfte wohl ein Anzeichen dafür sein, daß die je einen Einzelfleck hervorrufenden Sekundärstrahlen als paralleles Bündel aus dem Kristall heraustreten.

Es ist zu erwarten, daß die Erscheinung bei Kristallen des regulären Systemes übersichtlicher und leichter verständlich wird wie bei dem triklinen Kupfervitriol, weil man wohl annehmen darf, daß das zugehörige Raumgitter von der größtmöglichen Einfachheit ist. Als geeignet erschien uns die reguläre Zinkblende, mit der wir, wie schon erwähnt, Vorversuche gemacht und beträchtliche Intensität der Sekundärstrahlen erhalten hatten. Wir ließen von Steeg & Reuter in Homburg eine planparallele Platte aus einem

---

[1] Blendenöffnung B_4 bei diesem Versuch 1,5 mm.

guten Kristall parallel zu einer Würfelfläche (100) (senkrecht zu einer kristallographischen Hauptachse) schleifen von 10 × 10 mm Größe und 0,5 mm
Dicke. Diese Platte wurde in der oben beschriebenen Weise genau orientiert, so daß die Primärstrahlen den Kristall senkrecht zur Würfelfläche
durchsetzen. Das Resultat eines solchen Versuches zeigt uns Fig. 5, Taf. II.
Die Lage der sekundären Flecke ist völlig symmetrisch geworden in Bezug
auf den Durchstoßungspunkt. Man kann in die Figur zwei Paare zueinander senkrecht stehende Symmetrieebenen einzeichnen. Nimmt man irgendeinen der Flecken aus der Figur heraus und liegt dieser nicht auf einer der
Symmetrieebene, so kann man ihn durch Spiegelung und Drehung um 90°
mit noch 7 zugehörigen Punkten zur Deckung bringen. Fällt ein Fleck mit
einer Symmetrieebene zusammen, so kann man diesen naturgemäß nur mit
noch 3 entsprechenden zur Deckung bringen. Dies entspricht der holoedrischen Symmetrie des regulären Systems, trotzdem die Zinkblende in eine
hemiedrische Klasse gehört. Diese Tatsache, daß eine völlige Vierzähligkeit
auf der Platte vorhanden ist, ist wohl einer der schönsten Beweise für das
Raumgitter der Kristalle, und daß keine andere Eigenschaft als allein das
Raumgitter hier in Betracht kommt. Denn die Raumgitter zeigen stets die
holoedrische Symmetrie; Translationen von Raumgittern verschiedener
Natur gegen einander, wie sie zur Erklärung der Hemiedrieen angenommen
werden müssen, sind nach den Versuchen und unserer Theorie ohne Einfluß. Diese Anforderung der Symmetrie fand auch weiterhin ausnahmslos
Bestätigung durch die Versuche. Einmal ließen wir die Primärstrahlen senkrecht auf eine Oktaederfläche (111), dann auf eine Rhombendodekaeder-
fläche (110) auffallen. Fig. 7, Tafel III gibt die Dreizähligkeit wieder entsprechend der dreizähligen Achse, in der der Kristall bestrahlt wurde.

    Drehen wir den Kristall um den primären Strahl, so muß man aus dem
Vorhergehenden schließen, daß sich das Bild auf der Platte mitdreht. In der
Tat zeigten Versuche in dieser Richtung vollauf die Stichhaltigkeit dieses
Schlusses.

    Es war noch zu zeigen, eine wie genaue Orientierung des Kristalles erfor-
derlich ist, um bei Wiederholung eines Versuches identische Bilder zu
erhalten. Wir ließen den primären Strahl um 3° gegen eine vierzählige Achse
geneigt, doch so, daß die Ebene durch Strahl und Achse eine Symmetrieebene
war, durch den Kristall gehen. Das Resultat dieses Versuches gibt Fig. 11,
Tafel V. Wie wir sehen, ist die Vierzähligkeit verschwunden, wenngleich man
noch die Mehrzahl der Flecken in Fig. 5, Tafel II wiedererkennen kann.
Die eine Symmetrieebene zeigt sich auch hier.

    Drehten wir die senkrecht zur vierzähligen Achse geschliffene Platte so,
daß der primäre Strahl sie parallel zu einer dreizähligen Achse durchsetzte,
so ergab sich eine Figur, die sich von Fig. 7, Tafel III nicht in der Lage der

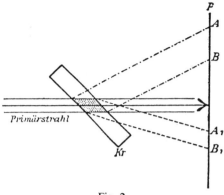

Fig. 2.

Flecke, sondern allein durch deren Größe unterschied. Auch nach der Symmetrie gleichberechtigte Flecken zeigten jetzt Größenunterschiede. Es beweist dies, daß die Begrenzung des durchstrahlten Kristallstückes ohne Einfluß auf die Lage der Intensitätsmaxima ist, während die Unterschiede in der Fleckengröße den Unterschieden der verschieden gerichteten Projektionen des durchsetzten Kristallstückes auf die photographische Platte entsprechen (siehe Fig. 2). Das schraffierte Gebiet stellt den durchleuchteten Teil des Kristalles Kr dar. AB und A_1B_1 sind die Projektionen dieses Teiles auf die Platte P und geben die Größe der Flecken an.

Außer den eben beschriebenen Versuchen haben wir weitere mit Zinkblende, Kupferkristall, Steinsalz und einer Diamantplatte angestellt. (Die Diamantplatte ist ein höchst dankenswertes Geschenk der Firma Ginsberg in Hanau an das physikalische Institut der Universität.) Wir sehen jedoch von der Mitteilung der Photogramme ab, weil die Versuche noch nicht abgeschlossen sind, hoffen aber in Kürze darüber berichten zu können. Wir wollen indessen noch auf zwei Versuchsergebnisse aus dieser Serie hinweisen, die uns von Bedeutung erscheinen.

Erstens haben wir beim Steinsalz gefunden, daß die Intensität der sekundären Flecke von der Dicke der durchstrahlten Schicht abhängt; denn bei gleicher Expositionszeit, gleicher Härte der Röhre und sonst gleichen Bedingungen war die Schwärzung bei 15 mm durchstrahlter Schicht des Kristalles wesentlich größer als bei einer 10 mal dünneren Schicht. Wir wollen diese Versuche mit anderem Material weiter fortführen.

Zweitens wollen wir einem Versuch mit dem Diamanten ein paar Zeilen widmen. Kohlenstoff zeigt nach Barkla keinerlei bisher nachgewiesene Eigenstrahlung. Es war also zu erwarten, daß selbst bei erheblichen Expositionen die Platten außer der durch die zerstreute Strahlung hervorgerufenen allgemeinen Schwärzung keine Flecken wie bei den anderen Kristallen zeigten, wenn diese auf Eigenstrahlung des Kristalles beruhten. Entgegen dieser Vermutung wiesen nicht nur die hinteren Platten P_4 und P_5 ähnliche Erscheinungen wie bei den früheren Aufnahmen auf, sondern sogar die Platten P_1, P_2 und P_3 ließen deutliche Flecken erkennen[1]. Ob diese auffallende Tatsache zusammenhängt mit dem kleinen Atomvolumen im Vergleich zu dem der übrigen Kristalle oder mit dem anomalen Verhalten des Diamanten gegenüber den Wärmeschwingungen, welches sich an der spezifischen Wärme zeigt, wollen wir vorläufig dahingestellt sein lassen[2]. Entscheidende Versuche hierüber sind ebenfalls in Vorbereitung.

Neben diesen bis jetzt beschriebenen Untersuchungen, die den Zusammenhang der Lage der Sekundärflecken und der Gitterstruktur erforschen sollen, haben wir den Charakter der die Flecken hervorbringenden Strahlen untersucht. Daß wir es in der Tat mit sekundären Röntgenstrahlen zu tun haben, macht der Umstand wahrscheinlich, daß die Strahlen durch beträchtliche Schichten von Metallen hindurchgehen, z.B. durch die Plattenhalter aus Stahlblech. Vorläufige Härtemessungen wurden mit dem Zinkblendekristall, der senkrecht zur vierzähligen Achse geschliffen war, auf folgende Weise angestellt. Da wir das Schwärzungsgesetz der Röntgenstrahlen nicht kennen, ist die Intensität der Strahlen proportional der durch sie hervorgerufenen Schwärzung gesetzt und diese mit einem Hartmannschen Mikrophotometer ausgemessen. Die Kristallsymmetrie bedingt, daß je acht einem Kreise zugeordneten Flecke dieselbe Schwärzung haben, was in der Tat der Fall ist. Wir brachten nun vor die Platte P_5 ein Aluminiumblech von 3 mm Dicke an, welches zwei gegenüberliegende Viertel der Platte bedeckte, die anderen beiden freiließ. Das Primärbündel ging, um Sekundärstrahlen des Aluminiumblechs zu vermeiden, durch eine zentrale Öffnung hindurch. Die Schwärzungsmessungen, die in folgender Tabelle zusammengestellt sind, zeigen, daß der Absorptionskoeffizient der Strahlen ungefähr 3,84 cm^{-1} für Aluminium ist. In Kolonne 1 stehen die Durchmesser der Kreise, auf dem die zueinander gehörenden Flecken liegen. In der zweiten die Schwärzung der Flecken ohne Aluminiumblech, während in der dritten Kolonne die Schwärzung nach dem Durchgang der Strahlen durch das Aluminiumblech verzeichnet ist. In der vorletzten Spalte sind die Werte der Schleierschwärzung der Platten eingetragen, während in die letzte die nach dem bekannten Absorptionsgesetz berechneten Absorptionskoeffizienten k für Al stehen. Das Absorptionsgesetz ist als exponentiell angenommen. Eine nach derselben Methode ausgeführte Härtemessung beim Diamanten ergab eine Härte der sekundären Strahlen von ungefähr derselben Größe. Die

---

[1] Auch bei tagelanger Exposition haben wir bei anderen Kristallen niemals auf den Platten P_1, P_2 und P_3 etwas anderes als allgemeine Schwärzung erhalten.
[2] Vgl. theor. Teil.

20

Härtemessungen nach der photographischen Methode sind jedoch nicht genau genug, um sichere Schlüsse hierüber ziehen zu lassen, da der gefundene Härteunterschied außerhalb der Meßgenauigkeit liegt. Mit einer elektrischen Methode, die wohl von den Zufälligkeiten der photographischen Methode, besonders den Plattenfehlern, verschieden harte Entwicklung etc. frei ist, werden diese Versuche wieder aufgenommen und es wird dann darüber berichtet werden.

Φ	ohne Al	mit Al	Schleier	k
50 mm	1,78	0,88	0,45	3,53 cm^{-1}
57,5 mm	2,02	0,79	0,45	4,71 cm^{-1}
74 mm	0,69	0,53	0,45	3,23 cm^{-1}
86 mm	0,84	0,55	0,45	3,89 cm^{-1}

Barkla findet für die Durchdringungsfähigkeit der Eigenstrahlung des Zinks einen wesentlich kleineren (für k also einen wesentlich größeren) Wert. Den Schluß nun daraus zu ziehen, daß wir es hier überhaupt nicht mit einer Eigenstrahlung zu tun haben, halten wir jedoch vorderhand nicht für unbedingt notwendig. Die folgende Tatsache spricht eher für eine Fluoreszenzstrahlung, die aber möglicherweise schon in der Primärstrahlung enthalten ist; die gleiche Härte der Strahlen beim Zinksulfid und Diamant läßt dies letztere vermuten. Während der Expositionszeit schwankte nämlich die Härte der Primärstrahlen besonders bei älteren Röhren, die ziemlich aufgebraucht waren und daher oft regeneriert werden mußten, in beträchtlicher Weise (von 6–12 Wehnelt). Dennoch blieben, wie die Photogramme zeigten, die sekundären Flecken scharf begrenzt und unverrückt. Eine Vergleichung der Härte der auf verschiedenen Ringen liegenden Strahlen untereinander läßt vermuten, daß diese von verschiedenem Durchdringungsvermögen sind. Es wäre dies freilich auch dann nicht auffallend, wenn es sich um Eigenstrahlung des Kristalles handeln sollte; denn da ja der Kristall aus Zink- und aus Schwefelatomen aufgebaut ist, so können sowohl die Zinkatome wie die Schwefelatome Strahlungen aussenden, die nach den sonstigen Erfahrungen von verschiedener Härte sind. Stammt die Eigenstrahlung aus der Antikathode selbst, so sind nach Barkla bei Platin tatsächlich mehrere Strahlungen zu erwarten.

Zum Schluß wollen wir besonders Herrn Prof. A. Sommerfeld, in dessen Institut diese Arbeit ausgeführt ist, für die bereitwillige Beschaffung der Apparate sowie sein stetiges Interesse und seine fördernden Ratschläge unseren herzlichsten Dank aussprechen. Wir möchten bei dieser Gelegenheit auch nicht versäumen, Herrn Geheimrat Röntgen und Herrn Geheimrat v. Groth für Überlassung von wertvollen Kristallen und Apparaten, sowie ihr reges Interesse ebenfalls verbindlich zu danken.

München, Institut für theor. Physik der Universität.

Crystallography thus affords to its sister science Chemistry the first visible proof of the accuracy of Dalton's atomic theory, and now enters into a new sphere of still greater usefulness. (...) Crystallography has thus become an exact science leading us to a practical knowledge of the hitherto mysterious world where Dalton's atoms and molecules reign supreme.

A. E. H. TUTTON,
Nature **90** (1912) 309

DO X-RAYS FOLLOW CRYSTAL-AVENUES?

2. Bemerkung über Zerstreuung und Absorption von β-Strahlen und Röntgenstrahlen in Kristallen, by J. STARK (1912)

━

3a,b. X-rays and Crystals, by W. H. BRAGG (1912)

━

4. Über die Kristallröntgenogramme, by GEORG WULFF (1913)

━

5. Kritische Bemerkungen zu den Deutungen der Photogramme von Friedrich und Knipping, by M. LAUE (1913)

━

2. Versuche[1] über das Eindringen von Kanalstrahlen in Kristalle haben es wahrscheinlich gemacht, daß diese Strahlen parallel ausgezeichneten Ebenen tiefer in das Innere von Kristallen einzudringen vermögen als parallel anderen Ebenen. In einem Kristall sind die elementaren Kraftfelder in geordneter Weise zusammengebaut; es lassen sich in ihnen Gerade oder gerade Kanäle ziehen, welche ausschließlich nur zwischenmolekulare Kraftfelder in regelmäßig wiederkehrender Anordnung durchsetzen; außerdem lassen sich geradlinige Kanäle ziehen, in welchen die Moleküle oder Atome in dichter Folge hintereinander liegen, welche also sehr starke inneratomische Kraftfelder umschließen. Ein von Atomen freier Kanal sei Kristallschacht genannt. Die Kristallstruktur bedingt, daß ein Schacht von bestimmter Richtung parallel seiner Achse in regelmäßigen Abständen durch den Kristall sich wiederholt. Ferner ordnen sich je nach der Kristallsymmetrie rings um eine kristallographische Achse gleichwertige Schächte von verschiedener Neigung an; auch kommen natürlich in demselben Kristall im allgemeinen auch ungleichwertige Schächte vor, die sich nach Querschnitt und Art der in ihnen aneinander gereihten zwischenmolekularen Kraftfelder unterscheiden.

Dringt nun ein elektromagnetisch empfindliches Teilchen so in einen Kristall ein, daß es auf Atome oder inneratomische Kraftfelder trifft, so erfährt es große Ablenkungen von seinem Wege oder wird von den Kraftfeldern festgehalten. Gelangt es dagegen in einen Kristallschacht parallel zu diesem, so wird es bei seiner Vorwärtsbewegung eine viel kleinere Ablen-

---

[1] J. Stark und G. Wendt, *Ann. d. Phys.* **38** (1912) 921.

kung durch die schwächeren zwischenmolekularen Kraftfelder erfahren; und wird es von den im Schacht aufeinanderfolgenden elementaren Feldern abwechselnd in entgegengesetzten Richtungen in gleich großen Beträgen abgelenkt, so wird es auf einer langen Strecke in einer sinusförmigen Bahn den Kristallschacht durchlaufen. In Kristallen werden demnach elektromagnetisch empfindliche Teilchen längs ausgezeichneten Achsen viel größere Schichtdicken zu durchdringen vermögen als in amorphen Körpern.

Außer der selektiven Absorption ist noch eine andere Erscheinung aus der atomistischen Ordnung der Kristalle zu folgern. Durch diese wird nämlich bedingt, daß sich die primären Strahlen in Gruppen teilen lassen, innerhalb deren die einzelnen Strahlen gleichartige elementare Kraftfelder längs homologen Punktreihen durchlaufen. Entsprechend der Kongruenz der Kraftfelder in diesen Punktreihen werden dann die primären Strahlen derselben Gruppe selektiv in derselben Richtung abgelenkt oder zerstreut. Es wird demnach in einem Kristall nicht bloß die Absorption, sondern auch die Zerstreuung von Strahlenteilchen selektiv in verschiedenen Achsen erfolgen. Damit darum parallel einer Achse die Intensität der zerstreuten, von einem Kristall durchgelassenen Strahlen groß wird, muß diese Achse gleichzeitig eine Kristallschachtachse und eine Achse maximaler Zerstreuung sein, oder wenigstens einer solchen nahe liegen.

Die vorstehenden Überlegungen lassen sich mit folgender Versuchsanordnung experimentell prüfen. Ein dünnes Strahlenbündel elektromagnetisch empfindlicher Teilchen läßt man auf eine Platte fallen, die in bestimmter Orientierung aus einem möglichst reinen Kristall geschnitten ist. Die Strahlenteilchen werden dann im Innern der Kristallplatte in mehr oder weniger großer Zahl eine Zerstreuung nach allen möglichen Richtungen erfahren. Diejenigen Teilchen indes, welche hierbei in einen Kristallschacht parallel dessen Achse gelenkt werden, werden im Schacht weiterfliegen. Infolgedessen werden auf der Rückseite der Kristallplatte die zerstreuten Strahlen nicht in allen Achsen in gleicher Intensität austreten, sondern in den Richtungen der Kristallschächte und der Achsen maximaler Zerstreuung in größerer Intensität als in den übrigen Richtungen. Wird darum hinter der Kristallplatte in einem Abstand von ihr, welcher groß ist im Vergleich zur Dicke des Strahlenbündels, eine gegen die Strahlen empfindliche Platte, z.B. eine photographische Platte, aufgestellt, so wird auf dieser erstens zentral die Spur des primären unzerstreuten Strahlenbündels sich abzeichnen, zweitens rund herum die Projektion des durchleuchteten Kristallstückes in den Achsen der Kristallschächte. Gleichwertige Kristallschachtachsen von gleicher Neigung gegen das primäre Strahlenbündel werden hierbei gleich intensive Zerstreuungsbilder liefern; in der Anordnung der Zerstreuungsbilder wird sich die Symmetrie des Kristalls zum

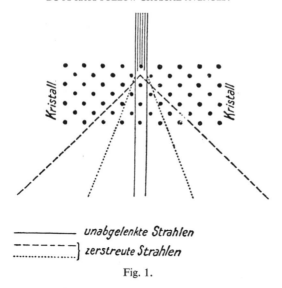

————————— unabgelenkte Strahlen
— — — — —⌉ zerstreute Strahlen
················⌋

Fig. 1.

Ausdruck bringen. In Fig. 1 ist schematisch der hier gedachte Versuch dargestellt.

Da ich an verschiedenen Stellen gewisse Eigenschaften der Röntgenstrahlen auf Grund der Lichtzellenhypothese[1] gedeutet habe, lag es für mich nahe, die obigen Überlegungen auch auf Röntgenstrahlen anzuwenden. Denkt man sich nämlich die Energie der elementaren Röntgenstrahlung bei der Fortpflanzung in einem kleinen Volumen lokalisiert bleibend, so wird ein Bündel von Röntgenstrahlquanten in einem Kristall ähnlich β-Strahlen eine selektive Zerstreuung und eine selektiv verringerte Absorption längs den Achsen von Kristallschächten erfahren und wird darum an einer Kristallplatte mehrere diskontinuierliche Zerstreuungsbündel liefern. Es ist natürlich nicht notwendig, daß die Röntgen- und die β-Strahlen an derselben Kristallplatte dieselbe Zerstreuungsfigur liefern.

Es ist bemerkenswert, daß ich auf Grund der Lichtzellenhypothese diese Überlegung anstellte, noch bevor mir die Beobachtungen[2] bekannt wurden, welche W. Friedrich und P. Knipping auf Anlaß von M. Laue über die Zerstreuung von Röntgenstrahlen in Kristallplatten machten, und welche diese Autoren als eine Interferenz von Röntgenstrahlen deuten. Ohne diese Auffassung für unzutreffend erklären zu willen, möchte ich immerhin darauf hinweisen, daß die bisherigen experimentellen Resultate die Zu-

[1] Vergl. J. Stark, *Die elementare Strahlung*, S. 259, S. Hirzel, Leipzig 1911.
[2] W. Friedrich, P. Knipping und M. Laue, *Interferenzerscheinungen bei Röntgenstrahlen.* Münch. Ber. 1912, S. 303.

lässigkeit der hier entwickelten Auffassung einer selektiven Zerstreuung und selektiven Absorption von Röntgenstrahlen in Kristallen nicht ausschließen. Es lassen sich alle von Friedrich und Knipping mitgeteilten Beobachtungen mit dieser Auffassung in Einklang bringen.

1. Wie leicht zu sehen ist, muß nach der Kristallschachthypothese ein jedes zerstreute Röntgenstrahlenbündel parallel sein, also auf photographischen Platten in verschieden großen Abstanden vom Kristall gleich große Zerstreuungsflecken liefern. Dies finden in der Tat Friedrich und Knipping.

5. Die Lage der Zerstreuungsflecken ist für eine bestimmte Kristallplatte unabhängig von der Absorbierbarkeit oder der Wellenlänge der Röntgenstrahlen, insofern alle Wellenlängen in dieselben Kristallschächte zerstreut werden. Eine jede Röntgenröhre liefert darum trotz starker Veränderlichkeit ihrer Härte während der Exposition, wie Friedrich und Knipping tatsächlich finden, scharfe Zerstreuungsflecken. Deren Lage ist folglich für eine bestimmte Kristallplatte auch unabhängig von der charakteristischen oder linienhaften Eigenstrahlung (Platin oder Kupfer) der Antikathode.

6. Die relative Lage und Anordnung der Zerstreuungsflecke hat nichts zu tun mit der linienhaften oder charakteristischen Röntgenstrahlung der Atome der Kristallplatte, sondern wird von allen chemischen Elementen geliefert und wird in erster Linie durch die kristallographische Symmetrie einer Kristallplatte bedingt. Dieselbe primäre Röntgenstrahlung liefert also an einer Bleiglanz-, Kupfervitriol-, Zinkblende-, Steinsalz- und Diamantplatte scharfe Zerstreuungsfiguren, wie Friedrich und Knipping in der Tat finden.

7. Die Symmetrie der Zerstreuungsfigur entspricht immer der Symmetrie der Kristallschachtachsen und somit immer der kristallographischen Symmetrie der verwendeten Platte. Für einen regulären Kristall von drei gleichen Kanten des Elementarwürfels ordnet sich also jeder Symmetrieachse eine entsprechende Zerstreuungsfigur zu, also einer zwei-, drei- bzw. vierzähligen Symmetrieachse in der primären Strahlenachse eine Zerstreuungsfigur von zwei, drei bzw. vier Symmetrieschnitten. Dies finden Friedrich und Knipping in der Tat für die reguläre Zinkblende.

9. Die verschieden große Intensität der Zerstreuungsflecke ist vermutlich auf die Ungleichwertigkeit verschiedener Kristallschachtachsen und auf die selektive Zerstreuung zurückzuführen. Je nach dem Querschnitt eines elementaren Kristallschachtes wird die zurückbleibende Absorption der zerstreuten Strahlen in ihm verschieden groß sein. Auch wird diese Absorption um so größer sein, eine je größere Schichtdicke die zerstreuten Strahlen im Kristall längs verschiedenen Schachtachsen zu durchsetzen haben. Diese

Vermutung scheint durch die Resultate von Friedrich und Knipping ebenfalls bestätigt zu werden.

10. Änderung der Neigung der Kristallplatte gegen die primäre Strahlenachse bedeutet Änderung der Richtung der elementaren ablenkenden Kraftfelder gegen die Richtung der primären Strahlen und damit Änderung der Menge Strahlen, welche in einen Kristallschacht von geänderter Neigung abgelenkt werden. Wird darum die Kristallplatte, welche, primär längs einer Symmetrieachse durchstrahlt, eine symmetrische Zerstreuungsfigur liefert, um einige Grad (3°) gegen diese Lage geneigt, so liefert sie zwar noch ebenso viele Zerstreuungsflecken wie zuvor, wenn auch in gestörter Symmetrie, da die sie hervorbringenden zerstreuten Strahlenbündel zusammen mit der Platte sich drehen; aber im allgemeinen ist das Verhältnis ihrer Intensitäten ein anderes als beim Zusammenfallen von Symmetrieachse und primärer Strahlenachse. Es ist möglich, daß sich in dieser Weise die merkwürdige Verschiedenheit der Intensitätsverhältnisse in Fig. 7 u. 8 und in Fig. 5 u. 11 der Arbeit von Friedrich und Knipping erklärt. Auf Grund der vorstehenden Überlegung sind auch, wie nicht weiter ausgeführt zu werden braucht, eigenartige Erscheinungen bei der Zerstreuung polarisierter Röntgenstrahlen in Kristallen zu erwarten.

Wenn nun auch die hier diskutierte Zerstreuungshypothese in guter Übereinstimmung mit den experimentellen Resultaten steht, so möchte ich ihr doch noch nicht den Vorzug vor der Interferenzhypothese geben. Eine Entscheidung zwischen ihnen können nur weitere Beobachtungen bringen.

Aachen, Physik. Institut der Techn. Hochschule, 26. August 1912

3a. Messrs. Friedrich, Knipping and Laue have recently published (*K. Bayer. Akad. der Wiss.*, 1912, p. 303) some remarkable effects obtained by passing a fine stream of X-rays through a crystal before incidence upon a photographic plate. A curious arrangement of spots is found upon the plate, some of them so far removed from the central spot that they must be ascribed to rays which make large angles with the original pencil.

The positions of these spots seem to depend on simple numerical relations, and on the mode in which the crystal presents itself to the incident stream. I find that when the crystal (zincblende) is placed so that the incident rays are parallel to an edge of the cube in the crystal [note the conditions! Ed.] the positions of the spots are to be found by the following simple rule. The atoms being assumed to be arranged in rectangular fashion, any direction which joins an atom to a neighbour at a distance na from it, where a is the distance from the atom to the nearest neighbours and n is a whole number, is a direction which a deflected (or secondary) pencil will take, and it will in doing so form one of the spots. In other words, we have to seek for all the cases in which the sum of three squares is also a square, and we then recover the positions of all the spots on the diagram. For example, secondary pencils take the directions (2, 3, 6) (4, 1, 8), and so on. In a few cases the sum of the squares is one short of a perfect square, *e.g.* (5, 7, 11), but in no case is it on the greater side; and there is at least one direction (2, 5, 14) which ought by the rule to be on the diagram and is not. Otherwise the rule is quite successful.

Until further experimental results are available, it is difficult to distinguish between various explanations which suggest themselves. It is clear, however, that the diagram is an illustration of the arrangement of the atoms in the crystal.

The rule has suggested itself to me as a consequence of an attempt to combine Dr. Laue's theory with a fact which my son pointed out to me, viz. that all the directions of the secondary pencils in this position of the crystal are 'avenues' between the crystal atoms.

Leeds, October 18

3b. In his discussion of Dr. Laue's diagrams Dr. Tutton (Nature, November 14, p. 309) invites me to consider their physical aspects in the light of the crystallographical details which he supplies.

The rule which I gave in a previous letter to Nature (October 24, p. 219), and which Dr. Tutton has in mind, is independent of all but the simplest facts of crystallography. It gives a numerical method of finding the positions of the spots on the diagrams, and its effect is merely to show that the positions of the spots give no information concerning the wave-length of the incident radiation.

In a paper read recently before the Cambridge Philosophical Society my son has given a theory which makes it possible to calculate the positions of the spots for all dispositions of crystal and photographic plate. It accounts also for the form of the spots and other details, and amongst other things it explains my numerical rule. It is based on the idea that any plane within the crystal which is 'rich' in atoms can be looked on as a reflecting plane; the positions of the spots can then be calculated by the reflection laws in the ordinary way. In this extended treatment the facts of crystallography are of importance, but it would take too long to discuss the matter in a letter.

I should like to refer to one other point. Dr. Tutton suggests that the new experiment may possibly distinguish between the wave and the corpuscular theories of the X-rays. This is no doubt true in one sense. If the experiment helps to prove X-rays and light to be of the same nature, then such a theory as that of the 'neutral pair' is quite inadequate to bear the burden of explaining the facts of all radiation. On the other hand, the properties of X-rays point clearly to a quasi-corpuscular theory, and certain properties of light can be similarly interpreted. The problem then becomes, it seems to me, not to decide between two theories of X-rays, but to find, as I have said elsewhere, one theory which possesses the capacities of both.

4. Die Theorie von J. Stark entspricht bei naheren Betrachtungen nicht genau den Tatsachen. Wenn wir mit J. Stark annehmen, daß die schwarzen Punkte des Kristallröntgenogramms den 'Kristallschächten' entsprechen, so sollten diese Punkte 1. den Richtungen mit einfachen kristallographischen Symbolen (Koordinaten) entsprechen, 2. auf den gewissen Geraden liegen (nach Zonen geordnet sein) und 3. sollten die Durchschnittspunkte dieser Geraden auch mit schwarzen Punkten besetzt sein. Bei der näheren Untersuchung der Kristallröntgenogramme wird keine der obigen Bedingungen befriedigt, und wenn die zwei ersteren doch annähernd befriedigt werden, so steht die dritte in auffallendem Widerspruche mit den Tatsachen.

5. Gegen die auch von Herrn Stark mit allem Vorbehalt ausgesprochene Hypothese scheinen mir die folgenden Gründe zu sprechen:

Wird der Kristall aus der Stellung, die er bei genanntem Photogramm hatte, ein wenig gedreht, so drehen sich sämtliche Kristallschächte mit. Es sollte somit nach Herrn Starks Ansicht auch das ganze Photogramm mitwandern und die einzigen Veränderungen in der Lage der Flecke zueinander müßen sich rein geometrisch durch die veränderte Lage der Platte zum Kristall erklären. Tatsächlich zeigt Photogramm 11, welches nach einer Drehung um drei Grad aus der vierzählig symmetrischen Stellung erhalten wurde, ein ganz anderes Bild als das vierzählig symmetrische Photogramm 5.

NET-PLANE REFLECTION ACCOUNTS FOR GEOMETRY OF LAUE PATTERN

6. The Specular Reflection of X-rays, by W. L. BRAGG (1912)

▬

7. On the Transmission of X-rays through Crystals, by T. TERADA (1914)

▬

8. Kritische Bemerkungen zu den Deutungen der Photogramme von Friedrich und Knipping, by M. LAUE (1913)

▬

6. It has been shown by Herr Laue and his colleagues that the diffraction patterns which they obtain with X-rays and crystals are naturally explained by assuming the existence of very short electromagnetic waves in the radiations from an X-ray bulb, the wave length of which is of the order 10^{-9} cm. The spots of the pattern represent interference maxima of waves diffracted by the regularly arranged atoms of the crystal. Now, if this is so, these waves ought to be regularly reflected by a surface which has a sufficiently good polish, the irregularities being small compared with the length 10^{-9} cm. Such surfaces are provided by the cleavage planes of a crystal, which represent an arrangement of the atoms of the crystal in parallel planes, and the amount by which the centres of atoms are displaced from their proper planes is presumably small compared with atomic dimensions.

In accordance with this, the spots in Laue's crystallographs can be shown to be due to partial reflection of the incident beam in sets of parallel planes in the crystal on which the atom centres may be arranged, the simplest of which are the actual cleavage planes of the crystal. This is merely another way of looking at the diffraction. This being so, it was suggested to me by Mr. C. T. R. Wilson that crystals with very distinct cleavage planes, such as mica, might possibly show strong specular reflection of the rays. On trying the experiment it was found that this was so. A narrow pencil of X-rays, obtained by means of a series of stops, was allowed to fall at an angle of incidence of 80° on a slip of mica about one millimetre thick mounted on thin aluminium. A photographic plate set behind the mica slip showed, when developed, a well-marked reflected spot, as well as one formed by the incident rays traversing the mica and aluminium.

Variation of the angle of incidence and of the distance of plate from mica left no doubt that the laws of reflection were obeyed. Only a few minutes' exposure to a small X-ray bulb sufficed to show the effect, whereas Friedrich and Knipping found it necessary to give an exposure of many hours to the plate, using a large water-cooled bulb, in order to obtain the transmitted interference pattern. By bending the mica into an arc, the reflected rays can be brought to a line focus.

In all cases the photographic plate was shielded by a double envelope of black paper, and in one case with aluminium one millimetre thick. This last cut off the reflected rays considerably. Slips of mica one-tenth of a millimetre thick give as strong a reflection as an infinite thickness, yet the effect is almost certainly not a surface one. Experiments are being made to find the critical thickness of mica at which the reflecting power begins to diminish as thinner plates are used. The reflection is much stronger as glancing incidence is approached.

The Cavendish Laboratory, Cambridge, December 8

7. The remarkable discovery made by Laue, Friedrich and Knipping concerning the transmission of X-rays through crystals, seems to have opened a wide field of researches which promise to throw a fresh light on the structure of matter and the nature of the radiation. As to the explanation of the phenomena hitherto observed, the opinions of physicists seem to be still differing in many respects. The following brief summary of the results of my experiments may not be out of place for those interested in this problem.

Examining photograms obtained with alum, borax, sugar etc., it was observed that the most conspicuous spots are arranged on a number of ellipses passing through the central spot formed by the incident ray. This was most remarkable with alum, when the incident rays were slightly inclined to one of the crystallographic axes; one ellipse was very conspicuous and the major axis of the ellipse varied with the inclination of the crystal. When the incident rays were made to coincide with the crystallographic axis, the ellipse disappeared entirely. These facts strongly suggested that the spots are formed by pencils of rays 'reflected' from a number of planes intersecting one another in the crystallographic axis. In this case, all the reflected pencils will lie on a circular cone having the incident pencil as one of the generating lines, which intersects the plane of the ellipse at the extremity of the major axis. It must be expressly remarked that, here and also in the following, nothing more is meant by the word 'reflected' or 'reflexion' than the geometrical relation of the deflected to the incident rays.

The spots formed by reflected beams are all of elongated shape, the length being nearly equal to the diameter of the undeflected spot. The directions of these elongated spots converge, if prolonged, to the point of the ellipse

31

just opposite to the undeflected spot. With the rocksalt crystal I have often observed a peculiar distortion of the spots which is probably due to the initial plastic deformation of the crystal. A piece of borax was melted down by a Bunsen flame during the observation; but the spots remained visible, until the piece was almost entirely melted.

The next experiment was to determine the position of the particular axes of crystals, which give rise each to a conical system of reflected beams. Rocksalt and fluorspar were chosen for this purpose, for the simplicity of the system of spots observed. The crystal fixed to the axis of a goniometer was rotated about one of its crystallographic axes, or about an axis bisecting the angle between two of the crystallographic axes. The axes of conical systems of deflected beams, which may properly be called *zonal axes* (Zonenachse), were successively sought, by bringing the spots into coincidence with the undeflected spot and taking the reading of the goniometer. The measurement can be made only roughly, since firstly the spots are of considerable size and secondly some spots become faint when they are brought too near to the bright undeflected spot. This is partly due to the optical illusion; but it was observed with certainty that many spots become actually faint when they approach the central spot. Nevertheless, the angles could be measured within one degree in most cases. After carrying out a series of measurements, it was found that the axes of cones always coincide with those directions in the crystal which are also crystallographically conspicuous. If we suppose the molecules of rocksalt arranged in a space-lattice such that each molecule is situated at the angular point of an elementary cube, the directions of the axes of the observed cones correspond to those of the rows of points (Punktreihe) connecting nearest sets of the points of the lattice. This way of finding the conspicuous zonal axes of crystals may be of no small importance for practical crystallography.

My next procedure was to determine the positions of spots belonging to conspicuous cones and compare them with those calculated on the assumption that these spots are formed by beams reflected from the net-planes (Netzebene) intersecting each other in the corresponding rows. Fig. 1, for example, diagrammatically shows the arrangement of spots obtained with rocksalt. O represents the spot formed by the incident beam, C the point at which the crystallographic axis z cuts the plane of the diagram, and AO represents the trace of the yz-plane. 1, 2, 3, ... 6 represent the spots belonging to the z-axis, C. If these spots are formed by beams reflected from planes intersecting in the axis C, the angle ϕ between one of these planes and the yz-plane may be found by the relation

$$\text{tg } \phi \cos \theta = \text{tg } \phi'$$

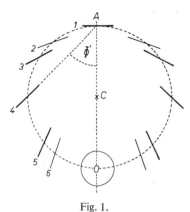

Fig. 1.

where ϕ' is the angle as shown in Fig. 1, and θ is the inclination of the z-axis to the incident ray. The angles ϕ' were measured on the photogram and the corresponding ϕ were calculated. On the other hand, the theoretical value of ϕ for possible net-planes were calculated. For this purpose, I took all lattice-points whose coordinates are less than 3, the side of the elementary cube being taken as unity, and calculated the direction-cosines of the net-planes determined by one of these points and z-axis. In the following table, observed and calculated values of ϕ are given; the last column gives the coordinates of the point which together with 000 and 001 determines the net-plane.

No. of spots in Fig. 1	Values of ϕ		Coordinates of the point determining the plane
	observed	calculated	
1	90°	90.0°	011
2	73°	71.6°	311
3	63°	63.4°	211
4	45°	45.0°	111
5	26°	26.6°	121
6	18°	18.4°	131

It will be seen that these planes are richest in lattice points, among all the net-planes.

Thus far, the results obtained with rocksalt, at least concerning the position of the spots, have been fairly explained by assuming reflecting planes determined by three neighbouring points of a simple space-lattice. The results with fluorspar allow of a similar treatment, but those obtained

33

with alum are not so simple as in the case of rocksalt and fluorspar. The spots arranged on the ellipse belonging to the crystallographic axis are decidedly more numerous than in the corresponding photogram for rocksalt and fluorspar. The angles ϕ observed were $18°$, $26°$, $32°$, $40°$, $45°$, $48°$, $54°$ and also many others greater than $54°$ which can not be separately measured, because the corresponding spots are so closely arranged as to form a continuous arc. Among the above values of ϕ, $18°$, $26°$ and $45°$ are the same as with rocksalt; but to explain the values $40°$ and $48°$, it is necessary to take points of the lattice far from the origin as determining the reflecting planes, if we confine ourselves to the simplest kinds of space-lattice as in the above explanation. This fact is of no small interest, since it seems to give a clue for revealing the internal structure of different crystals.

For some of the other crystals examined, the number of spots belonging to each zonal axis and also the number of these axes itself are still more numerous, which probably points to a more complex structure of crystal molecules.

Laue tried to explain the arrangement of the spots in the photograms obtained by Friedrich and Knipping, by assuming that they are due to the interference of different orders, of secondary waves produced by lattice points, and showed that a series of different wave lengths must be assumed to explain for all the spots observed. It seems to me not absolutely necessary to make this assumption. At least the position of the spots, may be explained by simple reflexion from different netplanes in the crystal.[1] Studying these photograms, I have remarked that all the spots in Figs. 5 and 7 of the photograms may be considered to be arranged on a number of circular cones having their common vertex at the crystal, and their axes coinciding with the most densely beset rows of points in a space-lattice consisting of elementary octahedrons. By means of a graphical method, I was able to find for all conspicuous spots in Figs. 5 and 7 of Laue's paper, the axes of the cones and the direction of the netplanes giving rise to these spots.

The elongated shape of the spots as observed in the visual observations and photograms, may be explained, if we take into account the divergent nature of the incident rays. The divergent beam is made more or less convergent by the parallel reflecting planes if the angle of incidence be sufficiently large. In this case, the length of the spot will be parallel to the trace of the reflecting plane on the screen or photographic plate. This explains why the directions of the spots converge to the point of the ellipse just opposite the undeflected spot. If a narrow slit is applied to the aperture of the dia-

---

[1] In the course of my investigation, I became aware of the paper of G. Wulff in which this point is clearly pointed out. He calls the spots 'Nullmaximum' corresponding to the interference of zero order, which is formally identical with reflexion. *Phys. ZS* **14** (1913) 217.

phragm, those spots which are parallel to the slit are not altered in shape, whereas those perpendicular to the slit are cut into a round spot.

As to the interesting variation of the intensity of spots with the inclination, the following may be remarked, though the details will be reserved for a subsequent communication. Most of the spots become generally fainter as they recede from the undeflected spot. But the decrease, is by no means gradual.

Thus far, I have considered the problem simply geometrically and made no assumption about the physical nature of the phenomena. To explain the facts hitherto observed, many hypotheses may be suggested. At present, the possibility seems not altogether excluded that a theory of the radiation on the line of corpuscular hypothesis may be worked up, if we make suitable assumptions on the structure of crystals. On the other hand, the wave or pulse theory as already proposed by several authorities seems very probable. For the decision of the question, the experimental data are still wanting concerning the exact nature of the reflected rays as well as the difference in behaviour of different crystals. The question, however, deserves consideration why the density of points on each of the net-planes generally determines the appearance of reflected spots, regardless of the fact that the volume of different primitive parallelopipeda is invariant. The answer is not so simple as it appears. The explanation seems to be sought in two directions. The one involves a hypothesis on the structure of crystal itself and is independent of the nature of the radiation. For example, we may consider that each of the crystal molecules placed at one point of the lattice, consists, in its turn, of a group of chemical molecules arranged in the form of a similar lattice with a finite boundary. Another alternative is to be sought in the nature of the radiation. One may perhaps seek the explanation on the assumption that the radiation consists of an assemblage of detached entities, though it seems rather difficult to proceed in this way[1].

At any rate, the difference of appearance of the system of spots for different crystals belonging to the same crystallographic system, is most probably due to the difference of the molecular grouping.

[1] A way of explanation, suggested by Prof. Tamaru in the meeting, during the ensuing discussion, is the following: Since the rays are divergent, the rays reflected by different parallel planes, m in number say, do not reach a spot on the screen simultaneously. Their effects, being produced successively, are simply added. The effects deflected from lattice-points on any one reflecting plane, however, reach the spot simultaneously and cause a disturbance (considered as a wave), in which the amplitude varies as the number, n say, of the effective points, so that the effect will be as n^2. Hence, the total effect will be as mn^2. mn being taken as constant, this effect is greater, the larger n is, i.e. the denser the lattice points are in each one reflecting plane. This may account for the fact that reflecting planes formed by nearer sets of points are only effective.

35

A further step which may contribute to the solution of the problem, is the investigation of the intensity of reflected beams due to different net-planes which we are now in a position to identify with sufficient certainty[1].

My best thanks are due to Prof. H. Nagaoka, Prof. S. Nakamura and Prof. T. Tamaru for kind guidance and useful instructions.

8. Von verschiedenen Autoren[2] ist die Deutung vorgeschlagen worden, daß jedes der Helligkeitsmaxima durch Spiegelung an gewissen Ebenen entsteht, deren Lage durch das Raumgitter bedingt ist.

Um den Zusammenhang der Spiegelungsauffassung mit der Interferenz-theorie klarzustellen, wollen wir die folgenden Betrachtungen anstellen.

Wie früher gezeigt, ist nach der Interferenztheorie ein Maximum dort zu erwarten, wo für eine der von den Gitterelementen (Atomen oder gewissen Atomgruppen) ausgehenden Sinusschwingungen von der Wellenlänge λ die drei Gleichungen

$$a_{1x}\alpha + a_{1y}\beta + a_{1z}\gamma = h_1\lambda + a_{1x}\alpha_0 + a_{1y}\beta_0 + a_{1z}\gamma_0$$

$$a_{2x}\alpha + a_{2y}\beta + a_{2z}\gamma = h_2\lambda + a_{2x}\alpha_0 + a_{2y}\beta_0 + a_{2z}\gamma_0 \qquad (1)$$

$$a_{3x}\alpha + a_{3y}\beta + a_{3z}\gamma = h_3\lambda + a_{3x}\alpha_0 + a_{3y}\beta_0 + a_{3z}\gamma_0$$

wenigstens genähert gleichzeitig erfüllt sind.

Da hier sowohl das Achsenkreuz x, y, z als die Einteilung des Raumgitters in Elementar-parallelepipeda noch ganz beliebig ist, können wir in irgendeine als Kristallfläche mögliche Ebene die xy-Ebene legen und die Vektoren a_1 und a_2 in derselben Ebene annehmen ($a_{1z} = a_{2z} = 0$). Fände an dieser Ebene eine Spiegelung statt, so wären die Richtungskosinus des gespiegelten Strahls

$$\alpha = \alpha_0, \ \beta = \beta_0, \ \gamma = -\gamma_0. \qquad (2)$$

Man erkennt, daß die beiden ersten Gleichungen (1) durch diese Werte mit $h_1 = h_2 = 0$ identisch erfüllt sind, während die dritte übergeht in:

$$2\gamma a_{3z} = h_3\lambda. \qquad (3)$$

---

[1] After the paper was read, I have received the paper of Mr. W. L. Bragg entitled *The diffraction of short electromagnetic waves by a crystal*, read before the Cambridge Philosophical Society on Nov. 11, 1912, and printed on Jan. 10, 1913, and became aware that my way of reconstructing Laue's photograms and of explaining the shape of the spots on them was essentially not new.

[2] W. H. und W. L. Bragg, *Nature* **90** (1913) 360, 410; *Proc. Cambr. Phil. Soc.* **17** (1913) 43; L. Mandelstam u. H. Rohmann, *Phys. Zs.* **14** (1913) 220.

Da a_{3z} dabei die Höhe des Elementar-parallelepipeds oder, was dasselbe sagt, der Abstand zweier mit Atomen besetzter Ebenen $z = $ const ist, so entspricht die letzte Gleichung ganz der Bedingung für das Auftreten eines Intensitätsmaximums bei den optischen Interferenzen an planparallelen Platten vom Brechungsindex 1. Die Interferenztheorie der in Rede stehenden Erscheinungen bei Röntgenstrahlen läßt also, sofern ebene Wellen einfallen, die Deutung zu, daß an solchen mit Atomen besetzten Ebenen Spiegelung eintritt, für deren Abstand im Raumgitter die Gleichung (3) erfüllt ist. Es steht also in Übereinstimmung mit der Interferenztheorie, wenn sich die Spiegelungsauffassung an der Lage der Helligkeitsmaxima empirisch bestätigt[3].

Der Unterschied zwischen beiden Auffassungen liegt nur in der Gleichung (3), welche nach der von mir vertretenen Auffassung noch neben den Bedingungen (2) (von denen nur zwei unabhängig sind) erfüllt sein muß, während für die Herren Bragg keine derartige dritte Bedingung besteht. [See, however, p. 46 of the paper *Proc. Camb. Phil. Soc.* (cited in note[1]!), this Vol. p. 40. Ed.] Sollte es sich herausstellen, daß die vom Kristall ausgehenden Röntgenstrahlen spektral so inhomogen sind, daß sie schon beim Gangunterschied von einigen Wellenlängen nicht mehr interferieren, so fiele diese dritte Bedingung fort und es näherte sich meine Auffassung der Braggschen. Ob dies aber der Fall ist, läßt sich wohl jetzt noch nicht endgültig entscheiden.

Der Vollständigkeit halber sei schließlich noch auf ein Argument hingewiesen, welches schon Herr Tutton[4] angeführt hat. Alle Deutungen der in Rede stehenden Erscheinungen haben der Einfachheit halber bisher nur von einfachen Raumgittern gesprochen. Tatsächlich liegen bei den Kristallen meist viel kompliziertere regelmäßige Punktsysteme vor. Daß diese Komplikation Änderungen bedingt, läßt sich leicht dartun. Aber die nach Herrn Bragg 'spiegelnden' Flächen dichtester Belegung müssen in ihrer Lage doch wesentlich dadurch bedingt sein. Es ist dann sehr merkwürdig, daß es hemiedrische Kristalle, wie die Zinkblende, gibt, die bei der Durchstrahlung die volle holoedrische Symmetrie ergeben [see this Vol. papers 21 and 22].

---

[3] Für einen speziellen Fall liefert schon G. Wulff, diese Zeitschr. **14** (1913) 217 diesen Nachweis. Seine Gleichung (8) [this Vol. p. 52.] ist mit (3) identisch.

[4] A. E. H. Tutton, *Nature* **90** (1912) 306 [this Vol. p. 94].

9. THE DIFFRACTION OF SHORT ELECTROMAGNETIC WAVES BY A CRYSTAL

by

W. L. Bragg, B. A., Trinity College

(communicated by Prof. Sir J. J. Thomson)
(Read 11 November 1912)

Herren Friedrich, Knipping, and Laue have lately published a paper entitled 'Interference Phenomena with Röntgen Rays'[1], the experiments which form the subject of the paper being carried out in the following way. A very narrow pencil of rays from an X-ray bulb is isolated by a series of lead screens pierced with fine holes. In the path of this beam is set a small slip of crystal, and a photographic plate is placed a few centimetres behind the crystal at right angles to the beam. When the plate is developed, there appears on it, as well as the intense spot caused by the undeviated X-rays, a series of fainter spots forming an intricate geometrical pattern. By moving the photographic plate backwards or forwards it can be seen that these spots are formed by rectilinear pencils spreading in all directions from the crystal, some of them making an angle of over 45° with the direction of the incident radiation.

When the crystal is a specimen of cubical zinc blende, and one of its three principal cubic axes is set parallel to the incident beam, the pattern of spots is symmetrical about the two remaining axes. Laue's theory of the formation of this pattern is as follows. He considers the molecules of the crystal to form a three-dimensional grating, each molecule being capable of emitting secondary vibrations when struck by incident electromagnetic waves from the X-ray bulb. He places the molecules in the simplest possible of the three cubical point systems, that is, molecules arranged in space in a pattern whose element is a little cube of side 'a', with a molecule at each corner. He takes coordinate axes whose origin is at a point in the crystal and which are parallel to the sides of the cubes. The incident waves are propagated in a direction parallel to the z axis, and on account of the narrowness of

---

[1] Sitzungsberichte der Königlich Bayerischen Akademie der Wissenschaften. June 1912.

the beam the wave surfaces may be taken to be parallel to the xy plane. The spots are considered to be interference maxima of the waves scattered by the orderly arrangement of molecules in the crystal. In order to get an interference maximum in the direction whose cosines are α, β, γ, for incident radiation of wave-length λ, the following equations must be satisfied

$$a\alpha = h_1\lambda, \quad a\beta = h_2\lambda, \quad a(1 - \gamma) = h_3\lambda \tag{1}$$

where $h_1 h_2 h_3$ are integers.

These equations express the condition that the secondary waves of wave-length λ from a molecule, considered for simplicity as being at the origin of coordinates, should be in phase with those from its neighbours along the three axes, and that therefore the secondary waves from all the molecules in the crystal must be in phase in the direction whose cosines are $\alpha\beta\gamma$.

Laue considers some thirteen of the most intense spots in the pattern. Owing to the high symmetry of the figure, the whole pattern is a repetition of that part of it contained in an octant. Thus these thirteen represent a very large proportion of all the spots in the figure. For these spots he obtains corresponding integers $h_1 h_2 h_3$ which are always small, the greatest being the number 10. But even if one confines oneself to integers less than 10, there are a great many combinations of $h_1 h_2 h_3$ which might give spots on the photographic plate which are in fact not there, and there is no obvious difference between the numbers $h_1 h_2 h_3$ which correspond to actual spots, and those which are not represented.

To explain this Laue assumes that only a few definite wavelengths are present in the incident radiation, and that equations (1) are merely approximately satisfied.

Considering equations (1) it is clear that when $h_1 h_2 h_3$ are fixed λ/a can only have one value. However if $h_1 h_2 h_3$ are multiplied by an integral factor p, equations (1) can still be satisfied, but now by a wave-length λ/p. By adjusting the numbers $h_1 h_2 h_3$ in this way, Laue accounts for all the spots considered by means of five different wave-lengths in the incident radiation. They are

$$\lambda = .0377a$$
$$\lambda = .0563a$$
$$\lambda = .0663a$$
$$\lambda = .1051a$$
$$\lambda = .143a.$$

However, this explanation seems unsatisfactory. Several sets of numbers $h_1 h_2 h_3$ can be found giving values of λ/a approximating very closely to the five values above and yet no spot in the figure corresponds to these numbers. I think it is possible to explain the formation of the interference pattern without assuming that the incident radiation consists of merely a small number of wave-lengths. The explanation which I propose, on the contrary, assumes the existence of a continuous spectrum over a wide range in the incident radiation, and the action of the crystal as a diffraction grating will be considered from a different point of view which leads to some simplification.

Regard the incident light as being composed of a number of independent pulses, much as Schuster does in his treatment of the action of an ordinary line grating. When a pulse falls on a plane it is reflected. If it falls on a number of particles scattered over a plane which are capable of acting as centres of disturbance when struck by the incident pulse, the secondary waves from them will build up a wave front, exactly as if part of the pulse had been reflected from the plane, as in Huygens' construction for a reflected wave.

The atoms composing the crystal may be arranged in a great many ways in systems of parallel planes, the simplest being the cleavage planes of the crystal. I propose to regard each interference maximum as due to the reflection of the pulses in the incident beam in one of these systems. Consider the crystal as divided up in this way into a set of parallel planes. A minute fraction of the energy of a pulse traversing the crystal will be reflected from each plane in succession, and the corresponding interference maximum will be produced by a train of reflected pulses. The pulses in the train follow each other at intervals of $2d\cos\theta$, where θ is the angle of incidence of the primary rays on the plane, d is the shortest distance between successive identical planes in the crystal. Considered thus, the crystal actually 'manufactures' light of definite wave-lengths, much as, according to Schuster, a diffraction grating does. The difference in this case lies in the extremely short length of the waves. Each incident pulse produces a train of pulses and this train is resolvable into a series of wave-lengths λ, $\lambda/2$, $\lambda/3$, $\lambda/4$ etc. where $\lambda = 2d\cos\theta$.

Though to regard the incident radiation as a series of pulses is equivalent to assuming that all wave-lengths are present in its spectrum, it is probable that the energy of the spectrum will be greater for certain wave-lengths than for others. If the curve representing the distribution of energy in the spectrum rises to a maximum for a definite λ and falls off on either side, the pulses may be supposed to have a certain average 'breadth' of the order of this wave-length. Thus it is to be expected that the intensity of the spot produced by a train of waves from a set of planes in the crystal will depend on the value of the wave-length, viz. $2d\cos\theta$. When $2d\cos\theta$ is too small the successive pulses in the train are so close that they begin to neutralize each other and when again $2d\cos\theta$ is too large the pulses follow each other at large intervals and the train contains little energy. Thus the intensity of a spot depends on the energy in the spectrum of the incident radiation characteristic of the corresponding wave-length.

Another factor may influence the intensity of the spots. Consider a beam of unit cross-section falling on the crystal. The strength of a pulse reflected from a single plane will depend on the number of atoms in that plane which conspire in reflecting the beam. When two sets of planes are compared which produce trains of equal wave-length it is to be expected that if in one set of planes twice as many atoms reflected the beam as in the other set, the corresponding spot will be more intense. In what follows I have assumed that it is reasonable to compare sets of planes in which the same number of atoms on a plane are traversed by unit cross-section of the incident beam, and it is for this reason that I have chosen the somewhat arbitrary parameters by which the planes will be defined. They lead to an easy comparison of the effective density of atoms in the planes. The effective density is the number of atoms per unit area when the plane with the atoms on it is projected on the xy axis, perpendicular to the incident light.

Laue considers that the molecules of zinc-blende are arranged at the corners of cubes, this being the simplest of the cubical point systems. According to the theory of Pope and Barlow this is not the most probable arrangement. For an assemblage of spheres of equal volume to be in closest packing, in an arrangement exhibiting cubic symmetry, the atoms must be arranged in such a way that the element of the pattern is a cube with an atom at each corner and one at the centre of each cube face. With regard to the crystal of zinc-blende under consideration zinc and sulphur being both divalent have equal valency volumes and their arrangement is probably of this kind. It will be assumed for the present that the zinc and sulphur atoms are identical as regards their power of emitting secondary waves.

Take the origin of coordinates at the centre of any atom, the axes being parallel to the cubical axes of the crystal. The distance between successive atoms of the crystal along the axes is taken for convenience to be $2a$.

All atoms in the xz plane will have coordinates $pa\ 0\ qa$ where p and q are integers and $p + q$ is even. See fig. 1 in text.

The same holds for atoms in the yz plane. In fig. 1, suppose the phase difference between vibrations from successive atoms along the three axes, when waves of wave-length λ fall on the crystal, to be $2\pi h_1, 2\pi h_2, 2\pi h_3$. Then in order that the vibrations from those atoms, which are arranged in the figure at the centres of the cube faces, should also be in phase, one must have $h_1/2 - h_3/2 =$ an integer, $h_2/2 - h_3/2 =$ an integer.

41

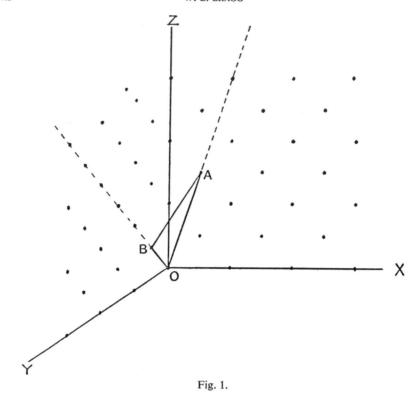

Fig. 1.

This condition is simply expressed by saying that h_1, h_2, h_3 must all be even or all odd integers. If the three simplest values of h_1, h_2, h_3 for a spot on the plate are not all odd, or all even, then these numbers must be doubled to make them even and the wave-length accordingly halved.

When this is done, it can be seen that for each value of h_3 there is a series of values of h_1 and h_2. These numbers all give spots in the photograph if the corresponding value of a/λ lies within a certain range.

The other arrangements of cubical point systems cannot, as far as I can see, give such a complete series. The other possible arrangements have for elements of their pattern (1) a cube with a molecule or atom at each corner, the arrangement which Laue pictured, or (2) a cube with a molecule at each corner and one at the centre. Neither arrangement will fit the system of planes given above. It is only the third point system, the element of whose pattern has a molecule at each corner and one at the centre of each cube face, which will lend itself to the system of planes found to represent spots in the photograph.

This last system, seeing that it forms an arrangement of the closest possible packing, is according to the results of Pope and Barlow the most probable one for the cubic form of zinc sulphide.

A photograph was taken of the crystal oriented so that the pattern obtained was perfectly symmetrical. The crystal was then tilted through 3° about a line perpendicular to the incident beam and to one of the cubical axes. This distorted the pattern considerably, but corresponding spots in the two patterns are easily to be recognised. The points which I wish to consider especially are the following.

In the first place, the spots in the distorted pattern are all displaced exactly as would be expected if they were reflections in planes fixed in the crystal. For instance, when the reflecting plane contains the line, about which the crystal was tilted through 3°, it can be ascertained that the movement of the spot corresponds to a deviation of the reflected beam through 6°. This alone is, I think, strong evidence that the wave-length λ is elastic, and not confined to a few definite values, and that equations (1) are satisfied rigorously and not merely approximately.

Besides the distortion of the figure due to the tilting of the crystal, a very marked alteration in the intensity of the spots is to be noticed. This is especially marked for those spots which are near the centre of the pattern, but not on or near the axis about which the crystal is tilted. This is probably due to the fact that for these spots a considerable change in wave-length has taken place.

When the angle of incidence θ of the primary beam on a set of reflecting planes varies, the value of $2d\cos\theta$ is altered and the alteration for the same $\delta\theta$ is greater the greater θ is.

One spot in particular changes from being hardly visible in the symmetrical pattern to being by far the most intense when the crystal is tilted. It can easily be calculated from the position of the spot that the value of $\cos\theta$ changes from .19 to .12 when the crystal is tilted. This corresponds to a change in the value of a/λ from 4.3 to 6.5, and it was found before that spots corresponding to the former wave-lengths were weak, those corresponding to the latter intense.

A curious feature of the photographs may be explained by regarding the spots as formed by reflection. As the distance of the photographic plate from the crystal is altered, the shape of each individual spot varies. At first round, they become more and more elliptical as the plate is moved further away. A reason for this is found in the following. If the incident beam is not perfectly parallel, but slightly conical, rays will strike the crystal at slightly different angles. Regard the crystal as a set of reflecting planes perpendicular to the plane of the paper (fig. 2). The rays striking the reflecting planes on the upper part of the crystal on the whole meet them at a less angle of incidence than those striking the planes at the bottom; the latter are deflected more, and the rays tend on reflection to come to a focus in a horizontal line. On the other hand, rays deviating from the axial direction in a horizontal plane diverge still more after reflection. Thus as the plate is removed from the crystal, the spots up to a certain distance become more and more elliptical.

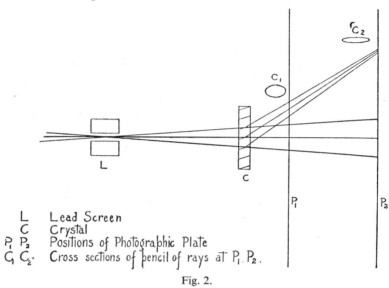

L   Lead Screen
C   Crystal
P₁ P₂   Positions of Photographic Plate
C₁ C₂·   Cross sections of pencil of rays at P₁ P₂.

Fig. 2.

The atoms of a crystal may be arranged in 'doubly infinite' series of parallel rows, as well as in 'singly infinite' series of planes. The incident pulse falls on atom after atom in one of these rows, if the row is not parallel to the wave front, and secondary waves are emitted, one from each atom, at definite time intervals. Along any direction lying on a certain circular cone with the row of atoms as axis, these secondary waves will be all in phase, one generator of the cone being, of course, parallel to the direction of the incident radiation. If the row of atoms makes a small angle with the direction, this cone with vertex at the crystal slip may now be considered to cut the photographic plate in an almost circular ellipse passing through the big central spot. Drawing the ellipses which correspond to the most densely packed rows of the crystal, a spot is to be expected at the intersection of two ellipses, for this means that pulses from a doubly infinite set of atoms are in that direction in agreement of phase. Thus it ought to be possible to arrange the spots in the photograph on these ellipses, in whatever way the crystal is oriented, and indeed they appear in all cases. They come out very strongly in the photographs taken with copper sulphate crystals.

So far it has been assumed that the atoms of zinc and sulphur act in an identical manner with regard to the production of secondary waves, but this assumption is not necessary. What is brought out so strongly by the analysis is this; that the point system to be considered has for element of its pattern a point at each corner of the cube and one at the centre of each cube face. In the arrangement assigned to cubical zinc sulphide and similar crystals by Pope and Barlow, this point system is characteristic of both the arrangement of the individual atoms regarded as equal spheres, and of the arrangement of atoms which are in every way identical as regards nature, orientation, and neighbours in the pattern. The atoms of zinc, for instance, in the zinc blende are grouped four together tetrahedron-wise, and as these little tetrahedra are all similarly oriented and are arranged themselves in the above point system, atoms of zinc identical in all respects will again be arranged in this point system. Which of these factors it is that decides the form of the interference pattern might be found by experiments with crystals in which the point system formed by the centres of all the atoms differs from that formed by the centres of identical atoms.

In conclusion, I wish to thank Professor Pope for his kind help and advice on the subject of crystal structure.

Kristalle von chlorsaurem Kali zeigen häufig eine sehr merkwürdige Erscheinung. Sie reflektieren analoge Farben, wie man sie bei dünnen Häutchen erhält, aber sehr glänzend und rein. Diese Farben sind von Stokes *untersucht worden, der fand, daß sie von einer periodischen Spaltung in einer Reihe äquidistanter Ebenen herrühren. Die Ebene, in der diese Spaltung erfolgt, bildet eine Unstetigkeit in dem Medium, und ein sehr kleiner Teil des auf die Ebene fallenden Lichtes wird reflektiert. Wenn weißes Licht auf den Kristall fällt, vereinigen sich diese Zwillingsebenen, um es in das Innere des Kristalls hinein zu reflektieren. Es ist eine sehr auffallende Eigentümlichkeit der Reflexion beim Auffallen weißen Lichtes auf den Kristall, daß das reflektierte Licht bei irgendeinem Einfallswinkel so rein ist, daß man es fast monochromatisch nennen kann. Beispielsweise kann der Kristall eine Bande im gelben Teile des Spek-*

trums reflektieren, deren Breite kaum größer ist als der Abstand zwischen den gelben Quecksilberlinien.[1] *Lord* Rayleigh *hat den Gegenstand mathematisch behandelt und gezeigt, daß wir in dem Kristall eine regelmäßige Wiederholung nahezu äquidistanter Zwillingsebenen annehmen müssen. 'Bei jedem Einfallswinkel gibt es eine besondere Wellenlänge, für welche die Phasen der verschiedenen Reflexionen untereinander übereinstimmen. Die Auswahl des Lichtes einer besonderen Wellenlänge würde somit nach demselben Prinzip erfolgen wie in Beugungsspektren und würde einen hohen Vollkommenheitsgrad erreichen können.'*

Die besonderen Merkmale der Reflexion sind sonach folgende: Wenn weißes Licht auf den Kristall auffällt, wird es von einer Gruppe paralleler Ebenen im Innern des Kristalls reflektiert und nicht von irgendeiner einzelnen Fläche. Das reflektierte Licht kommt einem monochromatischen Strahlenbündel nahe. Das weiße Licht geht durch den Kristall unverändert hindurch, davon abgesehen, daß sein Spektrum von einer dunklen Bande durchquert wird, welche dem Licht entspricht, das reflektiert worden ist.

Die Analogie zwischen diesem Effekt und der Beugung eines Röntgenstrahles durch einen Kristall liegt auf der Hand. In dem Kristall haben wir eine Gruppe von Netzebenen, die parallel und äquidistant sind, und von denen jede einzelne Bruchteil jeder über sie hingehenden Welle beugt. Im Innern des Kristalls wird daher die Reflexion eines Teiles des Röntgenstrahlenbündels erfolgen. Wenn wir annehmen, daß die einfallenden Röntgenstrahlen weißem Licht insofern entsprechen, als sie sämtliche Wellenlängen enthalten und ein kontinuierliches Spektrum besitzen, wird jede Gruppe von Netzebenen in dem Kristall eine schmale Bande des Spektrums reflektieren. Wenn ein schmales Röntgenstrahlenbündel auf einen kleinen Kristall als Ganzes auffällt, reflektieren die verschiedenen Netzebenensysteme des Kristalls die Strahlen, und wir haben dann eine Reihe reflektierter Strahlenbündel, die sich von dem Kristall aus nach allen Richtungen hin ausbreiten.

Die Reflexion unterscheidet sich von jener am Kaliumchloratkristall dadurch, daß bei letzterem nur eine Gruppe von Ebenen vorhanden ist, in denen der Kristall sich spaltet. Auf der anderen Seite ist eine unendliche Anzahl von Netzebenengruppen vorhanden, deren jede theoretisch eine schmale Bande der einfallenden Röntgenstrahlung reflektiert. In der Praxis braucht man nur eine begrenzte Anzahl dieser Reflexionen zu berücksichtigen. Die übrigen sind zu schwach, um wahrnehmbar zu sein.

W. L. Bragg,
Jahrb. d. Rad. u. Elektr. **11** (1915) 350

---

[1] Siehe R. W. Wood, *Physical Optics*, S. 161.

10. Über die Kristallröntgenogramme, by G. WULFF (1913)

▬

11. Loi générale de la diffraction des rayons Röntgen par les cristaux, by G. FRIEDEL (1913)

▬

12. M. LAUE (1913)

▬

13. G. FRIEDEL (1913)

▬

14. P. P. EWALD (1914)

102.2. M. Laue kommt zu den folgenden Resultaten seiner theoretischen Betrachtungen. Die von dem primären Röntgenstrahle getroffenen Kristallmoleküle werden zu Schwingungszentra, und die von ihnen ausgesandten Wellen interferieren untereinander. Die schwarzen Punkte des Kristallröntgenogramms entsprechen den entstandenen Richtungen der maximalen Helligkeit. Beziehen wir die ganze Erscheinung auf das rechtwinklige Koordinatensystem, dessen Anfang in einem Punkte des Raumgitters des Kristalls liegt, durch den der primäre Strahl geht, und nennen wir a_{1x}, a_{1y}, a_{1z}, a_{2x}, a_{2y}, ... die Projektionen der Kanten a_1, a_2, a_3 des Elementarparallelepipeds des Raumgitters auf die Koordinatenachsen, α_0, β_0, γ_0 die Richtungskosinus des primären Strahles und α, β, γ diejenigen des Helligkeitsmaximums, so kommen wir nach M. Laue zu den folgenden Gleichungen, die die Richtung des Helligkeitsmaximums bestimmen:

$$a_{1x}\alpha + a_{1y}\beta + a_{1z}\gamma = h_1\lambda + a_{1x}\alpha_0 + a_{1y}\beta_0 + a_{1z}\gamma_0,$$

$$a_{2x}\alpha + a_{2y}\beta + a_{2z}\gamma = h_2\lambda + a_{2x}\alpha_0 + a_{2y}\beta_0 + a_{2z}\gamma_0, \qquad (1)$$

$$a_{3x}\alpha + a_{3y}\beta + a_{3z}\gamma = h_3\lambda + a_{3x}\alpha_0 + a_{3y}\beta_0 + a_{3z}\gamma_0.$$

Hier ist λ die Wellenlänge und h_1, h_2, h_3 drei willkürliche ganze Zahlen.

Nun ziehen wir unmittelbar eine weitere Folgerung aus diesen Gleichungen. Multiplizieren wir die Gleichungen mit je einer ganzen Zahl ξ, η, ζ, die prim zueinander sind, und addieren.

Wir kommen zu der Gleichung:

$$(\xi a_{1x} + \eta a_{2x} + \zeta a_{3x})\alpha + (\xi a_{1y} + \eta a_{2y} + \zeta a_{3y})\beta + (\xi a_{1z} + \eta a_{2z} +$$
$$+ \zeta a_{3z})\gamma = \lambda(\xi h_1 + \eta h_2 + \zeta h_3) + (\xi a_{1x} + \eta a_{2x} + \zeta a_{3x})\alpha_0 +$$
$$+ (\xi a_{1y} + \eta a_{2y} + \zeta a_{3y})\beta_0 + (\xi a_{1z} + \eta a_{2z} + \zeta a_{3z})\gamma_0. \tag{2}$$

Die Größe $\xi a_{1i} + \eta a_{2i} + \zeta a_{3i}$ ist die Summe der Projektionen der drei Kanten eines Parallelepipeds auf die entsprechende Koordinatenachse. Es ist also die Projektion der Diagonale dieses Parallelepipeds auf diese Achse. Das auf den Kanten ξa_1, ηa_2, ζa_3 konstruierte Parallelepiped hat als Diagonale die Punktreihe des Raumgitters, deren kristallographisches Symbol $[\xi\eta\zeta]$ ist. Die Länge der Diagonale, die den Abstand der benachbarten Punkte dieser Reihe bestimmt—der Parameter der Punktreihe $[\xi\eta\zeta]$—, wollen wir durch P bezeichnen. Bezeichnen wir noch den Kosinus dieser Diagonale mit dem primären Strahle durch ω_0 und mit dem Helligkeitsmaximum durch ω, so können wir die Gleichung (2) in der von dem Koordinatensystem unabhängigen Form schreiben:

$$P(\omega - \omega_0) = \lambda(\xi h_1 + \eta h_2 + \zeta h_3). \tag{3}$$

Da $(\xi h_1 + \eta h_2 + \zeta h_3)$ ganze Zahl ist, so kann diese Gleichung folgendermaßen gelesen werden: 'Jede Punktreihe des Raumgitters (jede kristallographisch mögliche Kante des Kristalls) wird zur Achse von Helligkeitsmaxima, die eine Schar Kegel bilden. Jedem Kegel entspricht der Gangunterschied von gerader Anzahl Wellenlängen, die der Differenz der Projektionen des Parameters der Punktreihe auf die Erzeugende des Kegels und auf den primären Strahl gleich ist.'

3. Zwischen diesen Kegeln der maximalen Helligkeit zeichnen sich diejenigen aus, die dem Gangunterschiede Null entsprechen. Solche Kegel werde ich 'Nullkegel' nennen. Die Bedingung für diesen Kegel ist

$$\xi h_1 + \eta h_2 + \zeta h_3 = 0. \tag{4}$$

Diese Bedingung, in Worten gefaßt, kann folgendermaßen lauten:

'Die Achsen der Nullkegel sind die Punktreihen des Raumgitters, die in einer Netzebene (in einer möglichen Kristallfläche) liegen. Diese Ebene hat das kristallographische Symbol $(h_1 h_2 h_3)$, wo die Zahlen $h_1 h_2 h_3$ vom gemeinschaftlichen Divisor befreit sein sollen. Alle Kegel haben außer dem primären Strahle noch eine gemeinschaftliche Erzeugende, die das Hauptnullmaximum bildet. Dieses Hauptmaximum ist zugleich das Helligkeitsmaximum der Netzebene $(h_1 h_2 h_3)$ und ist von der Ordnung Null. Da dieses Maximum durch das Zusammensetzen einer ganzen Schar Maxima gebildet wird, die den einzelnen in der Netzebene gelegenen Punktreihen entsprechen, so übertrifft seine Helligkeit bei weitem die Helligkeit der einzelnen Komponenten.

Es liegt nahe vorauszusetzen, daß auf den Photogrammen nur dieses Maximum sichtbar wird, so daß die Punkte der Kristallröntgenogramme die Nullmaxima der Netzebenen des Raumgitters vorstellen. Ich werde deshalb die Punkte der Kristallröntgenogramme auch Nullpunkte nennen.

Aus dem oben Gesagten folgt unmittelbar, daß die Nullpunkte auf den Ellipsen (Nullellipsen) liegen sollen, die durch den Mittelpunkt der Interferenzfigur gehen[1]. Da die Netzebenen in den Punktreihen des Gitters sich schneiden, so müssen die Nullellipsen durch mehrere den verschiedenen Netzebenen entsprechende Nullpunkte gehen.

4. Wir sind jetzt zur Möglichkeit gekommen, die Kristallröntgenogramme mit dem Raumgitter des Kristalls in einen einfachen Zusammenhang zu bringen. Tragen wir die Nullpunkte auf die Kugeloberfläche auf. Es sei (Fig. 1) C der Mittelpunkt der Interferenzfigur und m ein Nullpunkt. Durch C und m gehen Nullkegel durch, deren Achsen auf einer Netzebene K liegen, die den Bogen Cm senkrecht halbiert. Das ist die Netzebene, die das Maximum m zum Nullmaximum hat. Auf diese Weise ist jedes Kristallröntgenogramm in eine stereographische Projektion des Kristalls leicht zu verwandeln. Die Anwendung auf die Kristallstruktur ist naheliegend.

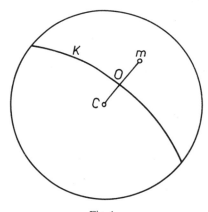

Fig. 1.

5. Bleiben wir bei den rechtwinkeligen Koordinatenachsen und bei der ebenen Projektion, so kommen wir zu der Beziehung zwischen den Kordinaten u, v, w der Normale der Netzebene und den Koordinaten x, y, z des

---

[1] Solche Nullellipsen sind sehr gut auf dem Photogramm, Fig. 8, Tafel III [not reproduced] der Arbeit von M. Laue, W. Friedrich und P. Knipping sichtbar. Dem Verfasser des vorliegenden Aufsatzes ist es neulich gelungen, durch alle Punkte der Fig. 5, Tafel II und der Fig. 7, Tafel III Nullellipsen zu ziehen; somit ist es bewiesen, daß diese Punkte wirklich Nullmaxima vorstellen.

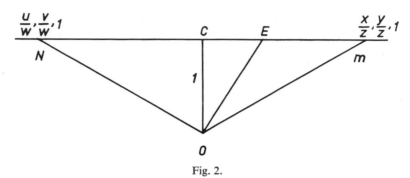

Fig. 2.

dieser Ebene entsprechenden Helligkeitsmaximums. Es sei ON (Fig. 2) die Normale der Netzebene OE, Om die Richtung des dieser Ebene entsprechenden Maximums und Nm die Ebene des Röntgenogramms im Abstande 1 vom Koordinatenanfang O. Da der Winkel COE den Winkel EOm gleich ist, so bekommen wir leicht die Beziehung

$$\frac{2w\sqrt{(u^2 + v^2)}}{u^2 + v^2 - w^2} = \frac{\sqrt{(x^2 + y^2)}}{z}$$

Diese Gleichung wird erfüllt, wenn

$$x : y : z = 2uw : 2vw : (u^2 + v^2 - w^2). \tag{5}$$

Dies ist aber die Beziehung, die M. Laue zwischen den Koordinaten des Helligkeitsmaximums und den Zahlen h_1, h_2, h_3 gefunden hat. Daraus ersehen wir, daß

$$u : v : w = h_1 : h_2 : h_3 \tag{6}$$

6. Wir sind jetzt imstande, die von W. L. Bragg[1] beobachtete Erscheinung zu erklären, die er für die Reflexion der Röntgenstrahlen hielt. Wir müssen dabei berücksichtigen, daß die Kristallmoleküle die Wellen nach allen Seiten aussenden, daß also die Erscheinung in der Interferenz der Eigenstrahlung der Moleküle besteht.

Wenn eine Kristallfläche oder eine Spaltungsfläche des Kristalls K (Fig. 3) gegen den primären Strahl SS_0 um den Winkel SON geneigt ist, wo ON die Normale der Fläche ist und wenn Ph die photographische Platte ist, so muß es einen Nullkegel S_0Om und ein Maximum m geben. Das Maximum m muß also so gelegen sein, daß der Winkel SON gleich mON ist, und daß

[1] *Nature* **90** (1912) 410.

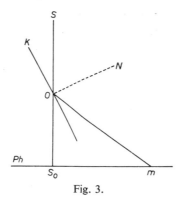

Fig. 3.

die Flächennormale *ON* in der Ebene von *SO* und *Om* liegt. Wir haben hier die Erscheinung, die mit der Reflexion formell identisch ist, die aber auch in den durchgehenden Strahlen beobachtet werden soll, da der Winkel *CO* (Fig. 1) dem Winkel *Om* gleich ist und da die Ebene *Cm* senkrecht auf *K* steht (die Normale von *K* enthält). Man kann also die ganze Erscheinung als die Reflexion des primären Strahles an den Netzebenen des Raumgitters auffassen, unabhängig davon, ob diese Netzebenen die äußere Begrenzung des Kristalls bilden, oder im Inneren desselben durchlaufen.

7. Spezialisieren wir jetzt unsere Betrachtungen auf den von M. Laue näher untersuchten Fall des kubischen Raumgitters, und zwar auf den Fall, wo der primäre Strahl parallel einer Würfelkante geht. Es seien das Nullmaximum einer Netzebene $(h_1h_2h_3)$ und die Punktreihe $[\xi\eta\zeta]$, die nicht in der Ebene $(h_1h_2h_3)$ liegt, gegeben. Für diesen Fall haben wir

$$P = a\sqrt{(\xi^2 + \eta^2 + \zeta^2)}$$

und

$$\omega_0 = \zeta/\sqrt{(\xi^2 + \eta^2 + \zeta^2)}.$$

Wenn wir noch die Beziehung (5) berücksichtigen, die zwischen den Koordinaten der Normale der Netzebene und denjenigen ihres Maximums bestehen, so bekommen wir für ω, die Formel

$$\omega = \frac{2h_1h_3\xi + 2h_1h_3\eta + (h_1^2 + h_2^2 - h_3^2)\zeta}{(h_1^2 + h_2^2 + h_3^2)\sqrt{(\xi^2 + \eta^2 + \zeta^2)}}.$$

Tragen wir diese Werte von P, ω_0 und ω ins (3) ein, so bekommen wir den Ausdruck

$$\lambda/a = 2h_3/(h_1^2 + h_2^2 + h_3^2), \tag{7}$$

den schon M. Laue gefunden hat. Dieser Ausdruck sagt, daß das Nullmaximum einer Netzebene aus den Wellen besteht, deren Länge von den Koordinaten der Netzebene abhängt. Um diesen Zusammenhang zwischen der Netzebene und der Wellenlänge näher zu enthüllen, wollen wir zuerst die Zahlen h_1, h_2, h_3 von dem gemeinschaftlichen Divisor befreien, da diese Zahlen gemäß der Gleichungen (1) nicht prim zueinander zu sein brauchen. Indem wir diesen Divisor mit m bezeichnen, bekommen wir die Formel

$$\frac{\lambda}{a} = \frac{2h'_3}{m(h'^2_1 + h'^2_2 + h'^2_3)}.$$

Diesen Ausdruck schreiben wir weiter in der Form

$$\frac{\lambda}{2} = \frac{1}{m} \frac{a^3}{a^2\sqrt{(h'^2_1 + h'^2_2 + h'^2_3)}} \frac{h'_3}{\sqrt{(h'^2_1 + h'^2_2 + h'^2_3)}}$$

Die Größe $a^2\sqrt{(h'^2_1 + h'^2_2 + h'^2_3)}$ ist der Flächeninhalt des elementaren Parallelogramms der Netzebene $(h_1 h_2 h_3)$, und a^3, dividiert durch diesen Flächeninhalt, ist gleich dem Abstande zweier benachbarten Netzebenen. Wir bezeichnen diesen Abstand durch Δ. Der Faktor $h'_3/\sqrt{(h'^2_1 + h'^2_2 + h'^2_3)}$ ist der Kosinus des Winkels zwischen der Normale der Netzebene und dem primären Strahle. Wir bezeichnen ihn durch ε. Als Resultat bekommen wir die Formel:

$$\frac{\lambda}{2} = \frac{\Delta\varepsilon}{m}. \qquad (8)[1]$$

Die Wellen werden also durch das Raumgitter sozusagen filtriert. Jedes Null-maximum enthält eine harmonische Reihe von Wellen, deren halbe Grund-welle gleich der Projektion der Schichtendicke des Raumgitters nach dieser Netzebene auf die Richtung des primären Strahles ist.

Wir kommen also zu dem Resultate, daß die Erscheinung wesentlich von der Lage des Kristalls gegen den einfallenden primären Strahl abhängt, und daß also jeder Lage des Kristalls eine besondere Interferenzfigur und ein besonderes Kristallröntgenogramm entsprechen kann. Das erklärt die Not-wendigkeit, die Kristallplatte genau zu justieren, um dasselbe Bild zu be-kommen; das erklärt auch, warum die Figuren der Abhandlung von M. Laue, W. Friedrich und P. Knipping, die nur um eine Neigung von 3° derselben Kristallplatte sich unterscheiden, in einer so auffallenden Weise verschieden sind. Das aber verhindert uns in keiner Weise, jedesmal das Kristallröntgenogramm in den einfachen Zusammenhang mit dem Raumgitter des Kristalls zu bringen, wie es oben erläutert wurde.

Moskau, Kristallographisches Laboratorium der städtischen Schaniawski-Universität

(Eingegangen 3. Februar 1913)

---

[1] [Note that paper 9, containing Bragg's reflection law, was not yet known to the author. Ed.]

11. G. Wulff a fait connaître récemment[1] une loi qui simplifie beaucoup l'interprétation des photogrammes de Friedrich et Knipping, de Broglie, etc. Le raisonnement de Wulff n'est pas rigoureux et fait intervenir une hypothèse inutile. Mais le résultat, ainsi que je me propose de le montrer est absolument général et subsiste quel que soit le réseau et quelle que soit l'incidence. Aucune hypothèse n'est nécessaire, si ce n'est les suivantes :

1° Le rayon incident comprend un spectre continu de longueurs d'onde qui sont de l'ordre de grandeur des paramètres cristallins.

2° Chaque nœud du réseau émet un système d'ondes sphériques en concordance de phase avec le rayon incident.

Ces hypothèses admises, le résultat de Wulff s'en déduit aisément.

D'abord il est clair que, si l'on considère un système de plans réticulaires parallèles du cristal, la direction D, définie par la loi de la réflexion régulière du rayon incident I sur ce système de plans, est celle d'un rayon diffracté possible. Considérons en effet un de ces plans P, et dans ce plan des points quelconque O, O_1, O_2, ... (par exemple des nœuds).

La différence de marche est nulle entre les rayons IOD, IO_1D, etc. Considérons ensuite le plan réticulaire P′, contigu du plan P, et, dans ce plan, des points quelconques (par exemple des nœuds) O', O'_1, O'_2, ... La différence de marche est nulle encore entre les rayons $IO'D$, IO'_1D, ... Quant à la différence de marche d entre les rayons IOD et $IO'D$, elle est égale au double de la projection de l'équidistance des plans PP′ sur le rayon incident. Pour tous les autres plans réticulaires P^n du système, la différence de marche entre IOD et IO^nD sera un multiple entier de d. Par suite, la direction D est celle d'un rayon diffracté dont la longueur d'onde est d ou l'une de ses harmoniques. Il suffira que le rayon incident contienne l'une des longueurs d'onde d, $d/2$, $d/3$, ..., pour que la direction D fournisse un rayon diffracté comportant cette longueur d'onde.

En second lieu, je dis que cette règle donne tous les rayons diffractés possibles. (...)

On peut donc poser en règle générale :

Chaque rayon diffracté suit la loi de la réflexion sur un des systèmes de plans réticulaires du cristal. Il comporte une longueur d'onde fondamentale et toutes ses harmoniques (pour autant que ces longueurs d'onde existent dans le rayon incident). Et la longueur d'onde fondamentale est le double de la projection de l'équidistance des plans du système sur le rayon incident.

On voit que les phénomènes de réflexion observés par de Broglie ne diffèrent pas du phénomène de Laue. Au surplus, la forme extérieure du fragment de cristal n'intervient en rien dans l'orientation des rayons diffractés.

---

[1] *Physikalische Zeitschrift*, t. **XIV** (1913).

La règle énoncée ci-dessus permet de transformer très rapidement les photogrammes en une projection stéréographique des pôles des plans réflecteurs, c'est-à-dire des plans réticulaires du cristal mis en évidence par la diffraction.

Dans le cas (seul utile à considérer en pratique) où le rayon incident est normal à la plaque photographique, la construction est des plus simples. Il suffit, en se servant par exemple du diagramme stéréographique de Wulff, de reporter sur ce diagramme les azimuts des taches de diffraction, puis de mesurer les distances de ces taches au centre de la tache centrale. Le rapport de cette distance à l'écartement du cristal et de la plaque photographique donne la tangente de l'angle que fait le rayon diffracté avec le rayon incident. La moitié de cet angle représente l'angle du plan réflecteur avec le rayon incident, c'est-à-dire l'angle du pôle de ce plan avec le plan de la projection stéréographique. Il est donc aisé de reporter ce pôle sur le diagramme.

12. Die sehr verwunderliche und noch unerklärte Tatsache, daß die spektral hochgradig inhomogenen Impulse der einfallenden Röntgenstrahlung im Kristall Schwingungen von recht genau definierter Wellenlänge hervorrufen (denn nur durch solche läßt sich die Schärfe der beobachteten Interferenzpunkte m. E. einfach erklären), hat gesprächsweise gelegentlich die Deutung gefunden, daß die Auswahl dieser Sinusschwingungen aus allen in den Impulsen vorhandenen eine Funktion des Raumgitters sei. Demgegenüber wollen wir zeigen, daß die (bei Vorhandensein der erforderlichen Schwingungen) nach (8)[1] möglichen Interferenzmaxima überall dicht liegen, so daß die photographische Platte vollständig geschwärzt werden müßte, wenn nicht die in den Funktionen $\Psi(\alpha, \beta)$ ausgesprochenen Eigenschaften der Gitterelemente eine bestimmte endliche Zahl aus den unendlich vielen Wellenlängen der ursprünglichen Strahlung aussonderten. Daß wir uns dabei auf den in den Gleichungen (8) betrachteten besonderen Fall beschränken, ist für das Ergebnis unwesentlich.

Führen wir in der Ebene der photographischen Platte ($z = $ const) Polarkoordinaten ρ, φ ein

$$x = \rho \cos \varphi, \quad y = \rho \sin \varphi,$$

so findet man nach (8) und der Identität $\alpha^2 + \beta^2 + \gamma^2 = 1$:

$$\operatorname{tg}\varphi = h_1/h_2, \quad \rho = (2z \sqrt{u})/|1 - u|, \quad \text{wo} \quad u = h_3^2/(h_1^2 + h_2^2).$$

[1] [this Volume, page 11.]

Es sind also in praxi alle Werte von φ möglich, weil man mit zwei ganzen Zahlen h_1 und h_2 stets das Verhältnis $h_2 : h_1$ jedem vorgeschriebenen Werte beliebig annähern kann. Ist dies Verhältnis festgesetzt, so kann man noch immer durch geeignete Wahl von h_1 und h_3 mit u bis auf einen beliebig kleinen Fehler jeden Wert erreichen, so daß dasselbe auch für den Radiusvektor ρ gilt.

13. Chaque tache en effet ne correspond pas à une longueur d'onde unique, mais à tout un ensemble d'harmoniques λ, $\lambda/2$, $\lambda/3$, ... Quelle est celle de ces harmoniques ou quelles sont celles de ces harmoniques qui concourent à la formation de telle tache? Il n'est pas aise de le discerner. Il semble que ce seront seulement des essais multipliés analogues à celui de Friedrich et Knipping, réalisés en inclinant graduellement la lame cristalline de manière à faire varier d'une manière continue la longueur d'onde fondamentale de chaque tache qui permettront, grâce aux fortes variations de la longueur d'onde que détermine, pour un même plan réflecteur, une faible inclinaison de la lame cristalline, d'explorer ce spectre et, par comparaison des taches entre elles, par l'observation de celles qui apparaissent ou disparaissent, de fixer les limites du spectre et d'évaluer l'intensité relative de ses diverses radiations simples.

14. In den Interferenzstrahlen treten keine beliebig kleinen Wellenlängen auf, sondern es gibt eine untere Grenze von λ/a (a = Gitterkonstante). Bei Vorhandensein aller Wellenlängen bis herab zu $\lambda = 0$ müßte, wie M. Laue gezeigt hat, die photographische Platte überall geschwärzt werden, weil zu jeder Richtung, deren Cosinus sich wie ganze Zahlen l, m, n verhalten, ein Interferenzstrahl möglich ist. Nun hat aber die überwiegende Mehrzahl von Richtungen ein großzahliges Verhältnis $l : m : n$ und die zugehörigen Wellenlängen sind sehr klein—in der Braggschen Sprechweise liegt dies daran, daß die reflektierenden Flächen hohe Indizes und daher sehr kleine Abstände haben—und daher bildet die Forderung einer unteren Grenze für die auftretenden Wellenlängen die einfachste Erklärung der beschränkten Punktzahl auf den Photographien. Es bleiben nur diejenigen Punkte bestehen, welche durch die Reflexion an den kristallographisch wichtigsten Ebenen von kleinen Indizes gebildet werden.

15. THE REFLECTION OF X-RAYS BY CRYSTALS

by

W. H. Bragg, M. A., F.R.S.

Cavendish Professor of Physics in the University of Leeds

and

W. L. Bragg, B. A.

Trinity College, Cambridge

(*Received April 7—Read April 17, 1913*)

In a discussion of the Laue photographs it has been shown[1] that they may conveniently be interpreted as due to the reflection of X-rays in such planes within the crystal as are rich in atoms. This leads at once to the attempt to use cleavage planes as mirrors, and it has been found that mica gives a reflected pencil from its cleavage plane strong enough to make a visible impression on a photographic plate in a few minutes' exposure. It has also been observed that the reflected pencil can be detected by the ionisation method[2].

For the purpose of examining more closely the reflection of X-rays in this manner we have used an apparatus resembling a spectrometer in form, an ionisation chamber taking the place of the telescope. The collimator is replaced by a lead block pierced by a hole which can be stopped down to slits of various widths. The revolving table in the centre carries the crystal.

When the actual relation between the angles of the crystal mirror and the ionisation chamber has been determined, the mirror and chamber may be swept together through an extended range, keeping the relation between the angles such that the chamber always shows the maximum current for each setting of the crystal. Curves for rock-salt are drawn in figs. 3, I, and 3, II. It will be observed that there are peculiar and considerable variations in the intensity of the reflection at different angles. The three peaks marked A, B, and C are common to the curves of all crystals so far investigated,

[1] W. L. Bragg, *Proc. Camb. Phil. Soc.*, vol. **17** Part I, p. 43 [this Vol. p. 38].
[2] W. H. Bragg, *Nature*, Jan. 23 (1913).

56

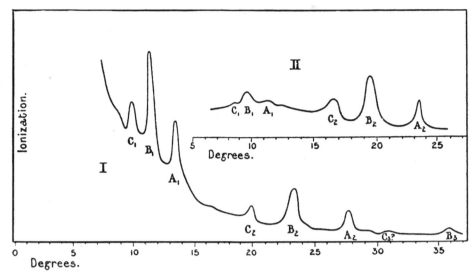

Fig. 3. Reflection (I) from face (100) and (II) from face (111) of rock-salt. The curves show the variation of strength of reflected beam with angle of incidence.

e.g. zinc blende, potassium ferrocyanide, potassium bichromate, quartz, calcite, and sodium ammonium tartrate. They are readily distinguishable by their invariable form, relative magnitudes, and spacings. Moreover, the absorption coefficients of the rays reflected at these separate angles do not vary with the nature of the crystal or the state of the bulb. The use of narrow slits permits a closer examination of these effects; but, of course, it takes much longer time to make, and more space to exhibit.

There can be little doubt the three peaks are, in all cases, due to the same three sets of homogeneous rays, rays which do not change with the state of the bulb, but may well do so with the nature of the anticathode. The absorption coefficient of the least penetrating set is very nearly that found by Chapman for the characteristic radiation of platinum.

The angles at which the special reflections of these rays take place are not the same for all crystals, nor for all faces of the same crystal. There can be little doubt as to the interpretation of these results. The three peaks A, B, and C represent three sets of homogeneous rays, which do not change with the state of the bulb, but may well do so with the nature of the anti-cathode. Rays of a definite quality are reflected from a crystal when, and only when, the crystal is set at the right angle. This is really an alternative way of stating the original deduction of Laue. The three sets of rays are not manufactured in the crystal, because all their properties are independent of the nature of the crystal. An absorbing screen may be interposed with the

57

same effect before or after the rays have struck the crystal. This was found by Moseley and Darwin[1], and we have verified it in the case of aluminium.

Since the reflection angle of each set of rays is so sharply defined, the waves must occur in trains of great length. A succession of irregularly spaced pulses could not give the observed effect. In the application of electromagnetic theory to monochromatic light on the one hand, and to homogeneous X-rays on the other, there is no difference to be considered beyond that of wave-length.

These results do not really affect the use of the corpuscular theory of X-rays. The theory represents the facts of the transfer of energy from electron to X-ray and vice versa, and all the phenomena in which this transfer is the principal event. It can predict discoveries and interpret them. It is useful in its own field. The problem remains to discover how two hypotheses so different in appearance can be so closely linked together.

---

[1] We learn that Messrs. Moseley and Darwin have lately been making experiments similar to some of those recorded here. Their results, which have not been published, agree with ours.

STRUCTURE DETERMINATION OF ROCKSALT, IRON PYRITE AND SPINEL

16. The Structure of Some Crystals as indicated by their Diffraction of X-rays, by W. L. Bragg (1913)

    ▬

17. The Analysis of crystals by the X-ray Spectrometer, by W. L. Bragg (1914)

    ▬

18. Die Berechnung der Kristallstruktur aus Interferenzaufnahmen mit X-Strahlen, by P. P. Ewald (1914)

    ▬

19. Structure of Some Crystals of Spinel Group, by S. Nishikawa (1914)

    ▬

16. It is the object of this paper to extend the analysis used in the case of the zincblende to some other crystals, particularly those of the simple alkaline halides.

In the diagram of the KCl pattern, fig. 3, the spots are represented by dots, their magnitude indicating the strength of the corresponding spot in the photograph. It will be seen how complete the pattern is, and how within a certain range each intersection is represented by a spot in the photograph. It suggests that the diffraction is due to a simple cubic space lattice, for when the elementary parallelepiped is a cube and its edges are taken as axes the indices of the planes naturally take these simple forms.

It is interesting to compare the simple pattern of potassium chloride with those of potassium iodide, potassium bromide, fluorspar, and zincblende. The stereographic projection of KBr (100) is given in fig 4, that of KI being very similar. Both of these are like the patterns of zincblende and fluorspar, and are in marked contrast to that of KCl.

It is evident that some factor has now entered which destroys the simplicity of the arrangement of spots characteristic of potassium chloride. Spots no longer appear at every intersection of the ellipses within a certain region, as in fig. 3.

An examination of the planes in which reflection takes place shows that there is a differentiation between those whose indices are wholly odd and those which have one or more even indices. If those planes alone are considered which have odd indices, the scheme is as complete as it was for the spots of the KCl crystal.

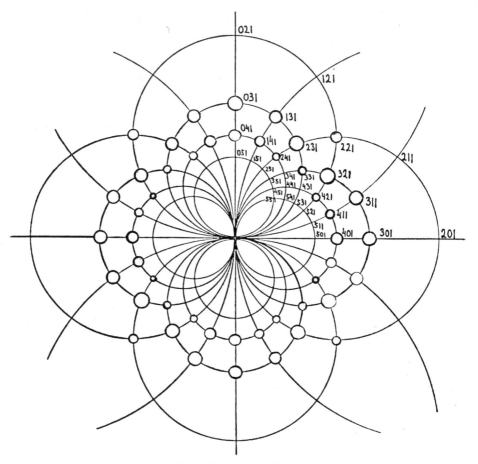

Fig. 3. Potassium chloride.

The same is true for those with an even index except that the intense spots are all further removed from the centre of the picture.

This difference can be explained without our being forced to assume that the diffracting system is anything more than a simple system of identical points. It is sufficient to suppose that the point system has points at the centres of the cube faces as well as at the cube corners. Let a cubic point system of the first kind be taken which has points at cube corners alone, and let points be introduced at the cube face centres in order to turn it into a point system of the so-called 'third kind'. (The 'second kind' is the centred cube.) The spacing of the planes which have odd indices (h, k, l) is not altered by the introduction of the new points, for they all lie on the original planes and only increase their point density. On the other hand, in the

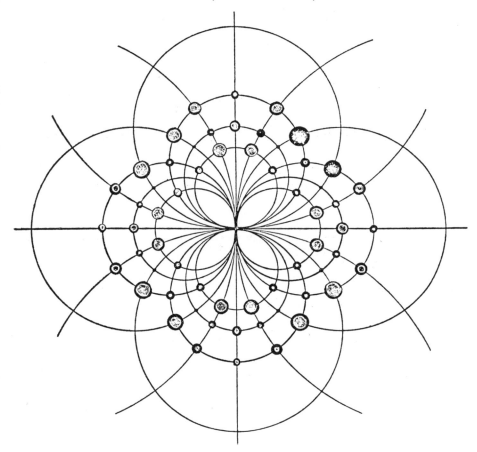

Fig. 4. Potassium bromide.

case of planes having an even index, some of the new points lie halfway between the original planes, the distance between the successive planes of this type must now be halved.

In the case of rock-salt, it is not possible to regard the pattern as completely characteristic of the one point system or the other. Photographs obtained using a thin section of crystal, about 1 mm thick, cut parallel to a cube face, show a pattern very similar to that given by potassium chloride, though in no case are they so simple as the pattern given by the latter crystal; for a considerable amount of difference between the 'odd' and 'even' planes is also evident. A photograph taken with a section 6 mm in thickness is more like one taken with potassium bromide or iodide, the difference between odd and even planes being more marked.

61

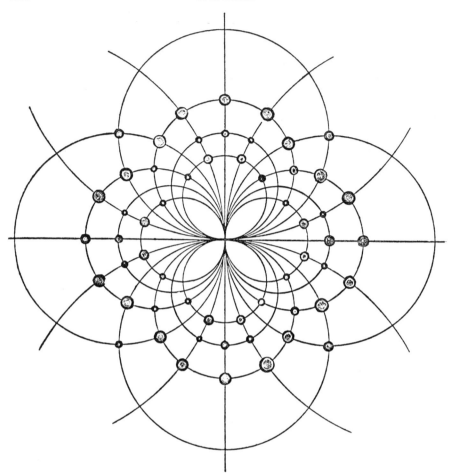

Fig. 9. Rock-salt, 2.5 mm thick.

I think that the rock-salt diffracting system is in some way intermediate between those of potassium chloride and potassium bromide. On comparing the evidence as to the nature of the diffracting systems in these crystals of sodium chloride, and of potassium chloride, bromide, and iodide, it would seem that a very simple explanation of their curious difference may be arrived at when it is considered that in each case diffraction is caused by two different atoms, and that the relative efficiencies of the two vary from crystal to crystal. Any explanation of these differences would be an extremely improbable one which did not assume a similar structure for the whole group of alkaline halides, for these crystals resemble each other very closely in their properties. Yet it has been seen that the space lattice of diffracting points is the simple cubic one in KCl; it is the facecentred cubic lattice in KBr and KI, and that in the case of NaCl the diffracting point system is in some way intermediate between the two space lattices.

Let us consider on what atomic properties the relative efficiencies might depend. It has been firmly established that the absorption of X-rays depends on the relative proportions of the various elements contained in the absorber. It is a purely additive property of the weight of each element per cubic centimetre of the absorber, and does not depend on the manner in which the elements are combined. Also the absorption of homogeneous X-rays increases steadily with the atomic weight of the absorber, except for a sudden discontinuity consisting of a large drop in the absorption coefficient when the atomic weight of the absorber passes through that of the element of which the homogeneous X-rays are the characteristic radiation. There are, however, no discontinuities in the absorption coefficient corresponding to the changes in chemical properties of the elements in the periodic table as one passes to higher atomic weights. It is reasonable, therefore, to assume provisionally that the weight of the atom in the main defines its effectiveness as a diffracting centre, and that two atoms of equal weight are equally effective. In the case of potassium chloride the atoms of potassium and chlorine, of atomic weight 39 and 35.5 respectively, are sufficiently close in atomic weight to act as identical diffracting centres. For rock salt this is no longer true; the atomic weight of sodium and chlorine differ considerably (35.5 to 23), and complications are introduced into the simple pattern characteristic of potassium chloride. In potassium bromide and iodide one atom preponderates so greatly over the other in atomic weight that the diffracting system consists practically of atoms of one kind only, and the pattern can again be assigned to a simple space lattice, but one which is of a different nature to that of potassium chloride. Yet the atoms of alkaline metal and halogen have precisely the same arrangement in all these cases.

Let us distinguish between two kinds of diffracting points by calling them black and white. Then the points must be arranged in such a way that—

1. There are equal numbers of black and white.

2. The arrangement of points black and white taken all together is that of the first cubic space lattice.

3. The arrangement of blacks alone or of whites alone is that of the third cubic space lattice.

An arrangement which gives this result is shown in fig 10.

In this diagram we may associate black centres with the alkaline metal, and white with the halogen, or vice versa. The space lattice formed by the whites is the same as that formed by the blacks, being in each case the face-

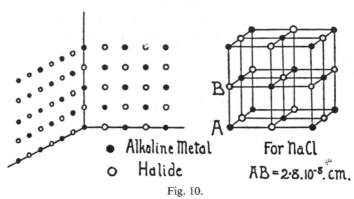

Fig. 10.

ccntred cube. If black and white centres become identical, as in potassium chloride, the diffracting lattice becomes the simple cubic one.

The evidence for this arrangement in the alkaline halides seems very strong, but this does not by any means complete the solution of their structure. It yet remains an open question whether one atom alone is to be associated with each point of the system, so that, for example, the black and white centres actually represent sodium and chlorine atoms in rock salt, or whether the crystal structure is of a more complex nature. It was with the object of discovering the complexity of the diffracting unit of these and other crystals that the series of crystal pattern analyses, which will now be described, were made; their results would seem to indicate clearly the association with each diffracting centre of a single atom.

In a paper to the Royal Society, read in April, 1913, a method was described of analysing the radiations from an X-ray bulb by reflecting them from the face of a crystal, and measuring the ionisation produced by the reflected beam. The results which we obtained with various crystals pointed to the existence of at least three components of the X-ray beam of definite wave-length, reflected from a crystal face when the condition

$$n\lambda = 2d\sin\theta$$

is satisfied for the component and crystal in question. Here λ is the wavelength, θ the glancing angle, and d the distance between successive planes of the crystal structure parallel to the reflecting face. The number n represents the 'order' of the reflection, for several peaks, which can be recognised as belonging to the same homogeneous radiation by the identity of their absorption coefficients, appear at a series of angles whose sines are in the ratio 1 : 2 : 3. This being so, one has a means of finding with some accuracy the ratio of the values of d, the distance between successive planes of the structure, for different crystals and different faces of the same crystal.

The angles at which these peaks are reflected from the various faces of a crystal, and from faces of different crystals, thus afford a great insight into the crystal structure; and, in fact, they supply just that information concerning the structure which the interference patterns do not, for by their means the dimensions of the lattices of different crystals can be accurately compared. The interference patterns only supply information concerning the nature of the lattices.

An analysis of the results obtained when different faces of the same crystal are used to reflect the X-rays in the spectrometer will show how this comparison is carried out.

In the curves for reflection from the three primary planes of the rock-salt crystal (100), (110), (111), (two of which are shown in fig. 16), the peaks occur for each face, but at different angles. From the equation

$$\lambda = 2d \sin \theta,$$

θ being the angle for the peak of the first order in each case, we have, for these three faces

$$d_{(100)} : d_{(110)} : d_{(111)} = 1/\sin \theta_{(100)} : 1/\sin \theta_{(110)} : 1/\sin \theta_{(111)},$$

where $d_{(100)}$ is the distance between planes parallel to the face (100), $\theta_{(100)}$ the angle at which the most prominent peak is reflected from the same face.

The angles for these three faces are 11.4°, 16.0°, 9.8°, respectively. This gives the result

$$d_{(100)} : d_{(110)} : d_{(111)} = 1 : 0.718 : 1.16,$$

whereas

$$1 : 1/\sqrt{2} : 2/\sqrt{3} = 1 : 0.707 : 1.15,$$

these being the theoretical relations for the face-centred cubic space lattice. This does not comprise all the information which a study of these three curves yields, they will be analysed more carefully below. For the present, it is sufficient to indicate what strong reasons there are for assuming that the distances d for the various faces can be accurately compared, by finding the angles at which these peaks occur.

It has been seen that the patterns given by potassium chloride, zincblende, fluorspar, and calcite can be ascribed to diffraction by points of a space lattice. It is now desired to compare the dimensions of the lattices of these crystals; since the absolute value of the wave-length λ of the radiation which forms the peaks is as yet unknown, the dimensions of each lattice will be expressed in terms of λ of the B peak of the Pt-rays as unit.

Since now both the form and the dimensions (in terms of λ) of the elementary parallelepiped are known, for the space lattice arrangement of

65

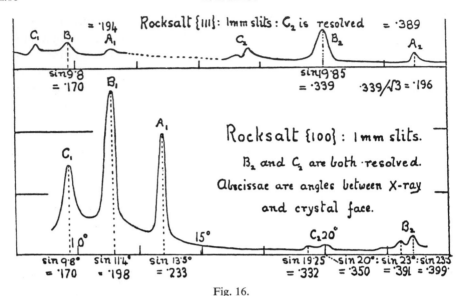

Fig. 16.

diffracting centres of these crystals, it is possible to calculate the volume of this parallelepiped; the volume is that associated with each point of the lattice, it is the inverse of the number of points per unit volume. A multiplication of this volume by the density of the crystal gives the mass associated with each diffracting centre, and it is to be expected that the comparison of these masses (for different crystals) will give some idea as to whether the centre consists of atoms, molecules, or groups of molecules. The results of these calculations for the various crystals are set forth in the table below:—

In this table—

θ = glancing angle of B peak, 1st order.

d = distance between planes parallel to the face investigated.

V = volume of elementary parallelepiped, calculated from this value of d and a knowledge of the nature of the lattice.

ρ = density of crystal.

M = molecular weight of substance.

The last column gives the value of $V\rho/\lambda^3 M$, the mass associated with each diffracting centre divided by the molecular weight of the substance [times λ^3]. This quantity is, therefore, proportional to the number of molecules associated with each centre. For each of these crystals, with the exception of potassium chloride, this quantity is the same within the errors [1] of experiment,

[1] It must be remembered that in calculating this quantity, any percentage error in the value for sin θ is trebled, since sin θ is raised to the third power.

Table X

Crystal	Lattice	Face	θ	d/λ	V/λ^3	ρ	M	$V\rho/\lambda^3 M$
			°					
Sylvine, KCl	Simple cubic	(100)	10.2	2.86	23.4	1.97	74.5	0.605
		(111)	18.0	1.62	22.2			
Rock-salt, NaCl	Face-centred cubic	(100)	11.4	2.53	32.5			
		(110)	16.0	1.82	33.9	2.15	58.5	1.22
		(111)	9.8	2.95	33.5			
Zincblende, ZnS	Face-centred cubic	(110)	16.5	1.76	30.8	4.06	97.0	1.28
Fluorspar, CaF$_2$	Face-centred cubic	(100)	11.7	2.46	29.8	3.18	78.0	1.18
		(111)	10.3	2.79	28.3			
Calcite, CaCO$_3$	Rhombohedral	(100)	10.5	2.74	44.8	2.71	100.0	1.22
		(111)	11.2	2.60				
Iron pyrites, FeS$_2$	Face-centred cubic?*	(100)	12.1	2.39	27.3	5.03	120.0	1.15

* The interference pattern of this crystal has not yet been obtained.

showing that in all these crystals the number of molecules associated with each diffracting centre is the same. Taking into consideration the very different constitution of these crystals, this fact seems to point to the association of one molecule, and one alone, with each diffracting centre; and since in zincblende, fluorspar, and calcite the molecule contains only one heavy atom, the conclusion is arrived at that the space lattice which the diffracting pattern indicates is that formed by the individual zinc or calcium atoms of these crystals.

Potassium chloride forms an apparent exception to this rule, for it has a value for $V\rho/\lambda^3 M$ half that given by the other crystals. The reason for this is clear when it is remembered that in potassium chloride there are two atoms of very nearly equal atomic weights. Each molecule provides two diffracting centres, these being arranged on the simple cubic space lattice. The mass associated with each centre is not that of a molecule, but half of this quantity, and again it is single atoms, but now of two kinds, which form the points of the diffracting space lattice.

It is clear that the argument given here cannot pretend to be a complete proof of this important point. It is conceivable, for example, that in all these crystals it just happens that the molecules are grouped together in fours, and that these groups form the diffracting centres. It is easy to picture such an arrangement for the alkaline halides, in fact this is the arrangement given to all such binary compounds by the theory of closest packing by Pope and

Barlow. Their arrangement would explain satisfactorily the patterns and peak relations of rock-salt, zincblende, and potassium bromide and iodide, for the black and white centres of the diagram given in fig. 10 are represented by tetrahedra composed of four spheres corresponding to atoms of either nature. This would also involve, however, the grouping in fours of the calcium atoms in calcite, and considerable difficulty is experienced in picturing an arrangement which does this. A similar difficulty arises in the case of fluorspar. Potassium chloride is also hard to account for on this arrangement, if it is granted that in this substance potassium and chlorine act almost identically on the X-rays, for the atoms are in the closest packed arrangement of the face-centred cube, while the diffraction pattern is characteristic of the simple cubic lattice. Many more comparisons of crystals are necessary to confirm this point, in the meantime it will be assumed that the simple structure correctly represents the truth, and that the diffracting centres are single atoms.

It has been seen how the comparison of the angles of reflection of a peak from various faces of the same crystal gives information concerning the space lattice structure of the crystal. Further information can be got by studying the dimensions of these peaks. For instance, the curves for two of the three primary planes (100), (110), (111) of rock-salt are given in fig. 16[1] and a reference to these curves will show the very marked difference which there is between the curves for the face (100) and that for the face (111). The (100) curve shows very marked first-order peaks, much smaller second-order peaks, and the merest indication of the peaks of the third order. The (111) curve on the other hand shows the second-order peaks very much stronger than those of the first order.

This difference of the curves corresponds to a difference in the nature of the planes parallel to these faces of the crystal. In the arrangement of black and white points given in fig. 10, it will be seen that the successive planes parallel to (100) contain equal numbers of black and white points; the same is true for the planes (110), which also give a strong first-order reflection. The planes parallel to (111), on the other hand, contain alternately all blacks and all whites. The black points alone form a face-centred lattice, for which the (111) planes are further apart than the (100) planes in the ratio $2/\sqrt{3}$. Thus the small first-order peaks reflected from the (111) face of rock-salt correspond to a periodicity of black planes alone, parallel to (111), the planes containing the heavy chlorine atoms. The presence midway between these planes of the planes containing sodium atoms does not

---

[1] For the experimental evidence in support of this part of my argument I am indebted to my father.

68

completely destroy this reflection of the first order, but it goes a long way towards doing so, while of course the reflection of the second order is reinforced and gives a large second-order peak. This explains the abnormal relative magnitudes of the (111) peaks of different orders as compared with those reflected from the faces (100) and (110).

In accordance with this, it is found that if the sodium is replaced by potassium, the first-order peak reflected from the (111) face becomes too small to be detected, the (111) curve for sylvine appears to have a peak of the first order, at an angle corresponding to planes $1/\sqrt{3}$ as far apart as the planes parallel to (100). In fact, the peaks are where they should be for the simple cubic space lattice.

This argument may be summed up as follows: The arrangement of the heavy atoms of these crystals (potassium chloride with its two equal atoms being an exceptional case) is that of the space lattice which is the skeleton of the crystal, one molecule containing one heavy atom being associated with each point of the lattice. The first-order peaks of the reflection curves are in the positions which theory would give for this space lattice, but the relative magnitudes of the peaks of the first and second orders on any curve are influenced by the positions of the lighter atoms in the crystal structure. If these lighter atoms are so disposed as to lie on the planes of the heavy atom space lattice parallel to the face investigated, then the reflection curve may be said to be of the normal type, it will have large peaks of the first order and small ones of the second. If the lighter atoms are arranged on planes situated halfway between the planes of the lattice, the first-order peaks will be diminished and those of the second order reinforced.

The curves for the faces (100) and (111) of fluorspar show this effect in a very marked manner (fig. 17). This crystal has as its skeleton the face-

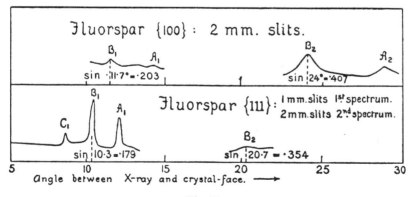

Fig. 17.

centred cubic lattice, the points of the lattice being represented by the calcium atoms. The fluorine atoms are so disposed that the reflection from the (111) planes is now of the normal type, in strong contrast to the curves for rock-salt. On the other hand, the first-order reflection from the face (100) has almost disappeared. The fluorine atoms must be arranged so as to lie on or near the (111) planes of the fundamental lattice, not on the planes (100) as are the sodium atoms of rock-salt.

It is hoped that an examination of the reflection from various faces of all these crystals may lead to the discovery of the exact positions of the lighter atoms in the crystal structure; as yet the experimental results are very incomplete. The results obtained so far seem to fix with some certainty the arrangement of the heavy atoms of these simple crystals, and in the case of the alkaline halides it is hoped that the positions assigned to atoms of both kinds are at any rate close approximations to the truth. A slight symmetrical distortion of the arrangement, which would reduce the crystal symmetry, would not affect any of the results which have been obtained here.

The analysis of crystal structures given here was initially undertaken with the object of discovering the absolute wave-length in centimetres of the homogeneous radiations issuing from the X-ray bulb. The positions of the peaks on the curves gave the wave-length of the corresponding radiations in terms of the dimensions of the crystal space lattice. As long as the complexity of the unit associated with each point of the lattice is unknown, the absolute wave-length cannot be calculated. If the arrangement here assigned to the alkaline halides is right, the dimensions of the lattice can be given in centimetres, for the mass associated with each centre of the lattice can be calculated from the known mass in grammes of the hydrogen atom.

For rock-salt, mass of 1 molecule of NaCl $= 58.5 \times 1.64 \times 10^{-24}$, therefore

$$58.5 \times 1.64 \times 10^{-24} = V\rho = 33.3 \times 2.15 \times \lambda^3,$$

$$\lambda^3 = 1.34 \times 10^{-24}, \qquad \lambda = 1.10 \times 10^{-8} \text{ cm.}$$

From the value for λ, and that for d/λ given in Table X, the dimensions of the lattice for any crystal in this table can be calculated.

Summary

For a number of simple crystals the interference patterns can be ascribed to diffraction of a 'white' radiation by a set of points on a space lattice.

Each of these points is a single atom; if one atom in the molecule is at least twice as heavy as any of the others, it is the lattice formed by these atoms alone which the diffraction pattern reveals. Two atoms of nearly the same atomic weight are nearly equivalent as diffracting centres. The lighter atoms of the molecule are not grouped closely round the heavy atom forming the diffracting space lattice, but occupy intermediate positions. For instance, in sodium chloride the sodium atom has six neighbouring chlorine atoms equally close with which it might pair off to form a molecule of NaCl. The reflection curves and interference patterns given by the alkaline halides agree in assigning the same structure to these salts, the atoms being arranged on a simple cubic space lattice in such a way that rows parallel to the cubic axes contain alternate atoms of either kind. The association of a single heavy atom with each point of the space lattice is indicated by the fact that the mass of each point is proportional to the molecular weight of the substance when each molecule contains one heavy atom. This relation is got from the reflection curves of different crystals. A knowledge of the mass of a hydrogen atom makes it possible to calculate the actual dimensions of a crystal lattice, and so to find the wave-length in centimetres of the homogeneous components of the X-ray beam, this being the object for which these analyses of crystal structure were undertaken.

17. In a former communication to the Royal Society [1], an attempt was made to determine for certain crystals the exact nature of the diffracting system which produces the Laue X-ray diffraction photographs. The crystals chosen for particular investigation were the isomorphous alkaline halides NaCl, KCl, KBr, and KI. As in the original experiments of Laue and his collaborators, a thin section of crystal was placed in the path of a narrow beam of X-rays, and the radiation diffracted by the crystal made its impression on a photographic plate. By noticing what differences were caused in the photograph by the substitution of heavier for lighter atoms in the crystal, a definite arrangement was decided on as that of the diffracting points of the crystalline grating.

Though it was found possible in the case of these simple salts to determine the position of the atoms of alkaline metal and halogen, which constitute the elements of the dimensional diffraction grating, yet this method, which may be called the photographic method, is very limited in its range of applications. It was only the extremely simple nature of the NaCl structure which made its analysis possible. On the other hand, the X-ray spectro-

---

[1] W. L. Bragg, *Roy. Soc. Proc.* A, vol. **89**, p. 249 [this Vol. p. 59].

meter, which has been devised by W. H. Bragg for the purpose of studying the reflection of X-rays by crystals, affords a very much more powerful method of research into the structure of the crystal.

The photographic method works by throwing on the crystal a beam of 'white' X-radiation, and comparing the strength of the beams reflected by various types of planes (nets) of the point system on which the atoms are arranged. The X-ray spectrometer employs a monochromatic radiation and faces are examined in detail one by one. In the first place, the spectrometer tells the distance in centimetres of plane from plane parallel to these faces. Moreover, if the successive planes are of identical composition, the results of the examination show this. If on the other hand the planes occur in groups, each group containing several planes of different nature, it is hoped that the results given below will show how the instrument can be made to give the exact spacing and relative masses of the planes of these groups. This means that we can obtain enough equations to solve the structure of any crystal, however complicated, although the solution is not always easy to find. In this paper I wish to indicate the solution for several types of crystals. For many of the experimental results I am indebted to my father, the rest have been obtained in Leeds with one of the spectrometers which he has constructed.

Parallel to any one of its possible faces, a crystal may be regarded as being built up of a series of planes. Each plane passes through the centres of one or more sets of atoms identical in all respects. The successive planes, encountered in proceeding in a direction perpendicular to the face under consideration, may not be identical in their character. They can always, however, be divided into groups in such a way that each group contains a sample of every kind of plane, arranged in an invariable order. It is proposed to call the distance between the groups $d_{(hkl)}$ when (hkl) are the indices of the crystal face. The pattern of the arrangement of planes repeats itself in the distance $d_{(hkl)}$.

For the structures of rocksalt, fluorspar, zincblende and diamond, the symmetry fixes exactly the position of each atom. Every atom is in such a position that the forces on it must obviously be in equilibrium. For instance, each sulphur in zinc blende is immediately surrounded by four zincs symmetrically placed so as to form the corners of a tetrahedron, of which the sulphur represents the centre of figure. The more distant zincs can be also seen to be so situated as to ensure that their actions on the sulphur atoms balance. The same is true for the other crystals. If we assume that the atoms themselves have no polarity and that their attractions and repulsions of neighbouring atoms are not a function of the orientation of the atoms, it follows that the structures assigned to crystals are those in which there is equilibrium. The stability or otherwise of this equilibrium is another matter.

We will now consider a case for which this does not hold good. The atoms in this case are no longer at the 'centres of the figure' of the structure, they are displaced by a very large amount from these ideal positions, and their exact situation is not fixed by the symmetry.

Iron Pyrites, FeS$_2$.—Cubic. Symmetry Tesseral Central. The spectra of iron pyrites are of a very much more complicated nature than those of fluor spar or zinc blende. A comparison of the molecular volumes and reflection angles of this crystal and those considered above shows that the iron atoms are again present in such numbers as they would be if arranged on a face-centred lattice. Since the first spectra are also in the positions to be expected for such a lattice, it is clear that this lattice is again the basis of the structure.

If the iron atoms were on the face-centred lattice and the sulphur atoms at cube centres, the structure would be similar to that of fluor spar. Since sulphur is approximately of half the atomic weight of iron, just as fluorine is of calcium, one would expect the spectra of these two crystals to resemble each other. This is far from being the case, and we must alter the structure in such a way as to explain the observed spectra.

The spectra for the face (100) are very peculiar. The first spectrum is pronounced, the second and third are absent, the fourth and fifth are of normal size compared to the first. This suggests that the arrangement of the pyrites (100) planes is somewhat similar to that of the planes (111) of fluor spar.

In order that this may be so we must displace the sulphurs from their positions at the cube centres. Normally each small cube possesses four trigonal axes intersecting in the centre of the cube. If the sulphur atom is moved from its position at the cube centre, this high symmetry is degraded, and some of the trigonal axes disappear. Therefore moving the sulphur atoms from the centre involves the sacrifice of some of the elements of symmetry. Four trigonal axes intersect in each iron atom, and of them one at least must be retained, in order that the crystal may be of the cubic system, and the iron atoms may remain identical with each other. This involves the retention of one trigonal axis as a diagonal of each small cube (fig. 4), and it is, therefore, along this diagonal that the sulphur must be displaced. It must lie on the diagonal, for if not each small cube would contain three atoms of sulphur arranged around the trigonal axis, while we know it only contains one.

It seems to follow, therefore, that the displacement of the sulphur atoms must be carried out in the following way. One diagonal of each cube is chosen to be preserved as a trigonal axis, the choice taking place in such a

73

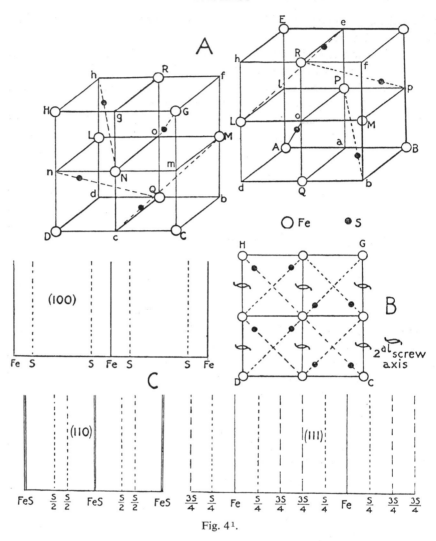

Fig. 4[1].

way that none of the trigonal axes intersect. Each of these diagonals then has an iron atom at one end and a vacant cube corner at the other. Then the sulphur atoms must be displaced along the selected diagonals on which they lie. All must be displaced towards the neighbouring iron atoms, or all away from them. The amount of the displacement is a variable quantity

---

[1] In fig. 4 the cube ABCDEFGH has been represented as divided into halves, in order to make the disposition of trigonal axes (the dotted diagonals) more clear. The lettering will show how the cubes are to be connected.

at our disposal. When this has been done, the structure possesses the symmetry characteristic of iron pyrites (Tesseral Central). The projection of the atoms in the unit cube ABCDEFGH as projected on the plane DHGC is shown in fig. 4B and it is clear that the tetragonal axes perpendicular to this face have been destroyed and that only digonal axes remain. The centres of symmetry are situated at every cube corner. Let the sulphur atom be displaced along the axis until it divides the diagonal in the ratio 4 to 1, the displacement taking place towards the unoccupied cube corner. The arrangement of the principal planes which then exists is shown in fig. 4C.

Being situated at 1/5th $d_{(100)}$ from the iron planes, the sulphurs will tend to cut out both the second and third (100) spectra. For if they were at $\frac{1}{4}d_{(100)}$ from the iron planes, they would just cut out the second spectrum; if at 1/6th $d_{(100)}$, they would cut out the third. In the plane (110), the presence midway between planes FeS of the pair of planes S/2 will tend to raise the second (110) spectrum as compared with the first. For the planes (111) the first spectrum will be small compared with the second, and the fifth will be abnormally large. This qualitative comparison of the spectra with those actually obtained will demonstrate that the position of the sulphur atom which we have assigned to it is not far from the truth.

Since in the case of iron pyrites the positions of the sulphur atoms are not fixed by the conditions of symmetry, the more or less qualitative analysis so far employed can only suggest their positions approximately. In order to fix these positions with accuracy, it is necessary to develop some quantitative comparison of the intensities of the first, second, third, fourth, and fifth spectra.

The Quantitative Comparison of Spectra

In the first place, experiments seem to indicate that the diffracting power of an atom varies as its atomic weight. The ratio of the diffracting power of two atoms is taken to be the ratio of the amplitudes of the diffracted wavelets which each would send out in identical circumstances, the same exciting wave passing over them. In the case of fluorspar, it has already been seen that the two fluorine atoms, whose combined atomic weights amount to 38, equal in diffracting power the single calcium of atomic weight 40. The series of carbonates isomorphous with calcite provide another case, which illustrates this law very clearly.

The spectra assign a very simple structure to these compounds, which belong to the rhombohedral holohedral crystal class. The exact structure of the calcite crystal is immaterial for present purposes; it is given in detail

75

at the end of this paper. It is only necessary to note that, perpendicular to the trigonal axis, the planes are evenly spaced, and contain alternately calcium atoms and groups of the composition CO_3. As is to be expected from its close structural relationship with calcite, sodium nitrate gives spectra in every way analogous to those of the calcite class. It is therefore included in the table below.

In Table II are given the relative intensities and angles for the first, second, third, and fourth spectra from faces (111) of the compounds $NaNO_3$, $CaMg(CO_3)_2$, $CaCO_3$, $MnCO_3$, $FeCO_3$. As before, the angles are those of the ionisation chamber, or double the glancing angles of reflection. It will be seen that, as the atomic weight of the metal approaches that of the group CO_3, the first spectrum becomes smaller compared with the second. This means that the planes R'' and CO_3 are becoming more nearly equal in diffracting power. Iron and manganese, with atomic weight of 56 and 55 respectively, must have approximately the same diffracting power as the group CO_3, for which $C + 3O = 12 + 48 = 60$, for the first spectrum has vanished in the case of $FeCO_3$ and $MnCO_3$. This must mean that diffracting power is proportional to atomic weight.

Table II

(111) face, calcite class. Pd rays.

Spectra	1st	2nd	3rd	4th
Na NO₃	100	50	0	0
23 62	11.6°	23.2°	–	–
CaMg (CO₃)₂	100	100	0	8
32 60	12.8°	24.5°	–	52.2°
Ca CO₃	30	100	0	14
40 60	11.2°	23.4°	–	48.2°
Mn CO₃	0	100	0	10
55 60	–	25.9°	–	52.5°
Fe CO₃	0	100	0	0
56 60	–	26.2°	–	–

Secondly, it has been seen that, when the rays are reflected from a series of planes which are regularly spaced and identical in all respects, the successive spectra diminish in intensity in a perfectly orderly manner. It can be further stated that, for all cases where the planes are of this type, the intensities of the successive spectra are approximately in the same ratio. If the first spectrum has an intensity 1, the second, third, fourth, and fifth spectra have intensities 0.2, 0.07, 0.03, 0.01. These numbers are only suggested as being very rough approximations. The faces (100) and (110) rock salt, (110) fluorspar and zinc blende, (100) and (110) diamond, are cases where the spectra intensities are of this normal type.

Let us now suppose that we are considering the reflection from faces of a crystal of a binary compound, composed of two elements, A and B, of atomic weights m_1 and m_2. The successive planes parallel to any one face may be identical in all respects, and contain both A and B atoms. Or, as often happens, they may alternately consist of A atoms alone and B atoms alone. In the first case the spectra will be of the normal type. The identical planes of composition AB may be considered as consisting of two sets of coincident planes of composition A and B. Now, let us suppose that the whole set of B planes is slighlty shifted relatively to the A planes, so that (1) passes into (2), fig. 5. The distance D remains the same as before; the shift of the B planes is equal to D/n.

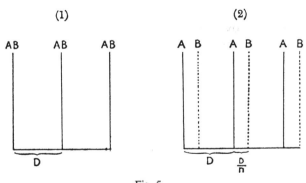

Fig. 5.

This causes the wavelets from the B planes to be in a different phase to the wavelets from the A planes. All other conditions remain the same; the same incident wave passes over the planes as would if they were coincident; it is absorbed to the same extent on reaching a corresponding depth; the emergent reflected wave is also equally absorbed by the superficial layers of the crystal. We can therefore compare with fairness the strength of the reflection from (1) with that from (2) under similar conditions, by comparing the reflection by a single plane AB with that by the pair of planes A and B. The amplitude of the wavelet reflected from planes A is proportional to m_1. That from planes B is proportional to m_2. They differ in phase by $2\pi/n$ for the first spectra, $4\pi/n$ for the second, and so on. Thus we may institute the following comparison:—

Order of spectrum	Intensities	
	Case I	Case II
1	$1(m_1 + m_2)^2$	$1[m_1^2 + m_2^2 + 2m_1m_2 \cos(2\pi/n)]$
2	$0.2(m_1 + m_2)^2$	$0.2[m_1^2 + m_2^2 + 2m_1m_2 \cos(4\pi/n)]$
3	$0.07(m_1 + m_2)^2$	$0.07[m_1^2 + m_2^2 + 2m_1m_2 \cos(6\pi/n)]$
4	$0.03(m_1 + m_2)^2$	$0.03[m_1^2 + m_2^2 + 2m_1m_2 \cos(8\pi/n)]$
5	$0.01(m_1 + m_2)^2$	$0.01[m_1^2 + m_2^2 + 2m_1m_2 \cos(10\pi/n)]$

The intensity of the spectrum is taken to be proportional to the square of the amplitude of the resultant reflected wavelet.

It is obvious that this reasoning may be extended to cases where the arrangement of planes is more complicated. It is only a question of finding the resultant of several wavelets of known amplitudes and phase relations, as against that of finding the resultant of two. We are now in a position to calculate theoretically the spectrum intensities to be expected for any structure assigned to a crystal. In this calculation the following assumptions are made:—

1. The diffracting power of an atom is proportional to its atomic weight.
2. The 'normal' spectra reflected from a simple series of identical planes have intensities in the ratio

$$1, \quad 0.2, \quad 0.07, \quad 0.03, \quad 0.01.$$

3. Neighbouring atoms diffract independently of each other.
This last has been tacitly assumed above.
The results of the calculation are given in Table III.

It will be seen by these results that the calculated and observed intensities obviously run parallel to each other. Taking into account the many experimental errors in the determination of the relative intensities, and the crude nature of the assumption which has been made, closer agreement could not be expected. The results certainly show that all the peculiar features of any set of spectra can be assigned to structural peculiarities of the crystal. If a certain spectrum is missing, or is unusually strong, a reason for it is found in the arrangement of the crystal planes.

Iron pyrites provides a good example. In order to account for the peculiar fact that the (100) planes have no second or third spectrum, we place the sulphur atoms in such a position as to divide the diagonal in the ratio 1 : 4. When the sulphur atoms are placed here the structure of the crystal is illustrated in fig. 4.

In this figure (A) represents the unit cube of the structure which is afterwards repeated without change parallel to itself. It is the unit of the

Table III

Spectra	Observed					Calculated				
	1st	2nd	3rd	4th	5th	1st	2nd	3rd	4th	5th
Rock salt—										
(100)	100	30	7	–	–	100	20	7	3	
(110)	100	24	7	–	–	100	20	7	3	
(111)	20	100	0	6	–	22	100	2	15	
Fluor spar—										
(100)	0	100	0	13	–	0	100	0	15	
(110)	100	16	6	–	–	100	20	7		
(111)	100	0	10	9	3	100	0	7	11	1
Zinc blende—										
(100)	40	100	0	0	–	53	100	5	3	
(110)	100	25	7	0	–	100	20	7		
(111)	100	5	8	–	–	100	4	11	8	
Iron pyrites—										
(100)	100	0	0	14	4	100	0	0	3*	2.5*
(110)	100	50	–	–	–	100	48*	17*	3*	4*
(111)	80	100	50	0	22	78	100	35	2*	21
Ideal spectrum						100	20	7	3	1

* [Values corrected according to *Jahrb. Rad. u. Elektr.* **11** (1914) 389.]

pattern, and its sides are the primitive translations of the group. Four iron atoms and eight sulphurs are associated with it. The cube is represented as being in two halves, in order to make the structure more clear. The diagonals which are marked are trigonal axes of the system. Every corner of the eight small cubes into which the structure is divided is a centre of symmetry. Through each side centre of these cubes passes a single digonal screw axis, parallel to one of the cube axes. Fig. 4B represents the structure as projected on a plane (100), and it is evident that this face has a digonal axis, and not a tetragonal axis, perpendicular to it.

The features are those characteristic of the crystal class to which iron pyrites belongs.

The way in which the spectra of iron pyrites have been calculated from the assumptions given above will be entered into rather fully here, as this case is a good instance of the quantitative analysis of strength of spectra.

The arrangement of planes parallel to the three principal faces of the crystal is given in fig. 4C, the sulphurs being placed so as to divide the diagonal in the 1 : 4 ratio. This is done in order to account for the fact that the face (100) has no second and third order spectra. For calculation then gives for the relative amplitudes of the first, second, and third spectra

$$56 + 2\{32 \cos (2\pi/5)\} = 56 + 21 = 77.$$
$$56 + 2\{32 \cos (4\pi/5)\} = 56 - 61 = -5.$$
$$56 + 2\{32 \cos (6\pi/5)\} = 56 - 61 = -5.$$

It is obvious that when these amplitudes are squared and multiplied by the factors for the normal spectrum, the second and third spectra will be vanishingly small compared to the first.

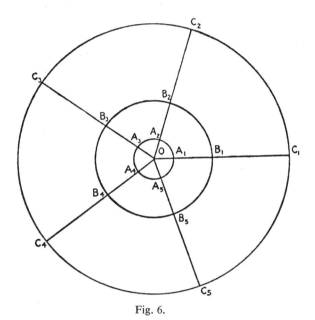

Fig. 6.

The planes parallel to (111) have a peculiar arrangement; their spectra can be worked out by the help of fig. 6. The three circles in the figure have radii proportional to $Fe = 56$, $S/4 = 8$, $3S/4 = 24$. Each circle is divided into five by the lines $OA_1B_1C_1$, $OA_2B_2C_2$, etc. The angle $A_1OA_2 = 2\pi/5 = 72°$. The wavelets which are reflected from one of these groups of planes and which go to build up the first spectrum have relative amplitudes and intensities represented by OB_4, OA_5, OC_1, OA_2, OB_3, these being due to the planes $3S/4$, $S/4$, Fe, $S/4$, $3S/4$ of a group. The amplitudes of these waves are 24, 8, 56, 8, 24 respectively, and their resultant is

$$56 + 2 \times 8 \cos (2\pi/5) + 2 \times 24 \cos (4\pi/5) = 56 + 5 - 38 = 23.$$

80

For the second spectrum the resultant of OB_2, OA_4, OC_1, OA_3, OB_5, is equal to $(56 - 13 + 15) = 58$. For now the 3S/4 planes are $8\pi/5$ out of phase with the Fe planes, and the S/4 planes $4\pi/5$ out of phase. The third spectrum is the resultant of these same components, and the amplitude of the reflected wave is proportional to 58. For the fourth we have the resultant of OB_4, OA_5, OC_1, OA_2, OB_3, as for the first spectrum. The resultant is again proportional to 23. For the fifth spectrum obviously all the components are in phase. The amplitude is measured by $56 + 64 = 120$.

Thus the amplitudes of these spectra are in the ratio

$$23 : 58 : 58 : 23 : 120.$$

So far, therefore, their intensities are in the ratio

$$(23)^2 : (58)^2 : (58)^2 : (23)^2 : (120)^2.$$

And when multiplied by the factors for the normal spectrum, these ratios become

$$(23)^2 : 0.2(58)^2 : 0.07(58)^2 : 0.03(23)^2 : 0.01(120)^2,$$

or

$$78 : 100 : 80 : 2 : 21.$$

If the sulphur atoms are placed so as to divide the cube diagonal in the ratio $1 : 3$ (see fig 4), the strengths of the spectra, as calculated above, become

$$100 : 56 : 38 : 0 : 8.$$

If they divide the diagonal in the ratio $1 : 5$, they can be calculated to be

$$19 : 100 : 24 : 7 : 17.$$

Therefore, we have the following comparison:—

Ratio	Intensities				
$1 : 3$	100	56	38	0	8
$1 : 4$	78	100	35	2	21
$1 : 5$	19	100	24	7	17
Observed intensities	75	100	50	0	22

The $1 : 4$ ratio seems, therefore, to be very nearly the true one. These three situations for the sulphur atom are very close. If $d =$ length of cube diagonal, the distance of the sulphur atom from the cube corner is $0.25d$, $0.20d$, $0.17d$ for the three cases. It seems reasonable to conclude from these figures that this distance lies between $0.19d$ and $0.21d$, or that the position of the sulphur atom on the diagonal may be found to 1 or 2 per cent. of the length of the diagonal.

The crystalline structure of hauerite, MnS_2, is, as far as has been investigated, identical with that of iron pyrites. The (100) planes have a strong first spectrum and no second and third. The planes (111) have the first, second, and third spectra in the ratio 32 : 100 : 50. As the only crystals available were small no great reliance is to be placed on these figures except as indicating that the structure is very nearly that of iron pyrites. This is surprising, considering the great difference in the molecular volume of hauerite, 34.4, as compared with that of pyrites, 23.5.

18. Die Berechnung der Kristallstruktur ist bisher nur von den Herren Bragg auf Grund von Reflexionsversuchen mit Röntgenstrahlen ausgeführt worden. Ihre Methode hat den Vorzug, die Struktur in großen Zügen verhältnismäßig leicht zu bestimmen, aber die Genauigkeit, die hierbei erreichbar ist, scheint mir aus zwei Gründen prinzipiell beschränkt zu sein. Der erste Grund ist, dass es große Schwierigkeiten bereitet, die Röntgenröhre während der ganzen Zeit der Reflexionsaufnahme an einer Fläche konstant zu halten, und daß daher die Intensitätsverhältnisse der verschiedenen Ordnungen selbst durch wiederholtes Messen nur annähernd festzustellen sind. Dies zeigt sich u.a. in den Angaben[1] über die Reflexion an Pyrit (111), wo das Intensitätsverhältnis zwischen erstem und zweitem Spektrum einmal (S. [this Vol. p. 81]) zu 0,75, kurz vorher (S. [this Vol. p. 79]) zu 0,80 angegeben ist[2].

Der zweite Grund liegt in der Schwierigkeit der Interpretation der erhaltenen Intensitäten. Um nämlich abzuschätzen, welche Schwächung etwa durch die Struktur bedingt ist, und um hieraus auf die Anordnung der reflektierenden Flächen zu schließen, muß der 'ideale' Intensitätsabfall der Spektren höherer Ordnung bekannt sein, d.h. sowohl der Abfall, der durch das wachsende Auflösungsvermögen der höheren Ordnungen bedingt ist (Lorentzscher Faktor $(h_1{}^2 + h_2{}^2 + h_3{}^2)^{-1}$) als auch die durch den zunehmenden Einfluß der Rauhigkeit der Flächen (infolge Wärmebewegung) hervorgerufene Intensitätsabnahme (Debyescher Faktor). Dieser 'ideale' Abfall ist nun wegen des Anteils der Wärmebewegung von Kristall zu Kristall verschieden und läßt sich ohne Kenntnis der Struktur und der thermischen Eigenschaften auch nicht im voraus berechnen.

Die Herren Bragg behelfen sich damit, allen Kristallen den idealen Abfall

---

[1] W. L. Bragg, *Proc. Roy. Soc. London* **89**A (1914) 468 [this Vol. p. 71].

[2] Herr Bragg schreibt mir, daß es ihm neuerdings gelungen sei, die Meßgenauigkeit zu erhöhen.

100 : 20 : 7 : 3 : 1 zugrunde zu legen; dabei wird kein Unterschied zwischen Steinsalz und Pyrit gemacht, obwohl ihre thermischen Eigenschaften und daher ihr individueller 'idealer Abfall' stark verschieden sind.

Es ist natürlich, daß man sich bei dieser Ungenauigkeit der Ausgangsdaten darauf beschränken muß, die gemessenen Intensitäten *ungefähr* durch eine geschickte Anordnung der reflektierenden Flächen wiederzugeben.

Wo nun—wie es sich z.B. bei Diamant nachträglich herausstellt—ein Grund für rationale Abstandsverhältnisse vorliegt, wird man sich mit der Reflexionsmessung an wenigen Flächen begnügen dürfen, welche eine Auswahl unter den rationalen Werten ermöglicht. Sind aber keine Anhaltspunkte für rationale Verhältnisse gegeben, was z.B. schon bei der sonst so ähnlichen Struktur der Zinkblende zutrifft, so erfordert die genaue Lagebestimmung die Messung der Reflexion an sehr vielen Flächen. Da das nach der Methode von Laue-Friedrich-Knipping hergestellte Interferenzbild die Reflexion an allen Flächen zeigt, so ist es geeignet, die Feinheiten der Struktur mit größerer Schärfe zu offenbaren, als es mit Reflexionsmessungen geschehen kann. [1]

Freilich gehört zu der Methode, die nun kurz auseinandergesetzt wird, daß die grobe Arbeit, nämlich die Bestimmung des Gittertypus, bereits erledigt ist; es soll sich nur noch darum handeln, einen Parameter, etwa —wie bei Pyrit—das Abstandsverhältnis auf der Diagonalenrichtung genau zu bestimmen.

Ein derartiger Fall liegt vor, wenn die Strukturen isomorpher Kristalle von einfacher Konstitution verglichen werden, denn diese unterscheiden sich nach den bisherigen Erfahrungen nur durch ihre Parameterwerte (vgl. Braggs [2] Angaben über Kalkspat, Dolomit, $NaNO_3$, Pyrit und Hauerit). Gerade bei diesen Kristallen liegt ein besonderes Interesse an der möglichst genauen Feststellung der Struktur.

In den Interferenzbildern macht sich die Struktur in der Intensität der Flecken bemerkbar; diese hängt außer von der Wellenlänge noch von dem mehr oder weniger guten Zusammenwirken der verschiedenen elementaren Raumgitter ab, aus denen die Struktur aufgebaut ist. Die Amplitude eines Interferenzstrahls wird durch den Strukturfaktor Σ gegeben, der gerade dadurch entsteht, daß die Interferenzmaxima der einzelnen Raumgitter einen bestimmten Phasenunterschied haben:

$$\Sigma = \textstyle\sum_\kappa \exp\{2\pi i(h_1\xi_\kappa + h_2\eta_\kappa + h_3\zeta_\kappa)/a\},$$

---

[1] [As known, modern analysis is based on the use of monochromatic radiation, all reflections of small crystals being involved. Ed.].
[2] *Loc. cit.*

hierin sind $\xi_\kappa, \eta_\kappa, \zeta_\kappa$ die 'Konstruktionspunkte', d.h. die Koordinaten der Anfangspunkte der elementaren Raumgitter.

Während beim elementaren Raumgitter die Intensität sich mit der Wellenlänge ganz allmählich ändert (die Kurve der spektralen Intensitätsverteilung ist 'glatt'), kann die durch den Strukturfaktor $\sum$ eines komplizierten Gitters bewirkte Verschiedenheit der Intensität auch für benachbarte Wellenlängen sehr groß sein, wenn diese in verschiedenen Flecken vertreten sind; ja, im Fall hemiedrischer Interferenzbilder (Pyrit, Hauerit, Natriumchlorat, vgl. G. Friedel[1]) haben die hemiedrischen Flecken allein wegen des Faktors $\sum$ verschiedene Helligkeit, obwohl ihre Wellenlänge, Absorption usw. identisch ist.

Ist nun bloß noch ein Parameter der Struktur unbekannt, so läßt sich für einige ausgewählte Flecken von gleicher oder benachbarter Wellenlänge die Änderung von $\sum$ mit dem Parameter feststellen, und es läßt sich dann mit großer Schärfe derjenige Parameterwert bestimmen, der am besten die Intensitäten erklärt.

Das Verfahren wird am deutlichsten durch eine Anwendung auf *Pyrit* werden. Seine Struktur, die z.T. in dieser Zeitschr. **15**, 78 (1914) von Herrn Bragg[2] angegeben worden ist, enthält als Parameter, dessen Bestimmung genauer zu geschehen hat, das Abstandsverhältnis der Atome auf den Diagonalenrichtungen. Herr Bragg findet, daß der Abstand zweier Schwefelatome $\frac{1}{5}$ des Abstandes von Eisenatomen ist, doch zeigt sich an der Interferenzaufnahme sofort, daß dieser Wert nicht richtig sein kann. (Die Flecken $37\bar{2}$ und $73\bar{2}$, sowie $18\bar{2}$ und $81\bar{2}$ sollten danach je gleiche Intensität haben, was nicht zutrifft[3]. Betrachtet man das allgemeinere System, dessen Abstandsverhältnis nicht $\frac{1}{5}$, sondern $\alpha/5$ ist, so lautet der Strukturfaktor für Flecken mit gemischten Indizes (teils gerade, teils ungerade) nach Zusammenfassung der Exponentialfunktionen zu trigonometrischen:

$$\sum = (-1)^{h_3} \cos (h_1 - h_2 - h_3)\pi\alpha/5 + (-1)^{h_1} \cos (-h_1 + h_2 - h_3)\pi\alpha/5 +$$

$$+ (-1)^{h_2} \cos (-h_1 - h_2 + h_3)\pi\alpha/5 + (-1)^{h_1+h_2+h_3} \cos (h_1 + h_2 + h_3)\pi\alpha/5.$$

Betrachten wir, um Diskussionen über das Spektrum ganz aus dem Wege zu gehen, die Flecken $25\bar{1}, 52\bar{1}; 37\bar{2}, 73\bar{2}; 18\bar{2}, 81\bar{2}$, welche paarweise gleiche

---

[1] *Comptes Rendus*, S. 1533, 29. Dez. 1913 [this Vol. p. 95]. Bezüglich der dort gezogenen Folgerungen über die Symmetrie der Interferenzbilder mag bemerkt werden, daß in der Tat nach Aufnahmen im hiesigen Institut Natriumchlorat (Klasse 28) hemiedrische Bilder liefert, und zwar rechts- und linksdrehende Kristalle die gleichen Bilder, wie es nach G. Friedel sein soll.

[2] Ausführlich *loc. cit.*

[3] Die Photogramme von Pyrit und Hauerit werden demnächst in den *Ann. d. Phys.* reproduziert erscheinen.

84

Wellenlänge haben. Werden diese Indizes in die Formel für $\sum$ eingesetzt, so läßt sich $\sum$ für $\alpha = 1$ berechnen, und gibt die Intensitäten, welche der von Herrn Bragg vorgeschlagenen Struktur zukommen; wird α nur wenig anders als 1 gewählt, so verändert sich $\sum$ bereits erheblich, und zwar ist für kleine Änderungen von α der Verlauf von $\sum$ hinreichend genau geradlinig darzustellen.

Man erhält so die Interpolationsfigur (S. unten) in der der absolute Betrag von $\sum$ als Funktion von α aufgetragen ist; es ist schön zu sehen, wie die Intensität von $52\bar{1}$, welche etwa $\frac{1}{4}$ von der von $25\bar{1}$ ist, bei $\alpha = 1$ überhaupt Null ist, sich aber dem richtigen Wert ($\sum_{52\bar{1}} = \frac{1}{2} \cdot \sum_{25\bar{1}}$) nähert, wenn α größer gewählt wird ($\alpha = 1,12$). Beobachtet ist ferner, daß $73\bar{2}$ bedeutend schwächer als $37\bar{2}$ ist, und $81\bar{2}$ überhaupt kaum sichtbar, während $18\bar{2}$ etwa gleich stark wie $37\bar{2}$ ist. Bei $\alpha = 1$ sind die Strukturfaktoren je zweier Flecke gleich, bei $\alpha = 1,12$ hingegen haben sie Werte, welche die Intensitäten aufs beste erklären. Es kann somit geschlossen werden, daß der wahre Wert von α zwischen 1,11 und 1,125 liegt, und somit das Abstandsverhältnis nicht $\frac{1}{5}$, sondern etwa 1,12/5 ist.

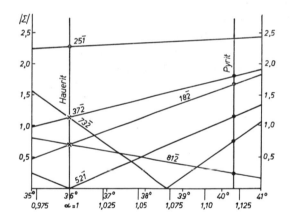

Sehr mühelos ist genaue Bestimmung des Aufbaues von Hauerit, indem dort sozusagen das Fehlen eines Fleckes den Wert von α sofort entscheidet. Während nämlich $25\bar{1}$ sehr stark ist, fehlt $52\bar{1}$ so vollständig, daß nicht die geringste Spur dieses Fleckes zu entdecken ist. Daher muß α mit großer Genauigkeit gleich 1 sein—bis auf weniger als 1 Proz. Dieser Wert stimmt auch für die anderen Flecke.

In den Beispielen des Pyrit und des Hauerit war die Benutzung der hemiedrischen Flecke besonders bequem, weil sie nicht die Kenntnis der Spektralkurve voraussetzt. Bei Kristallen mit holoedrischen Interferenzbildern müssen Flecke benutzt werden, die möglichst ähnliche

Wellenlängen haben, und deren Indizes außerdem nicht zu sehr verschieden sind. (Das letztere hängt mit der Verschiedenheit der Spektralkurven für verschiedene Aufzählungsindizes zusammen.) Doch erschwert dieser Umstand das Verfahren nicht wesentlich, namentlich nicht, wo es sich um den Vergleich innerhalb einer isomorphen Reihe handelt.

München, Institut für theoret. Physik

19. 1. Crystals of spinel group are found in perfect octahedra, belonging to the holohedral class of the regular system. They have chemical compositions of the type $R''R_2'''O_4$. In the present experiment, spinel $(Mg''Al_2'''O_4)$ and magnetite $(Fe''Fe_2'''O_4)$ have been investigated.

2. The method of investigations was as follows. Laue photographs taken with the white radiation from an ordinary focus tube (chiefly with platinum anticathode) at various orientations of the crystal were studied in a manner somewhat similar to that of Ewald[1]. Symmetrical photographs, which can be obtained with such an orientation of the crystal that one of its axes of symmetry is parallel to the incident beam, are generally convenient to find the indices of each Laue spot and the wave-length of the radiation corresponding to the spot. It was, however, sometimes advantageous to work with unsymmetrical photographs. For, on such a plate, spots having equivalent indices appear at different distances from the central spot, and enable us, at the same time, to study the reflexion of radiations of different wave-lengths from equally-spaced net-planes. In the latter case, the distance of each spot from the central one was measured on the plate, from which the sine of glancing angle θ could be calculated. The intensities of the spots were, on the other hand, roughly determined in an arbitrary scale by comparing them with a photographic wedge specially prepared for the purpose.

Taking the value of $\sin \theta/\sqrt{(h^2 + k^2 + l^2)}$, where h, k, l are the indices of the reflecting net-plane as the abscissa, and the corresponding intensity as the ordinate, each spot was diagrammatically plotted in fig. 1.

Now, to begin with, consider a simple cubic space-lattice of point system. Denoting the length of a side of an elementary cube by a, the 'grating space' or the distance between two consecutive net-planes (h, k, l) will be $a/\sqrt{(h^2 + k^2 + l^2)}$. We therefore have, as the fundamental equation of reflexion $\sin \theta/\sqrt{(h^2 + k^2 + l^2)} = n\lambda/2a$, where λ represents the wave-length of the rays reflected from the planes and n is an integer. Obviously the

---

[1] P. P. Ewald, *Ann. d. Phys.* **44** (1914) 257.

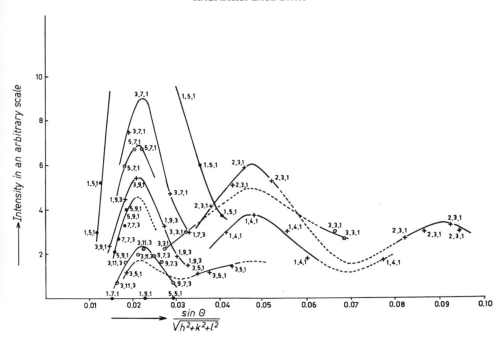

Fig. 1.

expression on the left hand side of the equation is the same as that taken for the abscissa. Since all the sets of planes with equal grating space are of equal surface densities, if a curve be drawn passing through the points corresponding to a given value of $h^2 + k^2 + l^2$ but of different values of θ, it will represent the intensity distribution in the spectrum of the primary rays, provided that the variation in reflecting power with the glancing angle in the absorption of the rays in the crystal could be neglected. A set of these curves are drawn in fig. 1. As will at once be seen, they are continuous, having maximum values at $\sin \theta / \sqrt{(h^2 + k^2 + l^2)} = .023$ for the first order, at .047 for the second and so on. Since in the ideal case the greater the value of $h^2 + k^2 + l^2$ the less is the reflecting power of the plane, the curves corresponding to larger values of $h^2 + k^2 + l^2$ will come below those corresponding to smaller ones. This is, however, not the case with the actual crystals in question as will be seen in fig. 1. To take an instance, the curve drawn through the points (3, 5, 1) is below that through the points (5, 9, 1). This evidently implies that the structure of the crystals is not so simple as can be treated as a simple cubic lattice. These points of departure from the ideal lattice, when closely investigated, may afford important knowledge as regards the actual arrangement of different constituent atoms.

87

As the manner of departure is so complicated in the case of spinel that it is difficult to find any general rule, it will be more convenient to study at first the case of magnetite which seems to be simpler in its chemical constitution as well as in the Laue photograph.

3. Magnetite ($Fe''Fe_2'''O_4$) is composed of two elements of widely different atomic weights. A Laue photograph taken with a thin plate cut perpendicular to a principal axis is reproduced in Plate V [not reproduced] the direction of the incident beam being slightly inclined to the axis. The curves in fig. 1 are the results obtained from the photograph by the procedure above mentioned. It may be seen that in the region of the first order spectrum no spot with even indices is present; that the spots (3, 3, 1) and (3, 5, 1) are much too weak in comparison with the spots (1, 5, 1) and (3, 7, 1); that the spots (1, 7, 1), (5, 5, 1) and (3, 7, 3) are not found, while those with much higher indices such as (7, 7, 3) or (3, 11, 3) are quite visible in the same region of the spectrum. Several other photographs obtained with various orientations of the crystal were examined in this way and the following points have been noted.

I. Reflecting net-planes may be classified with regard to their behaviours into four kinds according to their indices:

(*a*) Planes with two even integers: (1, 0, 0), (2, 0, 1), (2, 2, 1), ...

(*b*) Planes with one even integer: (1, 1, 0), (1, 2, 1), (1, 3, 0), ...

(*c*) Planes with odd integers only: (1, 1, 1), (1, 3, 1), (1, 3, 3), ...

(c_1) All the integers are $\pm$ 3 (mod. 8): (3, 5, 3), (3, 5, 5), ... or one of the integers is $\pm$ 3 (mod. 8): (1, 3, 1), (1, 5, 1), ...

(c_2) All the integers are $\pm$ 1 (mod. 8): (1, 1, 1), (1, 7, 1), ... or one of the integers is $\pm$ 1 (mod. 8): (3, 3, 1), (3, 5, 1), ...

II. A plane belonging to the category (*a*) does not give the first, second and third order spectra, the reflexion taking place first in the fourth order.

III. A plane (*b*) does not give first and third orders. Second and fourth orders are present, the latter of which being especially intense.

IV. A plane (c_1) shows an intense first order reflexion and a moderate second order.

V. A plane (c_2) shows a very weak first order reflexion, invisible in cases of planes with higher indices.

VI. The intensities of second order reflexion from the planes (*b*), (c_1) and (c_2) are nearly equal.

Turning now to the case of spinel, which must at any rate have something common with magnetite in its fundamental structure, we notice that the statements II and III can be applied to it while the others are only partially applicable. These considerations give us a clue for elucidating the structure of these crystals.

4. Firstly, the absence of odd order reflexions from planes with even indices ((a) and (b)) is a characteristic behaviour of the face-centred point-lattice. Secondly, the absence of the second order reflexion from planes with two even indices (a) is a striking feature of the diamond lattice after Bragg[1] for which, however, VI does not hold. Thirdly, to account for IV and V, it was found necessary to suppose that certain heavy atoms lie on the cube diagonal at a distance of $\frac{3}{8}$ of its length from each atom of the skeleton lattice.

After several trials, taking the above and many other points in consideration, the following structure was at last found to be the most simple and plausible.

A complete unit cube is made up of 8 molecules of $R''R_2'''O_4$. Of these, 8 atoms of the divalent metal R'' are situated in place of carbon atoms in the diamond lattice. 16 atoms of the trivalent metal R''' are distributed in the four vacant smaller cubes (i.e. in those four of the eight smaller cubes into which a unit cube is supposed to be divided), which are not occupied by the R'' atoms at their centres, so that each smaller cube contains $4R'''$ atoms in a tetrahedral configuration as in fig. 2C, in which cS : SM = 1 : 3. 32 atoms of oxygen are also placed on the cube diagonals but their positions depend on the nature of R'' and R''' atoms.

5. The lattice appears, at first sight, to be very complex and liable to some doubts with regard to the holohedrality of the crystal. The following consideration will, however, throw some light on this question. Suppose a face-centred cubic lattice consisting of 4 molecules of $R''R_2'''O_4$ or $R''(\frac{1}{2}R''')_4O_4$ which arrange themselves in the following manner: R'' atoms form skeleton lattice. $4(\frac{1}{2}R''')$ and $4O$ are grouped in two tetrahedra with a common centre as in fig. 2C, except that ⊙ in this case represents $\frac{1}{2}R'''$ instead of R'''. Consider this group placed in each alternate smaller cube of the skeleton lattice. The resulting lattice belongs undoubtedly to hemo-morph hemihedry of the regular system. Next, by means of inversion with respect to the centre of the skeleton lattice, construct another lattice of the same kind. Translate the new lattice as a whole from D toward F (fig. 2A) along the cube diagonal by a distance of $\frac{1}{4}DF$, so that every R'' atoms of the new lattice comes just at the centre of the vacant smaller cube of the original lattice. It will be seen that every $\frac{1}{2}R'''$ atom in one lattice comes in coincidence with that of the other, with which it forms one complete R''' atom. Thus, as the result of an interpenetration of the two hemi-hedral lattices, we obtain a holohedral one of the class O_h^7 according to Schönflies' notation[2]. General properties of this lattice are the same as

[1] W. H. Bragg, *Proc. Roy. Soc.* **A89** (1914) 277.
[2] Schönflies, *Krystallsysteme und Krystallstruktur*, Leipzig (1891), p. 548.

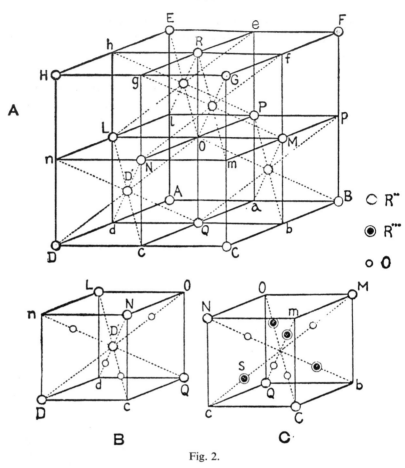

Fig. 2.

those of diamond, having tetragonal screw axes and 'glide planes' of symmetry[1].

6. The distribution of oxygen atoms on the cube diagonal is now to be considered. In order to determine this, the method employed by Terada[2] on an investigation of alum and that by Ewald and Friedrich[3] on an analogous case were applied. In the case of magnetite, the effect of O atoms is relatively insignificant, whereas in the case of spinel it is considerable, this depending on the atomic weight of metallic constituents relative to that of oxygen. On that account the position of O atoms can be determined with a far greater degree of accuracy for the spinel. In this case, the inter-

[1] See Braggs, *X-Rays and Crystal Structure*, London (1915), p. 147.
[2] T. Terada, *Tokyô Sûg.-Butu Kizi* 7 (1914) 292.
[3] P. P. Ewald and W. Friedrich, *Ann. d. Phys.* 44 (1914) 1183.

ference pattern is so complicated that the general properties IV and V stated above hold no longer. The following points are, however, to be noted from inspection of the photograph.

Indices (h, k, l)	$h^2 + k^2 + l^2$	$\sin \theta$	Intensities
3, 3, 1	19	0.23	weak
1, 5, 1	27	0.19	very strong
3, 5, 1	35	0.17	comparatively weak
1, 7, 1	51	0.14	0
5, 5, 1	51	0.14	nearly equal,
3, 7, 1	59	0.13	moderate
1, 7, 3	59	0.39	moderate
5, 5, 3	59	0.39	strong
3, 7, 3	67	0.37	weak
5, 7, 3	83	0.33	0
1, 9, 3	91	0.315	strong
7, 7, 3	107	0.29	faint
5, 9, 3	115	0.28	weak

In the above comparison, spots having like values of $h^2 + k^2 + l^2$ and of $\sin \theta$ are sorted out in separate groups. [Table only partly reproduced.] The intensities mentioned are to be understood as compared amongst the spots in each group. If the lattice were a simple cubic one, all the spots in each group would be nearly of the same intensity.

Now, in order to give a clear view of the general arrangements, a diagonal on which O atoms lie, is shown in fig. 3. Since O atoms are to be distributed symmetrically on the diagonal with respect to R'' atoms, it was suggested that they lie on a portion between D' and S (fig. 3). For, if one of the O atoms be present on the portion DD', there should be another on the same portion and the presence of two O atoms in such a small interval would be unlikely. A rough trial resulted in favour of the above suggestion, and the distance x of the seat from D' was found to be about $\frac{1}{3}D'S$. To determine x more accurately, the intensity distribution was examined by giving for x various values slightly different from $\frac{1}{3}D'S$, the calculation being made

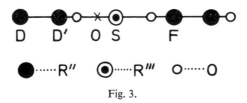

Fig. 3.

91

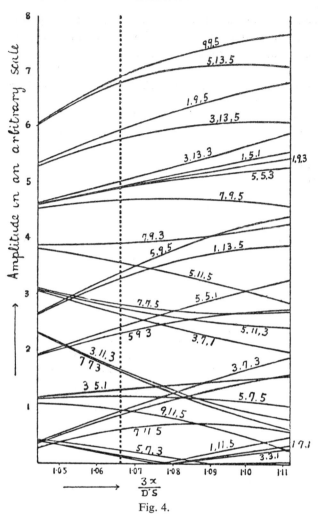

Fig. 4.

by a method similar to that employed by Ewald[1]. The results are shown in fig. 4. The abscissa represents the distance x and the ordinate gives, in an arbitrary scale, the resultant amplitude of the reflected wave from different net-planes whose indices are noted down alongside each corresponding curve. It will be seen that for $x = 1.07/3 \cdot D'S$ the intensities agree in a remarkable way with the complicated experimental results already described. A further verification was made for spots with even indices and the agreement between the calculated and experimental results was equally good.

[1] *Loc. cit.*

In the case of magnetite, the effect of O atoms being not so considerable as in the case of spinel, they may be shifted along the diagonal within a certain sensible range. After a close examination it was found that the probable position is a point at a distance $\frac{1}{3}D'S$ from D', or rather in the interval between $\frac{1}{3}$ and 1.05/3.

Summary

The molecular structure of the crystals of the spinel group was found to be a space-lattice having the same symmetry properties as the diamond-lattice. It consists of two hemihedral face-centred lattices interpenetrating each other, the elementary cube being made up of 8 molecules of $R''R_2'''O_4$. The position of O atoms varies according to the nature of the atoms of R'' and R'''.

In conclusion, I wish to thank Professor Nagaoka for placing the resources of the Laboratory at my disposal and for his kind interest during the progress of the experiment. My thanks are also due to Professors S. Nakamura and T. Terada for their valuable criticism.

P.S. During the proof-reading, I received '*Nature*', issued on 22 July, 1915, in which Prof. Bragg has communicated a letter on the same subject. As far as can be judged from the brief note, the result of his investigation seems to agree with that of mine. [Full paper in *Phil. Mag.* **30** (1915) 305–315. Ed.]

HEMIEDRISM AND X-RAY INTENSITIES

see W. Friedrich, P. Knipping *and* M. Laue, *this Vol. p.* 18, *l.* 13–22.

20. A. E. H. Tutton (1912)

▬

21. Sur les symétries cristallines que peut rélever la diffraction des rayons Röntgen, by G. Friedel (1913)

▬

22. Eine Bemerkung über die Interferenzfiguren hemiedrischer Kristalle, by W. L. Bragg (1914)

▬

23. Über die Symmetrie der Kristall-Röntgenogramme, by M. v. Laue (1916)

▬

20. The tetragonal nature of the axis of symmetry along which the Röntgen rays were travelling through the ZnS crystal is most strikingly apparent in the photograph. One recognises at once also the presence of two perpendicular planes of symmetry in the arrangement of the spots. In fact, the figure corresponds to the holohedral or full symmetry (class 32) of the cubic system, in spite of the fact that zinc blende belongs to the hexakistetrahedral class 31 (one of the so-called hemihedral classes) of cubic symmetry. Now this interesting fact affords the most beautiful and perfect proof that it is the space-lattice (Raumgitter) of the crystal structure which is affording the figure, and that no other property than this space-lattice is concerned. For space-lattices alone always possess holohedral symmetry, and they determine the crystal system and angles and obedience with the law of rational indices. Interpenetrations, translations, and coincidence-movements of space-lattices, which afford those of the sixty-five Sohncke regular point-systems which account for the simpler cases of hemihedrism (types of crystals of lower than holohedral symmetry), are here obviously not concerned; still more emphatically, if possible, is this true of the 165 yet more complicated point-systems involving mirror-image symmetry made known to us by von Fedorow and Barlow.

In other words, it is not the stereographic arrangement of the elementary atoms which is revealed by the photographs, but the underlying space-lattice, which is arrived at by taking the atoms of the same chemical element which are similarly (sameways, identically) situated throughout the whole structure.

94

21. Diverses choses inexactes ont été dites sur les symétries que les radiogrammes peuvent révéler dans les cristaux. C'est ainsi que Laue s'est étonné de ne pas trouver trace, sur les radiogrammes de la blende, de l'antihémiédrie de ce minéral. Le même auteur croit pouvoir découvrir dans les radiogrammes du quartz une différence entre le quartz droit et le quartz gauche. Il est aisé de voir que non seulement de telles dissymétries dans les radiogrammes n'existent pas, mais qu'on ne peut les concevoir et qu'on devait, *a priori*, s'attendre à ne pas les constater.

Dans une symétrie holoèdre, donc centrée, à tout plan de symétrie correspond un axe binaire (ou en général pair) qui lui est normal, et réciproquement. Lorsqu'on passe de l'holoédrie à une hémiédrie, de ces trois éléments, axe, plan et centre, deux disparaissent nécessairement ensemble. Si le plan et le centre font défaut, on a affaire à l'hémiédrie holoaxe; si ce sont l'axe et le centre, à l'antihémiédrie; si ce sont l'axe et le plan, à la parahémiédrie.

Or, imaginons deux rayons diffractés A et A' symétriques par rapport à un plan de symétrie, dans la diffraction produite par un cristal holoèdre convenablement orienté. Ces deux rayons sont aussi bien symétriques l'un de l'autre par rapport à l'axe binaire normal au plan. Par contre, chacun est son propre symétrique par rapport au centre. Supposons maintenant que le cristal, au lieu d'être holoèdre, ait l'une des deux hémiédries non centrées, c'est-à-dire l'holoaxie ou l'antihémiédrie. En ce cas, il subsiste toujours, de l'holoédrie, soit l'axe binaire, soit le plan de symétrie. Cela suffit pour que les deux rayons A et A', identiques par symétrie dans le cas de l'holoédrie, restent forcément identiques par symétrie dans le cas de l'hémiédrie. Par suite, *en aucun cas, les radiogrammes ne pourront révéler l'absence de centre.* Au contraire, s'il s'agit de la parahémiédrie, où l'axe et le plan disparaissent ensemble et où le centre subsiste seul, le rayon A reste symétrique de lui-même et non de A'. Il n'y a plus de raison pour que A et A' soient identiques. La parahémiédrie pourra se manifester dans les radiogrammes.

Telle est la raison pour laquelle la blende fournit des radiogrammes à symétrie cubique holoèdre et le quartz des radiogrammes à symétrie ternaire holoèdre. Il est d'ailleurs impossible de concevoir sous quelle forme (tant qu'on n'aura pas découvert dans les rayons X la polarisation circulaire ou elliptique) les radiogrammes pourraient montrer la dissymétrie holoaxe. Ce qui a été dit plus haut suffit à le démontrer.

En résumé, les seules symétries que puissent déceler les radiogrammes sont les holoédries et les parahémiédries.

95

22. Es ist oft bemerkt worden, daß die Röntgenstrahleninterferenzphotogramme mit einem Zinkblendekristall, wie sie ursprünglich Herr M. v. Laue und seine Mitarbeiter erhalten haben, keine Andeutung der hemiedrischen Natur dieses Kristalls aufwiesen. Ein Photogramm, das aufgenommen wurde, während die einfallenden Strahlen senkrecht zu einer Würfelfläche (100) waren, zeigt eine vollkommene vierfache Symmetrie, obgleich die auf dieser Fläche senkrechte Symmetrieachse des Kristalls nur eine zweifache ist. Andererseits liefern Eisenpyrite unter ähnlichen Verhältnissen starke Anzeichen für die zweifache Natur der zu einer Würfelfläche senkrechten Achse; es zeigt sich eine ausgesprochene Abweichung von der vierfachen Symmetrie in der Intensität der Flecke in dem Photogramm. Herr Friedrich hat derartige Photogramme erhalten[1], und ich habe einige, die denselben Punkt beleuchten.

Meines Erachtens ergibt sich eine einfache Erklärung für diese Tatsachen, wenn man den Bau dieser Kristalle betrachtet. Die Struktur der Zinkblende haben mein Vater und ich in unserer Arbeit über die Struktur des Diamants[2] angegeben. Die Anordnung der Atome in Eisenpyriten habe ich in einer noch unveröffentlichten neueren Mitteilung an die Royal Society angegeben. In beiden Fällen stimmt die Symmetrie des Punktsystems mit jener des wirklichen Kristalls überein.

Die Hemiedrie der Zinkblende besteht darin, daß sie Achsen dreifacher Symmetrie besitzt, die polar sind. Die Fläche (111) am einen Ende einer solchen Achse ist von der Fläche ($\overline{1}\overline{1}\overline{1}$) am andern Ende verschieden, obwohl in einem Kristall der holoedrischen Klasse diese Flächen identisch sein würden. Nach unserer Ansicht über die Struktur haben die zur Fläche (111) parallelen Ebenen des Kristalls die in Fig 1 schematisch dargestellte Anordnung, bei der solche Ebenen, die nur Zinkatome enthalten, und solche, die nur Schwefelatome enthalten, paarweise gruppiert sind.

Es ist klar, daß die zu diesen Ebenen senkrechte Achse eine polare ist. Trotzdem würden wir nach der Theorie erwarten, daß die Reflektion von Röntgenstrahlen an der Ebene ($\overline{1}\overline{1}\overline{1}$) mit der Reflektion an der Ebene (111)

Fig. 1.

[1] Vgl. v. Laue, *Physikal. Zeitschr.* **14** (1913) 1078.
[2] W. H. Bragg and W. L. Bragg, 'The Structure of the Diamond.' *Proc. Roy. Soc.* A. **89** (1913) 277.

identisch sein würde. Jede Ebene der Struktur reflektiert nur einen winzigen Bruchteil einer über sie hinweggehenden einfallenden Welle. Ein auftreffender Impuls wird von den Schwefelebenen als ein Wellenzug reflektiert und von den Zinkebenen als ein Wellenzug, der mit dem ersten nicht in Phase ist. Bei der Reflektion an der Fläche (111) wird die erste Gruppe ein wenig gegen die zweite in Phase verzögert, bei der Reflektion an der Fläche ($\overline{111}$) eilt sie in Phase vor. In beiden Fällen aber werden sich die beiden Gruppen vereinigen und dieselbe Resultierende liefern.

Dies ist nur ein Beispiel für eine allgemeine Regel, nämlich dafür, daß die Flächen an den beiden Enden einer polaren Achse dieselbe Reflektion der Röntgenstrahlen liefern werden, vorausgesetzt, daß jedes einzelne Atom die Röntgenstrahlen ganz unabhängig von seinen Nachbaratomen beugt. Wir müssen ferner annehmen, daß die Phasendifferenz solcher Wellen, die an einem derartigen Paar von Zink- und Schwefelebenen reflektiert werden nur von dem Unterschiede des durchlaufenen Weges abhängt, und daß die Natur des Atoms auf die Phase keinen Einfluß hat. [see papers 82 and 83]

23. § 1. In der Literatur findet sich vielfach die wohl auf Friedel[1] zurückgehende Behauptung, die Röntgenstrahlinterferenzen an Kristallen besäßen ebenso wie der Vorgang der Lichtfortpflanzung an sich ein räumliches Symmetriezentrum, sodaß man unter keinen Umständen an ihnen erkennen könnte, ob der Kristall ein solches Zentrum hat oder nicht, und daß es infolgedessen dafür nicht 32, sondern nur wie für die Optik 11 unterscheidbare Kristallsysteme gäbe. Die Überlegungen, durch welche Friedel dies erweisen will, lauten:

'Dans une symétrie holoèdre, donc centrée, à tout plan de symétrie correspond un axe binaire (ou en général pair) qui lui est normal, et réciproquement. Lorsque on passe de holoédrie à une hémiédrie, de ces trois éléments, axe, plan et centre, deux disparaissent nécessairement ensemble. Or, imaginons deux rayons diffractés A et A' symétriques par rapport à un plan de symétrie, dans la diffraction produite par un cristal holoèdre convenablement orienté. *Ces deux rayons sont aussi bien symétriques l'un de l'autre par rapport à l'axe binaire normal au plan. Par contre, chacun est son propre symétrique par rapport au centre.* Supposons maintenant, que le cristal, au lieu d'être holoèdre, ait l'une des deux hémiédries non centrées, c'est-à-dire l'holoaxie ou l'antihemiédrie. En ce cas, il subsiste toujours de l'holoédrie, soit l'axe binaire, soit le plan de symétrie. Cela suffit pour que les deux rayons A et A', identiques par symétrie dans le cas

---

[1] G. Friedel, *Compt. rend.* **157** (1913) 1533 [this Vol. p. 95].

de l'holoédrie, restent *forcément* identiques par symétrie dans le cas de l'hémi-édrie. Par suite, en aucun cas, les radiogrammes ne pourront révéler l'absence de centre ...'

Dieser Beweis scheint uns in mehr als einer Hinsicht anfechtbar. Schon der Anfangssatz schließt das trikline System von der Betrachtung aus, da es bei seiner Holoedrie keine Symmetrieebene oder -achse gibt. Die beiden kursiv gedruckten Sätze sind sodann zum mindesten unklar, weil darin von der Richtung des einfallenden Strahles nicht die Rede ist; hält man letztere Richtung fest, so sind sie falsch, wie der erste Blick auf die Versuchsergebnisse zeigt. Aber setzen wir einmal den für Hrn. Friedel günstigen Fall, daß er den gebeugten Strahl und seinen Gegenstrahl bei umgekehrter Richtung des einfallenden miteinander vergleicht (in diesem Fall treffen die kursiv gedruckten Sätze tatsächlich zu), so bleibt immer noch der durch das 'forcément' bekräftigte Schluß unverständlich. Er ließe sich gerade so gut auf irgend zwei kristallographische Richtungen A und A' anwenden und zeigte dann, daß es überhaupt keine Kristallsysteme ohne Symmetriezentrum geben kann.

Wir wollen im Gegensatz hierzu zeigen, daß die Richtigkeit des Satzes: 'Der Vorgang der Röntgenstrahlbeugung hat an sich ein Symmetriezentrum' von einer Voraussetzung physikalischen Inhaltes abhängt, die, nach den vorliegenden Versuchen zu urteilen, zwar immer erfüllt ist, sich aber ihrem ganzen Wesen nach nicht geometrisch beweisen läßt. Die mathematisch genaue Form dieses Satzes aber scheint uns zu lauten: *Unterwirft man bei festgehaltener Richtung und Intensität des einfallenden Strahles den Kristall einer Inversion, so bleibt Richtung und Intensität jedes gebeugten Strahles erhalten. Oder, was dasselbe sagt: Kehrt man in einem und demselben Kristall die Richtung des einfallenden Strahles bei gleichbleibender Intensität um, so kehrt auch jeder gebeugte Strahl seine Richtung ohne Intensitätsänderung um.*

§ 2. Wir gehen aus von den Gleichungen für die Lage eines gebeugten Strahles. Sind $\mathfrak{a}_1$, $\mathfrak{a}_2$, $\mathfrak{a}_3$ die Kanten des Elementarparallelepipeds des Raumgitters, $\mathfrak{s}_0$ und $\mathfrak{s}$ zwei Einheitsvektoren in der Richtung des einfallenden und eines gebeugten Strahles, die ganzen Zahlen h_1, h_2, h_3 die Ordnungszahlen des letzteren, und ist λ die Wellenlänge, so gehorcht $\mathfrak{s}$ den drei Gleichungen

$$(\mathfrak{a}_1, \mathfrak{s} - \mathfrak{s}_0) = h_1\lambda, \quad (\mathfrak{a}_2, \mathfrak{s} - \mathfrak{s}_0) = h_2\lambda, \quad (\mathfrak{a}_3, \mathfrak{s} - \mathfrak{s}_0) = h_3\lambda. \quad (1)$$

Bei gleichzeitiger Umkehr von $\mathfrak{s}$ und $\mathfrak{s}_0$ bleiben diese Gleichungen bestehen, nur daß die Zahlen h ihr Vorzeichen wechseln. Achten wir also nur auf die Richtung, nicht auf die Intensität des gebeugten Strahles, so trifft die in Rede stehende Behauptung ohne weiteres zu. Da durch die

Vektoren $\mathfrak{a}_1$, $\mathfrak{a}_2$, $\mathfrak{a}_3$ nur ein *einfaches* Raumgitter gegeben ist, das selbst ein Symmetriezentrum besitzt, so ist das keineswegs zu verwundern.

§ 3. Im allgemeinen sind aber nicht nur die Eckpunkte der soeben genannten Elementarparallelepipede mit Atomen besetzt, sondern es finden sich solche der gleichen oder einer anderen Art auch in deren Inneren.

Die Intensität des Strahles ist dann proportional zum 'Strukturfaktor':

$$\left| \Psi + \Psi' \exp\left\{ \frac{2\pi i}{\lambda}\, (\mathfrak{r}', \mathfrak{s} - \mathfrak{s}_0) \right\} + \Psi'' \exp\left\{ \frac{2\pi i}{\lambda}\, (\mathfrak{r}'', \mathfrak{s} - \mathfrak{s}_0) \right\} + \dots \right|^2 \quad (2)$$

Es fragt sich, ob auch er bei einer gleichzeitigen Umkehr von $\mathfrak{s}$ und $\mathfrak{s}_0$ seinen Wert behält.

Die Antwort auf diese Frage hängt offenbar ganz wesentlich von den Beugungsfaktoren Ψ ab. Von vornherein läßt sich über sie nur sagen, daß sie im allgemeinen komplexe, von den Richtungen $\mathfrak{s}$ und $\mathfrak{s}_0$ sowie von der Wellenlänge λ abhängige Größen sind. Man macht nun wohl immer die Annahme, daß wenigstens für den Beugungseinfluß auf Röntgenstrahlen jedes Atom zentrische Symmetrie besitzt, ja, daß es sich dabei sogar als Punkt, also wie mit Kugelsymmetrie begabt, verhält. Dann muß Ψ von den Richtungen $\mathfrak{s}$ und $\mathfrak{s}_0$ unabhängig sein. Das ist keineswegs selbstverständlich. Aber für die Beugung wird diese Annahme theoretisch durch die heutige Vorstellung vom Bau der Atome sehr wahrscheinlich gemacht, nach der die Röntgenstrahlen überhaupt nur durch den innersten Kern der Atome beeinflußt werden, der in seinen Abmessungen gegen den mechanisch gemessenen Atomdurchmesser äußerst klein ist; und außerdem hat sie sich bei den kristallographischen Untersuchungen der Hrn. Bragg, denen sie stets zugrunde liegt, trefflich bewährt. Wir wollen sie im folgenden stets beibehalten.

Ist aber auch Ψ nur von der Wellenlänge und der Atomart abhängig, so kann es doch eine komplexe Größe ($= |\Psi| \exp(i\theta)$) sein; θ ist dann die Phasendifferenz zwischen der einfallenden Welle und der von ihr im Atom erzwungenen Schwingung.

§ 4. Hat der Kristall selbst ein Symmetriezentrum, so zeigt sich dies natürlich ohne weitere Voraussetzung auch bei der Beugung der Röntgenstrahlen. In diesem Fall muß der Strukturfaktor (2) eine Umkehr aller $\mathfrak{r}'$, $\mathfrak{r}''$ ... ohne Wertänderung zulassen, weil diese die Kristallstruktur nicht verändert. Die Umkehr von $\mathfrak{s}$ und $\mathfrak{s}_0$ wirkt aber auf jenen Faktor genau so wie die Umkehr aller $\mathfrak{r}'$ ...; es wechseln die Exponenten in (2) ihr Vorzeichen, doch bleibt der Faktor selbst unverändert.

§ 5. Hat der Kristall kein Symmetriezentrum, so können wir für alle Atome in ihm

$$\mathfrak{r}' = \beta_1'\mathfrak{a}_1 + \beta_2'\mathfrak{a}_2 + \beta_3'\mathfrak{a}_3,$$

$$\mathfrak{r}'' = \beta_1''\mathfrak{a}_1 + \beta_2''\mathfrak{a}_2 + \beta_3''\mathfrak{a}_3$$

usw. setzen, wobei die β beliebige echte Brüche mit den Grenzfällen 0 und 1 sind. Unter Rücksicht auf (1) nimmt der Strukturfaktor (2) dann die Form

$$|\Psi + \Psi' \exp\{2\pi i(\beta_1'h_1 + \beta_2'h_2 + \beta_3'h_3)\} +$$

$$+ \Psi'' \exp\{2\pi i(\beta_1''h_1 + \beta_2''h_2 + \beta_3''h_3)\} + \ldots|^2 \qquad (2a)$$

an, wobei die Exponenten ebenfalls gebrochene Zahlen sind. Bei der Umkehr von $\mathfrak{s}$ und $\mathfrak{s}_0$ wechseln nach § 2 die ganzen Zahlen h ihr Vorzeichen. Dafür, daß dabei (2a) unverändert bleibt, wie man auch die Zahlen h wählen mag, ist notwendig und hinreichend, daß alle Beugungsfaktoren

$$\Psi = |\Psi| \exp(i\theta), \quad \Psi' = |\Psi'| \exp(i\theta'), \quad \Psi'' = |\Psi''| \exp(i\theta'')$$

usw. entweder dasselbe θ haben, oder daß sich die verschiedenen θ nur um π voneinander unterscheiden.

Damit also ohne Rücksicht auf die Symmetrie des Kristalls für die Röntgenstrahlbeugung ein Symmetriezentrum vorhanden ist, ist (abgesehen von der vorausgesetzten Punktförmigkeit der Atome für diesen Vorgang) notwendige und hinreichende Bedingung, daß alle Atome auf eine auffallende Röntgenwelle entweder mit der gleichen Phasendifferenz ansprechen, oder daß nur zwei um π verschiedene Werte bei diesen Phasendifferenzen vorkommen. Die Herren Bragg haben bei ihren so erfolgreichen Untersuchungen über den Kristallbau stets gleiche Phasendifferenzen stillschweigend vorausgesetzt. Ob nicht auch Phasendifferenzen π vorkommen, muß dahingestellt bleiben.

§ 7. Das Bisherige zusammenfassend können wir sagen: Der Satz, daß der Vorgang der Röntgenstrahlbeugung an sich ein Symmetriezentrum besitzt, ist keineswegs geometrisch abzuleiten. Tatsächlich scheint er nach den bisher vorliegenden Versuchen durchweg zuzutreffen.

Wenn sich also jener Satz in der Erfahrung bestätigt, so ist daraus zu schließen, daß alle Atome auf Röntgenstrahlwellen mit der gleichen Phasenverzögerung ansprechen; oder daß doch nur zwei um π verschiedene Phasenverzögerungen vorkommen. Es fragt sich, ob wir hierin eine Eigentümlichkeit der Atome oder lediglich eine Wirkung der Raumgitteranordnung sehen sollen; es ist nämlich zu bedenken, daß die Beugungsfaktoren Ψ für das einzelne und für das dem Gitter angehörende Atom nicht übereinzustimmen brauchen.

§ 8. Eine bestimmte Antwort auf diese Frage läßt sich zurzeit mangels einer hinreichend sichergestellten Atomdynamik wohl nicht geben. Ersetzen wir die Atome durch Dipole, welche nach der klassischen Dynamik unter dem Einfluß einer quasielastischen Kraft reibungsfrei um eine Ruhelage schwingen, so läßt sich aber zeigen, daß die erwähnte Eigentümlichkeit der Beugungsfaktoren allein aus der Anordnung hervorgeht. Wir werden die gegenseitige Beeinflussung der Atome im Raumgitter am einfachsten ermitteln, wenn wir uns mit Ewald[1] den Kristall nach allen Richtungen hin unendlich ausgedehnt denken. Ewald hat zwar nur ein einfaches rhombisches Raumgitter untersucht, doch werden wir sein Ergebnis, daß in ihm ein System ebener Wellen möglich ist, die in der Richtung mit dem einfallenden und dem gebeugten Wellen unserer Betrachtungen übereinstimmen, unbedenklich auf beliebige kompliziertere Gitter übertragen können; spricht doch auch der Grenzübergang von unserer Theorie des endlichen Kristalls dafür daß bei über alle Grenzen wachsendem Kristall nur in den genannten Richtungen Strahlen übrig bleiben. Nun läßt sich bekanntlich an den Maxwellschen Gleichungen für den leeren Raum zeigen, daß zu jedem elektromagnetischen Vorgang seine Umkehrung möglich ist, die sich von ihm lediglich in der Richtung der magnetischen Feldstärken und im Ablaufssinn der Zeit unterscheidet; die Strahlrichtungen sind dabei gerade die entgegengesetzten wie zuvor. Ebenso läßt die Newtonsche Mechanik zu jedem reibungsfreien mechanischen Vorgang die Umkehrung zu, die sich von ihm im Ablaufssinn der Zeit unterscheidet. Daraus folgt, daß in unserem Raumgitter aus reibungsfreien Dipolen zu dem genannten Wellenvorgang auch die Umkehrung möglich ist, die aus ihm durch Umkehr aller Strahlrichtungen unter Aufrechterhaltung der zugehörigen Intensitäten hervorgeht. Damit wäre wohl auf die einfachste und tiefgehendste Weise gezeigt, daß der Vorgang der Röntgenstrahlbeugung an sich ein Symmetriezentrum hat, wenn man die Atome als reibungsfreie Dipole auffassen könnte.

Man bestätigt auch leicht, daß dann nur Phasenverzögerungen θ auftreten können, die einander gleich sind oder sich um π unterscheiden. Der einzelne Dipol hätte trotz seiner vorausgesetzten Reibungsfreiheit eine Dämpfung als Folge der Ausstrahlung elektromagnetischer Energie; infolge dessen würde er periodische erzwungene Schwingungen mit einer Phasenverzögerung gegen die erregende Kraft ausführen, die alle möglichen Werte zwischen 0 und π haben kann. Im Raumgitter von unendlicher Ausdehnung fällt die Ausstrahlung und die damit verbundene Dämpfung aber fort; oder in anderer Ausdrucksweise, die elektromagnetische Dämpfungskraft des einzelnen Dipols wird durch die Einwirkung der anderen

[1] P. P. Ewald, *Physik. Zeitschr.* **14** (1913) 465; *Ann. d. Phys.* **49** (1916) 117, § 7.

Dipole aufgehoben. Dann aber spricht er auf eine periodische erregende Kraft entweder mit der Phasenverzögerung 0 oder π an, je nachdem deren Frequenz kleiner oder größer ist, als seine Eigenfrequenz. Im Raumgitter müssen also alle Phasenverzögerungen 0 oder π sein, was mit dem Satz von § 5 übereinstimmt. *Im reibungsfreien Dipolraumgitter ist es also lediglich eine Folge der Gitteranordnung, daß ein Symmetriezentrum für die Röntgenstrahlbeugung auftritt und daß die Phasenverzögerungen nur zwei um π verschiedene Werte annehmen können, die Reibungslosigkeit scheint dabei aber notwendige Voraussetzung.* Bei wirklichen Atomen, bei denen wir freilich diese Folgerung aus der klassischen Mechanik nicht ohne weiteres anwenden dürfen, haben wir stets Absorption der Röntgenstrahlen. Es wäre eine interessante Frage für den Versuch, ob sich nicht, namentlich bei stark absorbierenden Kristallen, und wenn die Frequenz der einfallenden Strahlung nahe einer Eigenfrequenz des Atomes liegt, doch Ausnahmen von beiden Sätzen feststellen lassen. [see papers 82 and 83].

24.   THE INTENSITY OF REFLEXION OF X-RAYS
BY CRYSTALS

by

W. H. Bragg, M.A., F.R.S.

Cavendish Professor of Physics in the University of Leeds

It is of importance, that the intensities should be measured with as much accuracy as is possible. It happens that this method of analysis is extraordinarily powerful, and that very rough measurements coupled with general assumptions have been sufficient to lead to definite conclusions. The measurements which were used, could only be considered as provisional, under the circumstances. They were sufficient, however, for the determination of several complicated crystals, such as iron pyrites, the calcite series, and so on.

If, therefore, it has been possible to find so much from the early and rough measurements of intensity, it ought to be possible to do far more if the measurements are made more accurate.

There are other reasons for attempting to increase the accuracy of the intensity determinations. In the first place, it will be possible in this way to test theories which profess to explain the general process of reflexion of X-rays by crystals. And again, it is important to be able to determine to what extent the intensities are dependent on the temperature of the crystal. The thermal movements of the atoms should affect the reflexion; indeed, Debije has calculated the extent to which they should do so [1]. Experiment should therefore be of great use in this direction also.

For these various reasons I have endeavoured to increase the degree of accuracy with which intensities can be compared by means of the spectrometer. This paper contains a brief account of the method which appears to be the most suitable, and gives some results of its application to rocksalt and to the diamond. Although much greater accuracy is no doubt still obtainable, the determinations already made seem capable of being applied usefully.

[1] *Verh. d. Deutsch. Phys. Ges.* 15 (1913) 678, 738, 857; also *Ann. d. Phys.* **43** (1914) p. 49 [this Vol. p. 152 and 162].

Let us first attempt to give a definite meaning to the term intensity of reflexion.

Imagine a fine pencil of homogeneous [1] X-rays to proceed from a source at A, to be limited by a slit at B, and to be incident upon a crystal C, so placed that a reflected ray is formed which passes into the ionization chamber D. Let the crystal be so adjusted as to give the maximum value of the reflected ray; and let the ionization current in D be measured in the usual way, the current being allowed to run for a stated time, say t seconds.

We may now remove the crystal and turn the ionization chamber round until the primary beam enters it directly: and we may again measure the ionization current for a given time.

The comparison of these two quantities so obtained does not, however, give us a proper measure of the intensity of reflexion. For, whereas the current in the latter position is proportional to the width of the slit at B, the reflexion in the former case is not proportional to the width of the same slit. Reflexion takes place only when the angle between ray and crystal is

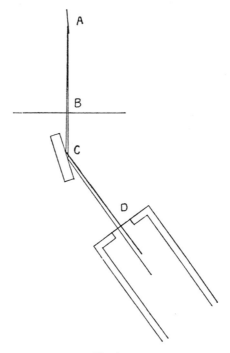

Fig. 1.

[1] Homogeneous pencils have been used in these experiments because they are definite, and can be readily obtained intense and pure.

very exactly adjusted. If we consider the rays which come from a single point in the source at A and fall upon a perfect piece of crystal, a very narrow slit at B will let through all the rays which can be reflected at one time, and the reflexion is not increased by opening the slit any wider. The comparison of quantities will therefore bring in the width of the slit, and it cannot be eliminated without a better knowledge of theory than we possess.

But if we turn the crystal by a succession of small steps through the angle at which reflexion takes place, measuring the ionization current at each step, and if we plot the results in a curve, the area of that curve is a measure of the reflexion effect which does contain the width of the slit as a factor. If we open the slit at B we prolong in proportion the range over which the crystal is able to reflect. When we compare the quantity obtained in this way with the ionization by the direct primary current the width of the slit disappears. Obviously the height of the slit is of no consequence to a first order of approximation. In fact, the ratio is only affected now by the times during which the current is allowed to run in each part of the experiment, and the magnitude of the steps through which the crystal is turned. As these quantities may be kept constant in different experiments, or altered in known proportions, the ratio is now a true comparative measure of the intensity of the reflexion of an X-ray of given quality by a given crystal face in a given order.

In some measurements I have found it convenient to observe the ionization current for a given time at each step in the movement of the crystal and subsequently to add together all the currents observed. This is of course equivalent to plotting the curve and integrating it. At other times I have left the rays in action and advanced the crystal one step at each beat of the clock: movement of the crystal is begun at an angle at which there is no reflexion, it is taken through the reflexion angle, during which time the leaf of the electroscope moves rapidly, and the rays are turned off when the crystal has ceased to reflect. By this method the integration above mentioned is effected automatically. If it were necessary it would be easy to move the crystal at a uniform rate by clockwork, but in practice the simpler methods are quite sufficient for the purpose. The method of steady revolution has been used by de Broglie[1] in obtaining photographs of the spectra.

We may now compare the method of the revolving crystal with the methods by which the earlier measurements of intensity were made. The method then used was to move crystal and ionization chamber together, the latter at twice the rate of the former. In this way a 'spectrum' was mapped out, in

---

[1] *C. R.* Nov. 17, 1913.

which the occurrence of 'peaks' marked the existence of homogeneous pencils of greater or less strength; and the height of the peak was taken to represent the strength of the reflexion, and used as a means of comparing the relative strengths of various orders of reflexion. This method would be as good as the other if crystals were perfect. But they are not. Rocksalt, for example, is very far from being uniform: it consists rather of an agglomeration of smaller and more perfect crystals put together in imperfect alignment. In consequence, a pencil of X-rays passing through a fine vertical slit and falling on a vertical crystal face, is not reflected simultaneously at all points of the narrow vertical band along which it meets the crystal. It is reflected first in one part, then in another as the crystal turns round, and one piece of it after another presents itself to the rays at the proper angle for reflexion. Since reflexion does not occur within close limits but is spread over a wide range, the highest point of the peak is much lower than it would be if the crystal were perfect, and is no true measure of the intensity of the reflexion.

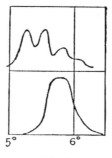

$5°$ $6°$

Fig. 2.

For example, the curves of fig. 2 show the result of measuring the intensity of the reflexion of the first order spectrum in the (100) face of rocksalt, the incident rays being limited to a fine pencil. The abscissæ represent the angular positions of the crystal, the ordinates the measured ionization currents. It will be observed how very irregular the curves are; and still more remarkable is the difference between them, for they were obtained from neighbouring portions of the same face. Clearly no measure of intensity is to be obtained from the maximum ordinate of either of these curves. The areas of the curves are nearly the same, however. The specimen of rocksalt which was used was very irregular. It is easy to find much better.

If a wide pencil of rays is used the results of irregularities are far less obvious. Portions of the crystal lying on the narrow vertical band above mentioned may not be reflecting when they should, but other portions which lie off the band are reflecting when they should not. The errors average out. But there is an especial risk in using a wide pencil. When the crystal is set at the fine glancing angles of first order reflexion, five or six degrees it may be, there is danger that some part of the pencil may not fall on the crystal face, unless the latter is very wide. It appears probable that in earlier measurements the magnitudes of several first order reflexions were under-estimated on this account.

When, however, the newer method is employed, the effects of crystal irregularity largely disappear even when fine pencils are used. Each piece of the face on which the pencil of X-rays falls gets its chance in turn, and when all is added up, it is as though the differently set pieces had all acted together. This is a very important consideration.

Although the crystal irregularities prevent all parts of it from acting together, the reflected rays from all parts pass through the slit of the ionization chamber even when it is quite narrow. This curious focussing effect has already been explained in the case of a perfect crystal[1]. It is dependent on the equality of the distances from the crystal to the source and to the slit of the ionization chamber, respectively. It may be shown that it holds good to a sufficient extent even when the crystal is not perfect. This is a very convenient circumstance, because the slit of the ionization chamber may therefore be set in position to take in the reflected rays of a given wave-length for all positions of the crystal, and at the same time its width may be limited so that there is no chance of other wave-lengths entering the chamber. For instance, there are two strong rhodium lines, and it is easy to use the one and not the other. The stronger line is really a doublet, and in the higher orders it is possible to use one constituent of the doublet and not the other.

One difficulty, apparently of minor importance, should be mentioned: it is easiest to explain it by a numerical illustration. Suppose the glancing angle is 6°, and the crystal has to be turned through the range from 5° to 7° in order to give all parts of the crystal on which the rays impinge the chance of reflecting. Then it is clear that this area is larger when the angle is small (5°) than when it has the large value (7°). Parts of the crystal are acting in the one case which are not acting in the other. If the crystal were perfect, it must be noticed, this would be quite proper; but an irregular crystal would only give an approximately true value through averaging. It appears probable, however, that this effect is not important. Of course it is well to choose for experiment as good a piece of crystal as is possible.

Some of the crystal faces must be prepared, since natural faces are

---

[1] *Proc. Roy. Soc.* A **38** 433.

limited in number. A prepared face should be cut so as to be nearly true, say within half or a quarter of a degree. Want of truth makes very little difference in the determination of the angle of reflexion, but may affect an intensity measurement seriously. This may be seen at once from the figure.

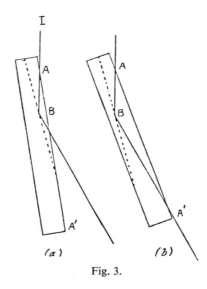

Fig. 3.

If the prepared face AA' is not parallel to the crystal planes, whose direction is shown by the dotted line, it will make a considerable difference whether it is set as represented in (a) or as in (b). The primary pencil IA enters the crystal at A and is reduced to a certain value when it reaches B, B being any point on the path and AB the same length in the two figures. In the one case, however, the reflected pencil has to traverse a much smaller mass of crystal before emerging than it has to do in the other, and the reflexion appears correspondingly greater. This effect is very marked in practice. For example, a (111) face of rocksalt, which reflects the principal rhodium ray at a glancing angle of 11°, was cut 5° out of truth. The intensity of reflexion was then twice as great in the one position as in the other. In the case of a prepared face it is therefore well to measure the intensity effects for both positions and to take the mean, in case the face has not been cut quite truly.

We may now consider some experimental results in the case of rocksalt.

The anticathode A (see fig. 1) was so placed that the rays left it at a grazing angle in order to pass through the slit at B. The slit was half a millimetre wide, and was placed as close to the crystal as possible. The distance from A to B was 17 cm, from B to C 3 cm, from C to D 12 cm. Although the distances AC and CD were not equal, the focussing was sufficiently good.

The crystal was turned by hand, five minutes at a time, one movement for each beat of the clock. About three degrees of total movement was sufficient to take in all the reflexion the crystal could give. The rays used were those constituting the principal line of rhodium. To increase the ionization current the chamber was filled with methyl bromide.

The measurements were very consistent, consecutive observations differing by not more than one or two per cent. The results are given in the following table, in which the intensity of the first order reflexion is put equal to 100 and the rest are given as percentages.

	1st order	2nd order	3rd order	4th order
Face (100)	100	18.7	6.25	
Face (110)	41	7.05		
Face (111)	16.5	24.4	3.1	4.2

The results for the first two faces show the rapid decline of intensity with increasing order of reflexion which has already been referred to. The planes parallel to the (111) face contain, alternately, sodium atoms only, and chlorine atoms only: as has already been mentioned, the spectra of even orders are therefore much stronger than those of odd orders.

A new experimental fact appears in this, that the intensities of the different faces are comparable with each other. We plot the intensity of each order

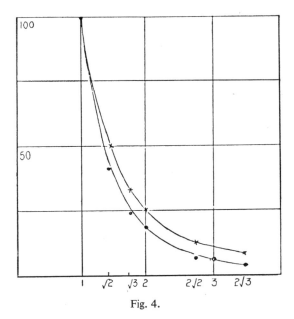

Fig. 4.

against the ratio of the sine of its glancing angle to the sine of the glancing angle of the first order of the (100) face. We then find that they all lie nearly on one curve (fig. 4, lower curve), no matter what face they belong to, excepting, however, the first and third spectra of the (111) face. These last, however, are peculiar, and differ from all the others in that they arise from a difference in atomic weights. In the case of sylvine, where potassium has replaced sodium and the weights of potassium and chlorine are nearly equal, these two spectra do not appear.

Considering, therefore, all the reflexions in which the effects of the various atoms add together directly, there is not a different law for each face, but one law for all the faces; and it is of especial interest that those reflexions from the (111) planes, in which the effects of the two kinds of plane add together, fell in with the rest.

It will be observed that the intensities fall away somewhat more rapidly than the inverse square of the sine of the glancing angle. For convenience of comparison, the upper curve in the figure shows how the observed points would have been placed if the law had been that of the inverse square.

It will be possible eventually to express each of the intensities in the above table in absolute terms, which are independent of all circumstances of the experiment and depend only on the nature of the crystal, the order of the spectrum, or more generally the glancing angle, the temperature, and the wave-length of the rays reflected. I have not attempted to do this so far. It will be necessary to use as primary rays a pencil which has been sorted by reflexion.

THE FOURIER METHOD

25 [1]. If we know the nature of the periodic variation of the density of the medium we can analyse it by Fourier's method into a series of harmonic terms. The medium may be looked on as compounded of a series of harmonic media, each of which will give the medium the power of reflecting at one angle. The series of spectra which we obtain for any given set of crystal planes may be considered as indicating the existence of separate harmonic terms. We may even conceive the possibility of discovering from their relative intensities the actual distribution of the scattering centres, electrons and nucleus, in the atom; but it would be premature to expect too much until all other causes of the variations of intensity have been allowed for, such as the effects of temperature, and the like.

[1] W. H. BRAGG, Bakerian Lecture, *Phil. Trans. A* **215** (1915) 254.

CHAPTER II

The Reciprocal Lattice

THE RECIPROCAL LATTICE

26a. Das 'reziproke Gitter' in der Strukturtheorie. Teil I: Das Reziproke eines einfachen Gitters, by P. P. EWALD (1912)

■

27. Geometrische Konstruktion der Interferenzrichtungen, by P. P. EWALD (1912)

■

26b. Das 'reziproke Gitter' in der Strukturtheorie. Teil II: Das Reziproke eines zusammengesetzten Gitters, by P. P. EWALD (1912)

■

26a. Durch die Erforschung des Feinbaues der Kristalle mit Röntgenstrahlen haben die mathematischen Untersuchungen über Kristallstruktur den spekulativen Charakter verloren, der ihnen früher in den Augen mancher Forscher anhängen mochte. Auch ist die Anzahl derer, die sich mit Strukturtheorie befassen, seit der Laueschen Entdeckung von 1912 viel größer geworden und man wird jetzt geneigter sein, als vordem, eigene Methoden auszubilden, die den Zwecken der Strukturtheorie angepaßt sind. Darum dürfte es nicht ungelegen sein, hier teils zusammenfassend, teils fortführend eine Methode darzustellen, die sich schon auf physikalischem Gebiet, nämlich bei der Untersuchung der Interferenzerscheinungen mit Röntgenstrahlen, bewährt hat, die Methode des 'reziproken Gitters'.

Der erste Teil der vorliegenden Arbeit enthält keine neuen Ergebnisse. Er bringt die Bekanntschaft mit dem reziproken eines einfachen Translationsgitters. Mögen diejenigen, denen die Darstellung mit Vektoren ungewohnt ist, die ersten §§ benutzen, um Sätze, die ihnen vielleicht in Determinantenschreibweise geläufig sind, in der prägnanten Kurzschrift der Vektoralgebra wiederzufinden. Ich habe mich nicht entschließen können, auf die Erleichterungen, die die vektorielle Ausdrucksform für jeden, der sie kennt, mit sich bringt, zu verzichten. § 1 bringt einen Vergleich zwischen den 'reziproken' und den verschiedenen 'polaren' Achsen (Bravais, Grassmann). Das Ende des ersten Teiles bildet eine kurze formale Darstellung der Röntgeninterferenzen, auf welche später Bezug genommen wird.

Teil II ist neu und man kann sagen, nur vorläufig abgeschlossen. Er bringt die Ausdehnung der Methode auf zusammengesetzte Gitter, die mancherlei Überraschendes zeigt, das sich aber im ganzen zu einem schönen System abzurunden verspricht. Rein geometrisch ist der Ausgangspunkt, durch rein geometrische Gesichtspunkte ist der Gedankengang geleitet

—und plötzlich, das ist das Erstaunliche, ist ein reziprokes Gitter entstanden, das im engsten Zusammenhang mit den Angaben steht, die uns zunächst bei Erforschung der Struktur mit Röntgenstrahlen geliefert werden. So ist es wohl nicht vermessen, die Hoffnung auszusprechen, daß sich mit Hilfe des reziproken Gitters ein sicherer Weg finden lassen wird, der von den Meßergebnissen mit Röntgenstrahlen zu der Kristallstruktur hinüberführt—ein Übergang, der bisher trotz mannigfacher Hilfsmittel, nur in den einfachsten Fällen zwangläufig erfolgen konnte, in verwickelteren Fällen jedoch eines eigenen Spürsinnes bedurfte.

TEIL I. DAS REZIPROKE EINES EINFACHEN GITTERS

§ 1. *Die reziproken Kristallachsen*

Ein Kristall sei auf drei Achsen bezogen, die wir nach Richtung und Länge durch drei Vektoren $\mathfrak{a}_1\,\mathfrak{a}_2\,\mathfrak{a}_3$ darstellen.

Zu dem System der $\mathfrak{a}_i$ wird in der Vektorrechnung das System der 'reziproken Vektoren' $\mathfrak{b}_i$ definiert (Gibbs) durch folgende Eigenschaften. Es ist

$$(\mathfrak{a}_i\mathfrak{b}_k) = 0, \quad (\mathfrak{a}_i\mathfrak{b}_i) = 1 \quad (i, k = 1, 2, 3). \tag{1}$$

Die erste Gleichung sagt aus, daß jeder Vektor $\mathfrak{b}_k$ auf zwei Vektoren $\mathfrak{a}_i$ senkrecht steht, denn diese Tatsache bedeutet das Verschwinden des skalaren Produktes. Die $\mathfrak{b}_i$ bilden also zu den $\mathfrak{a}_i$ die Polarecke. Die zweite der Gl. (1) gibt hingegen die Normierung von $\mathfrak{b}_i$; dieses soll so lang gewählt werden, daß seine Projektion auf die Richtung $\mathfrak{a}_i$ die Länge $1/a_i$ hat, wenn wie üblich a_i die Länge des Vektors $\mathfrak{a}_i$ bedeutet. Durch diese Art der Normierung unterscheiden sich die 'reziproken' von den seit Bravais' Zeiten für strukturtheoretische Zwecke wohlbekannten polaren Achsen.

Auf Grund der Eigenschaften (1) läßt sich leicht der Ausdruck der $\mathfrak{b}_i$ durch die $\mathfrak{a}_i$ finden, nämlich:

$$\mathfrak{b}_1 = \frac{[\mathfrak{a}_2\mathfrak{a}_3]}{(\mathfrak{a}_1[\mathfrak{a}_2\mathfrak{a}_3])}, \quad \text{und zykl. Vertauschungen.} \tag{2}$$

Man bestätige hieran die Gl. (1) und das über die Richtung der Achsen gesagte und beachte sodann, daß

$$(\mathfrak{a}_1[\mathfrak{a}_2\mathfrak{a}_3]) = (\mathfrak{a}_2[\mathfrak{a}_3\mathfrak{a}_1]) = (\mathfrak{a}_3[\mathfrak{a}_1\mathfrak{a}_2]) = v_a \tag{2'}$$

das Volumen des Parallelepipeds bedeutet, welches von den Achsen $\mathfrak{a}_i$ als

Kanten gebildet wird. Man hat also

$$\mathfrak{b}_1 = \frac{1}{v_a}\,[\mathfrak{a}_2\mathfrak{a}_3], \qquad \mathfrak{b}_2 = \frac{1}{v_a}\,[\mathfrak{a}_3\mathfrak{a}_1], \qquad \mathfrak{b}_3 = \frac{1}{v_a}\,[\mathfrak{a}_1\mathfrak{a}_2]. \qquad (2'')$$

Die Achsensysteme $\mathfrak{a}_i$ und $\mathfrak{b}_i$ stehen in einem reziproken Verhältnis, d.h. so gut wie die $\mathfrak{b}_i$ als reziproke zu den $\mathfrak{a}_i$, können diese als reziproke zu den $\mathfrak{b}_i$ angesehen werden. Aus der vollkommenen Symmetrie der Gl. (1) in $\mathfrak{a}$ und $\mathfrak{b}$ folgt sofort, daß ebenso wie Gl. (2″) auch gelten muß:

$$\mathfrak{a}_1 = \frac{1}{v_b}\,[\mathfrak{b}_2\mathfrak{b}_3], \qquad \mathfrak{a}_2 = \frac{1}{v_b}\,[\mathfrak{b}_3\mathfrak{b}_1], \qquad \mathfrak{a}_3 = \frac{1}{v_b}\,[\mathfrak{b}_1\mathfrak{b}_2], \qquad (3)$$

wobei

$$v_b = (\mathfrak{b}_1[\mathfrak{b}_2\mathfrak{b}_3]) = \ldots \text{(zykl. Vert.)} \qquad (3')$$

das von den $\mathfrak{b}_i$ aufgespannte Volum ist. Für sein Verhältnis zu v_a ergibt sich, wenn man in (3′) $\mathfrak{b}_1$ gemäß (2) ersetzt und das skalare Produkt aus zwei Vektorprodukten unter Beachtung von (1) ausführt[1]:

$$v_a . v_b = 1. \qquad (4)$$

Die Normierung bewirkt, daß die Volumina von Ecke und reziproker Ecke reziprok sind.

Durch die Gl. (1) oder (2) sind die Dimensionen festgelegt: haben die Kristallachsen die Dimension von Längen, so sind die reziproken Achsen Vektoren von der Dimension 1 : Länge.

Indem wir die Reziprozität in dem Verhältnis zwischen primären und polaren Achsen in den Vordergrund rücken, führen wir eine abweichende Normierung ein, welche den reziproken Achsen die Eigentümlichkeit verleiht: *die reziproken von den reziproken sind die ursprünglichen Achsen.* (Bei den anderen Polarachsen treten noch Faktoren hinzu.) Bezeichnen wir symbolisch den Übergang von Primär- zu Polarachsen mit R, so ist

$$(\mathfrak{b}_i) = R(\mathfrak{a}_i), \quad RR(\mathfrak{a}_i) \equiv (\mathfrak{a}_i) \text{ oder } RR \equiv 1. \qquad (5)$$

Primäre und reziproke Achsen bilden eine *Gruppe.*

§ 2. *Das reziproke Gitter*

Wir verstehen unter einem Gitter zunächst ein 'einfaches' Gitter, d.h. ein solches, dessen 'Basis' nur aus einem Atom besteht. Ein einfaches Gitter

---

[1] Es ist: $([\mathfrak{a}\mathfrak{b}][\mathfrak{c}\mathfrak{d}]) = (\mathfrak{c}\mathfrak{a})(\mathfrak{d}\mathfrak{b}) - (\mathfrak{d}\mathfrak{a})(\mathfrak{c}\mathfrak{b}).$

läßt sich stets durch affine Verzerrung aus dem triklinen Bravaisschen Gitter gewinnen—, was auch als Definition des einfachen Gitters gelten mag.

Seien $\mathfrak{a}_i$ primitive Translationen eines einfachen Gitters, welches wir als das Primärgitter bezeichnen. Wir gewinnen aus dieser einen Angabe alle Kenntnis des Gitters, wenn wir uns die Fahrstrahlen zu den Gitterpunkten —am besten in vektorieller Form—hinschreiben:

$$\mathfrak{R}_l = l_1\mathfrak{a}_1 + l_2\mathfrak{a}_2 + l_3\mathfrak{a}_3 = \sum_i l_i\mathfrak{a}_i. \tag{6}$$

Neben den Koordinaten der Gitterpunkte verlangen wir aber auch die Richtungen der Netzebenen zu kennen. Eine solche mit den Millerschen Indizes h_1, h_2, h_3 hat mit den Achsen die Durchstoßpunkte gemein, deren Fahrstrahlen proportional zu $\mathfrak{a}_1/h_1$, $\mathfrak{a}_2/h_2$, $\mathfrak{a}_3/h_3$ sind. Ihre Normalenrichtung erhalten wir durch das Vektorprodukt aus den beiden ihr parallel gelegenen Vektoren (Fig. 1)

$$\overrightarrow{12} = \frac{\mathfrak{a}_2}{h_2} - \frac{\mathfrak{a}_1}{h_1}$$

und

$$\overrightarrow{23} = \frac{\mathfrak{a}_3}{h_3} - \frac{\mathfrak{a}_2}{h_2}.$$

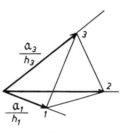

Fig. 1.

Dies Produkt ist:

$$[\overrightarrow{12}, \overrightarrow{23}] = \frac{[\mathfrak{a}_2\mathfrak{a}_3]}{h_2 h_3} - \frac{[\mathfrak{a}_1\mathfrak{a}_3]}{h_1 h_3} + \frac{[\mathfrak{a}_1\mathfrak{a}_2]}{h_1 h_2} = \frac{v_a}{h_1 h_2 h_3} \{h_1\mathfrak{b}_1 + h_2\mathfrak{b}_2 + h_3\mathfrak{b}_3\}.$$

Wir benutzen nun die Achsen $\mathfrak{b}_i$ als primitive Translationen zur Herstellung des 'reziproken Gitters' und bezeichnen mit $\mathfrak{h}$ den Fahrstrahl vom Anfangspunkt zu einem Gitterpunkt dieses Gitters:

$$\mathfrak{h} = h_1\mathfrak{b}_1 + h_2\mathfrak{b}_2 + h_3\mathfrak{b}_3 = \sum_i h_i\mathfrak{b}_i. \tag{7}$$

So gewinnen wir den von den Polargittern her bekannten Satz: der Fahrstrahl zum Gitterpunkt $h_1 h_2 h_3$ des reziproken Gitters hat die Richtung der Normalen der Netzebene mit den Millerschen Indizes $h_1 h_2 h_3$ im Primärgitter.

Betrachten wir den kürzesten Fahrstrahl $\mathfrak{h}^*$ von gegebener Richtung. Für ihn sind $h_1^* h_2^* h_3^*$ teilerfremd. Seine Länge hat eine einfache Bedeutung. Die gleichung einer Ebene von der Normalenrichtung $\mathfrak{n}$ (Einheitsvektor), die im Abstand d vom Nullpunkt vorbeigeht, heißt in Vektorschreibweise, wenn $\mathfrak{r}$ die laufenden Koordinaten zusammenfaßt:

$$(\mathfrak{n}\mathfrak{r}) = d.$$

Suchen wir diejenige zu $\mathfrak{h}^*$ senkrechte Ebene auf, welche der durch den Nullpunkt $\mathfrak{R}_l = 0$ gehenden Ebene benachbart ist, so haben wir für $\mathfrak{n}$ zu setzen $\mathfrak{h}^*/|\mathfrak{h}^*|$ und entnehmen als Netzebenenabstand d^* den kleinsten Wert, den das skalare Produkt

$$\frac{1}{|\mathfrak{h}^*|}(\mathfrak{h}^*\mathfrak{R}_l) = \frac{1}{|\mathfrak{h}^*|}\{h_1^* l_1 + h_2^* l_2 + h_3^* l_3\} = \frac{1}{|\mathfrak{h}^*|}\Sigma_i(h^*_i l_i)$$

annehmen kann, wenn nicht gleichzeitig $l_1 = l_2 = l_3 = 0$ ist. Da $h_1^* h_2^* h_3^*$ keinen gemeinsamen Teiler haben, sind mit dem Zähler alle ganzen Zahlen darstellbar und der kleinste Wert ist

$$d^* = 1/|\mathfrak{h}^*|. \tag{8}$$

Der Fahrstrahl zum ersten Gitterpunkt einer gegebenen Richtung im reziproken Gitter is gleich dem Reziproken des Abstandes der entsprechenden Netzebenen im Primärgitter.

Hiernach scheinen nur die jeweils kürzesten Fahrstrahlen im reziproken Gitter eine eigentliche geometrische Bedeutung zu haben. Denn den Längen der Fahrstrahlen zu zweiten, dritten, ... Gitterpunkten würden im Primärgitter Netzebenen vom halben, drittel, ... Abstand entsprechen, welche nicht vorhanden sind.

§ 4. *Reziprokes Gitter und Fourierentwicklung*

Das hervorstechende Merkmal des Kristallgitters ist seine Periodizität. Viele Ortsfunktionen im Gitterraum werden deshalb ebenfalls rein periodisch, andere lassen sich durch Abspaltung von Faktoren oder additiven Größen auf periodische reduzieren (z.B. das optische Feld). Periodische Funktionen werden im ganzen Raum durch Fourierreihen dargestellt, die aus diesem Grund von besonderer Bedeutung in der Gittertheorie sind.

119

Das reziproke Gitter gestattet, den Ausdruck der Fourierreihe in invarianter und besonders anschaulicher Form aufzustellen, wie hier angedeutet werden mag.

Wir betrachten zunächst eine 'eindimensionale' Fourierentwicklung, die wir in folgender Form am einfachsten schreiben:

$$f(x) = \frac{1}{a} \Sigma_{-\infty}^{+\infty} A_h \exp(2\pi i h x / a) \tag{10}$$

h ist der Summenzeiger, A_h der Fourierkoeffizient und a der Entwicklungsbereich. Die Periodizität der Darstellung erhellt, wenn man x um ein beliebiges ganzes Vielfaches n von a vermehrt: jedes Summenglied multipliziert sich mit dem Faktor exp $2\pi i h n$, der 1 ist. Die Summation geht von $-\infty$ bis $+\infty$; durch Zusammenfassung der Glieder mit $-h$ und $+h$ erhält man die Summe in der üblichen Form mit cos- und sin-Funktionen.

Das einzelne Glied in (10) stellt eine Welle dar, deren Wellenlänge a/h beträgt. Denken wir an die Saite von der Länge a, auf welche diese Darstellung oft angewandt wird, so bedeutet dies Glied ihre h^{te} Oberschwingung, A_h deren Amplitude. Um diese aus der gegebenen Funktion f zu gewinnen, multipliziert man bekanntlich die Gl. (10) mit exp$(-2\pi i h' x / a)$ und integriert von $x = 0$ bis $x = a$: die Integrale der Summenglieder sind Null bis auf das Glied, für welches $h' = h$ ist und es bleibt

$$A_h = \int_0^a f(x) \exp(-2\pi i h x / a) dx.$$

Wir wollen die Form der Fourierreihe im eindimensionalen Fall so darstellen, daß sie ohne weiteres auf beliebige mehrdimensionale Gebiete übertragen werden kann. Dazu formulieren wir die obigen Tatsachen so:

Der Entwicklungsbereich 0 ... a wird dargestellt durch einen Vektor $\mathfrak{a}$ des eindimensionalen Gebietes. Seine Länge a fassen wir als 'Inhalt' auf und schreiben demgemäß auch v_a dafür. Wir konstruieren den zu $\mathfrak{a}$ reziproken Vektor $\mathfrak{b}$, der zur Erfüllung der Definitionsbedingung $(\mathfrak{a}\mathfrak{b}) = 1$ gleichen Sinn wie $\mathfrak{a}$, aber die Länge $1/a$ haben muß. Mit $\mathfrak{b}$ führen wir das 'reziproke Gitter' auf, zu dessen Punkten die Fahrstrahlen $\mathfrak{h} = h\mathfrak{b}$ (h ganzzahlig) führen. Fassen wir schließlich x als den eindimensionalen Fahrstrahl $\mathfrak{r}$ auf, so lautet die Fourierentwicklung

$$f(\mathfrak{r}) = \frac{1}{v_a} \Sigma_h A_h \exp 2\pi i (\mathfrak{h}\mathfrak{r}); \quad A_h = \int f(\mathfrak{r}) \exp\{-2\pi i (\mathfrak{h}\mathfrak{r})\} dv. \tag{11}$$

Die Summe ist über alle Punkte des reziproken Gitters, die Integration über alle 'Volumelemente' dv des Entwicklungsbereichs zu erstrecken.

Diese Fassung der Fourierentwicklung gilt auch für zwei-, drei- und mehrdimensionale Gebiete, und zwar einerlei, ob diese rechtwinklig oder schiefwinklig abgegrenzt sind.

Im dreidimensionalen durch drei Vektoren $\mathfrak{a}_i$ bestimmten Entwicklungsgebiet gilt insbesondere für die Darstellung einer Funktion f von $\mathfrak{r} = (x, y, z)$: Man bilde die reziproken Achsen $\mathfrak{b}_i$, aus ihnen das Gitter mit dem Fahrstrahl $\mathfrak{h}$ der Gleichung (7). $\mathfrak{h}$ übernimmt die Rolle der Wellennormalen für das einzelne Glied der Fourierentwicklung, denn dieses hat konstante Werte auf den Ebenen $(\mathfrak{h}\mathfrak{r}) = $ konst., die senkrecht zu $\mathfrak{h}$ stehen. Die Summe über alle Punkte des reziproken Gitters ist natürlich eine dreifach unendliche und der Index h am Entwicklungskoeffizienten repräsentiert ein Indextripel (h_1, h_2, h_3).

Warum gerade $\mathfrak{h}$ auftreten muß, erkennen wir in der auch für das folgende ungemein wichtigen Eigenschaft dieses Vektors: Sei nach (6) $\mathfrak{R}_l$ der Fahrstrahl zu einem Punkt des Primärgitters, so hat das skalare Produkt $(\mathfrak{h}\mathfrak{R}_l)$ den Wert

$$(\mathfrak{h}\mathfrak{R}_l) = (\textstyle\sum_i h_i \mathfrak{b}_i . \sum_k l_k \mathfrak{a}_k) = h_1 l_1 + h_2 l_2 + h_3 l_3 = \textstyle\sum_i h_i l_i. \qquad (12)$$

Es ist also unter allen Umständen ganzzahlig. Infolgedessen ändert das einzelne Glied der Reihe (11) den Wert nicht, wenn statt $\mathfrak{r}$, $\mathfrak{R}_l + \mathfrak{r}$ gesetzt wird. *Das auftreten von $\mathfrak{h}$ ist durch die Periodizität bedingt.*

27. GEOMETRISCHE KONSTRUKTION DER INTERFERENZRICHTUNGEN

Damit alle Zellen im ganzen Gitter phasengleich zusammenwirken, so ist notwendig dass jeweils die auf den Kristallachsen benachbarten Atome zusammenwirken. Dies gibt die Laueschen Interferenzbedingungen:

$$\left.\begin{array}{l} (\mathfrak{a}_1, \mathfrak{s} - \mathfrak{s}_0) = h_1 \lambda \\ (\mathfrak{a}_2, \mathfrak{s} - \mathfrak{s}_0) = h_2 \lambda \\ (\mathfrak{a}_3, \mathfrak{s} - \mathfrak{s}_0) = h_3 \lambda \end{array}\right\} h_1 h_2 h_3 \text{ drei ganze Zahlen.} \qquad (2')$$

Im allgemeinen Fall vereinigt man die drei skalaren Gleichungen (2') zu einer völlig äquivalenten und besonders übersichtlichen Vektorgleichung:

$$\mathfrak{s} - \mathfrak{s}_0 = \lambda\mathfrak{h} \quad \text{Fundamentalgleichung.} \qquad (2)$$

Hierin ist $\mathfrak{h} = h_1 \mathfrak{b}_1 + h_2 \mathfrak{b}_2 + h_3 \mathfrak{b}_3$ der schon oben eingeführte Fahrstrahl im reziproken Gitter; die Gleichung entsteht aus den vorigen (2') durch Multiplikation dieser mit $\mathfrak{b}_1$ bzw. $\mathfrak{b}_2, \mathfrak{b}_3$ und Addition auf Grund der für jeden beliebigen Vektor $\mathfrak{v}$ (hier $\mathfrak{s} - \mathfrak{s}_0$) gültigen Identität:

$$\mathfrak{v} = \mathfrak{b}_1(\mathfrak{a}_1\mathfrak{v}) + \mathfrak{b}_2(\mathfrak{a}_2\mathfrak{v}) + \mathfrak{b}_3(\mathfrak{a}_3\mathfrak{v})$$

Gleichung (2) führt sofort zu einer geometrischen Konstruktion der Interferenzrichtungen, die zu einer gegebenen Einfallsrichtung $\mathfrak{s}_0$ und Wellenlänge λ gehören. Trägt man nämlich (Abb. 73) im reziproken Gitter vom Ursprung O aus den Vektor $- \mathfrak{s}_0/\lambda$ ab, so gelangt man zu dem 'Ausbreitungspunkt' A. Da $\mathfrak{h}$ ein Gitterfahrstrahl und $\mathfrak{s}/\lambda$ ein Vektor von der Länge $1/\lambda$ sein muß, ergeben sich die Interferenzrichtungen als die Vektoren vom Ausbreitungspunkt A zu irgendwelchen Gitterpunkten, die auf der um A geschlagen Kugel vom Radius $1/\lambda$ (die durch den Nullpunkt geht) liegen[1].

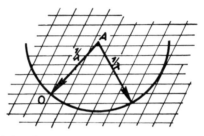

Abb. 73. Konstruktion der Interferenzrichtungen mit der Ausbreitungskugel.

Diese Konstruktion mit Hilfe der 'Ausbreitungskugel' gibt oft den besten Überblick über die Gesamtheit der Interferenzerscheinung und insbesondere über Symmetrieverhältnisse. Sie gestattet auch sofort den 'Reziprozitätssatz'[1] abzulesen, der so ausgesprochen werden kann: Das Bündel der Interferenzstrahlen ist eine Einheit; es ist ganz gleichgültig, welcher der Interferenzstrahlen eines Bündels als Primärstrahl angesehen wird, es entsteht stets das gleiche Bündel. Dieser Satz bildet die Grundlage der dynamischen Theorie.

Betrachtet man in der Konstruktion Abb. 73 den Primärstrahl und einen beliebigen Interferenzstrahl, so baut sich über dem Vektor $\mathfrak{h}$ ein gleichschenkliges Dreieck von der Schenkellänge $1/\lambda$ auf. Da aber $\mathfrak{h}$ die Normalenrichtung der Ebene $(h_1\,h_2\,h_3)$ ist, so erkennt man hieraus die Berechtigung der von W. L. Bragg[2] ausgesprochenen Auffassung: Jeder Interferenzstrahl entsteht aus dem Primärstrahl durch 'Spiegelung' an einer (inneren oder äußeren) Netzebene des Kristallgitters; dabei gehört zur Interferenz $(h_1\,h_2\,h_3)$ gerade die Millersche Ebene $(h_1\,h_2\,h_3)$ als Spiegelebene. Sind die $(h_1\,h_2\,h_3)$, die nach ihrer Bedeutung als Gangunterschiede sehr wohl

[1] P. P. Ewald, *Phys. Zs.* **14** (1913) S. 465; M. v. Laue, *Enzyklopädie der mathematischen Wissenschaften* Bd. V, S. 24.
[2] W. L. Bragg, *Proc. Cambridge Phil. Soc.* **17** (1913) S. 43 [this Vol. p. 40].

einen gemeinsamen Faktor haben können, nicht teilerfremd, und bezeichnet man mit $h_1^* h_2^* h_3^*$ das gekürzte Flächensymbol, so schreibt man

$$(h_1 h_2 h_3) = n(h_1^* h_2^* h_3^*) \tag{3}$$

und nennt die Interferenz auch die Reflexion n-ter Ordnung an der Fläche $(h_1^* h_2^* h_3^*)$. Die Reflexion 6. Ordnung an (110) ist also auch (660) zu schreiben.

Interessiert man sich für die Reflexe an einer bestimmten Fläche, so hat man die Gittergerade im reziproken Gitter zu betrachten, die das Bild dieser Fläche ist. Damit außer einem Anfangspunkt ein weiterer Punkt $n\mathfrak{h}^*$ dieser Geraden (Punktabstand $|\mathfrak{h}^*| = 1/d_h$) auf der Ausbreitungskugel vom Radius $1/\lambda$ liegt, muß der Ausbreitungspunkt so liegen (Abb. 74), daß

$$n|\mathfrak{h}^*| = (2 \sin \theta)/\lambda$$

oder

$$n\lambda = 2d_h \sin \theta \tag{4}$$

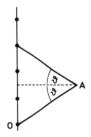

Abb. 74. Ableitung des Braggschen Gesetzes.

ist. Dabei ist d_h der Abstand der Netzebenen $(h_1 h_2 h_3)$ und θ der gegen die Spiegelebene gemessene Einfalls- bzw. Reflexionswinkel (sog. 'Glanzwinkel', eine auch in der geometrischen Optik gebräuchliche Bezeichnung). Die zweite Form dieser Gleichung ist die vielgebrauchte Braggsche Reflexionsbedingung, neben (2) die wichtigste Formel der ganzen Theorie.

26b. TEIL II. DAS REZIPROKE EINES ZUSAMMENGESETZTEN GITTERS

§ 5. Ziel und Zweck der Verallgemeinerung

Die bisherigen Überlegungen haben dazu geführt, zu einem 'einfachen' Primärgitter ein reziprokes zu konstruieren, derart, daß es ganz gleichgültig ist, ob von einem Gitter die Primärform oder die reziproke Form der Beschreibung bekannt ist. Denn von der einen Form kann man zur andern durch die eindeutige Operation, die oben mit R bezeichnet wurde, übergehen. Während die Primärform das Gitter durch Angabe der *Punktlagen* $\mathfrak{R}_l$ beschreibt, wird das gleiche Gitter in der reziproken Form durch Angabe der *Ebenenlagen* $\mathfrak{h}$ geschildert.

Ein gleicher Dualismus in der Beschreibung muß offenbar auch möglich sein, wenn das Primärgitter nicht 'einfach', sondern 'zusammengesetzt' ist. Nehmen wir gleich das allgemeine Gitter, so sind seine Punkte zu beschreiben durch die Angabe:

1. von drei nicht in einer Ebene gelegenen Translationen $\mathfrak{a}_1\,\mathfrak{a}_2\,\mathfrak{a}_3$,
2. von Lagen $\mathfrak{r}_s$ und Massen m_s der 'Basis' Bestandteile.

Besteht die mit den Translationen $\mathfrak{a}_i$ periodisch sich wiederholende Basis aus S Bestandteilen (Atome, Elektronen, Radikale, kurz Atome genannt), so treten zu den drei vektoriellen Angaben $\mathfrak{a}_i$ noch weitere S vektorielle und S skalare Angaben $\mathfrak{r}_s$ und m_s. Die Angaben m_s, die wir der Kürze halber als *Massen* der Basisatome bezeichnen, sind irgend welche Parameter, die die Atomsorten des Gitters in bezug auf den gerade interessierenden Gesichstpunkt charakterisieren—seien es nun wirkliche Massen, oder Kernladungszahlen, oder Streuungsvermögen für Röntgenstrahlen, oder Ionenladungen, oder optische Eigenfrequenzen — wesentlich ist nur, daß in diesen Parametern eine ähnliche Diskontinuität herrscht, wie sie für die Atome kennzeichnend ist, bei denen keine stetigen Übergänge von einer Sorte zur anderen existieren[1].

Wir suchen nun das für die einfachen Gitter hinreichend bekannte reziproke Gitter derart auszugestalten, daß es auch von dem zusammengesetzten Gitter eine vollständige und eindeutige Beschreibung liefert, die zu der eben vorgenommenen Beschreibung insofern ein Gegenstück bildet, als nicht die Punktlagen, sondern die Ebenenlagen darin klar zum Ausdruck kommen sollen.

Während im 'einfachen' Gitter die Ebenen, die einer und derselben Schar angehören, gleichwertig sind, d.h. sich in gleichen Abständen folgen und gleiche Belastung (Masse der Punkte pro Quadratzentimeter) aufweisen, ist dies im zusammengesetzten Gitter nicht der Fall. Die Beschreibung des Gitters durch seine Ebenen muß also die *Abstandsfolgen und die verschiedenen Belastungen innerhalb einer Ebenenschar* erkennen lassen.

Es sei schon hier darauf hingewiesen, daß die Röntgenuntersuchung gerade eine derartige Beschreibung des Gitters liefert: Abstandsfolgen und

[1] Auch der skalare Charakter der 'Massen' ist nicht wesentlich. Es könnten auch die Polarisationen $\mathfrak{p}_s$ benutzt werden, um die Atomsorten in ihrem Verhalten gegenüber Licht- oder Röntgenwellen zu unterscheiden.

Belastungen der Ebenen sind es, die aus den Intensitäten der Interferenzen gewonnen werden. Bezeichnen wir mit Bragg die Interferenzen als Reflexionen an den Netzebenen, so ist es einleuchtend, daß durch sie immer nur Aussagen über die Netzebenen, nicht über die Punktlagen gewonnen werden können. Wir werden deshalb vermuten dürfen, daß die beabsichtigte Beschreibung des Gitters in einem engen Zusammenhang mit der experimentellen Erforschung der Gitter stehen wird.

§ 6. *Vorläufige Gewichtsbestimmung aus der Periodizität des Gitters*

Denken wir uns zunächst das Gitter aus der Atomsorte 1 vorhanden, so ist dies ein einfaches Gitter von den Translationen $\mathfrak{a}_i$ und es gehört zu ihm ein reziprokes Gitter, dessen Fahrstrahl

$$\mathfrak{h} = \Sigma_i h_i \mathfrak{b}_i \qquad (15)$$

ist. Setzen wir nun die weiteren $S - 1$ kongruenten und parallelen Gitter aus den andern Atomsorten in das erste ein, so entstehen hierdurch keine neuen Ebenenrichtungen mit Belastungen, die von 0 verschieden sind. Denn innerhalb der einzelnen Teilgitter existieren nur die gleichen Ebenenrichtungen, wie im ersten Gitter. Werden aber Atome aus verschiedenen Teilgittern durch eine Ebene verbunden, so wird diese Ebene entweder noch durch unendlich viele analoge Atomgruppen gehen und also zu den rationalen Ebenen gehören, die auch im Teilgitter 1 schon vertreten waren, oder aber die Ebene hat eine irrationale Lage—dann enthält sie nicht unendlich viele Punkte und ihre Belastung, sowie ihr Abstand von der parallelen Nachbarebene sind Null, und sie ist keine eigentliche Gitterebene.

Halten wir daran fest, daß die Fahrstrahlen im reziproken Gitter die Normalen der Ebenen im Primärgitter sein sollen, so dürfen wir demnach nicht etwa das reziproke Gitter dadurch verallgemeinern, daß wir statt seiner Punkte eine Basis einsetzen, denn das würde neue Richtungen $\mathfrak{h}$ ergeben. Der geometrische Anblick des reziproken Gitters muß vielmehr der gleiche sein, wie für eines der Teilgitter.

Es bleibt nur die Möglichkeit, den Punkten des reziproken Gitters verschiedenes *Gewicht* beizulegen. Die Gewichtsfunktion wird abhängen:

1. von der Punktlage $\mathfrak{h}$ im reziproken Gitter;
2. von der geometrischen Konfiguration der Basis, also den S Vektoren $\mathfrak{r}_s$;
3. von der Natur der Basisatome, also ihren 'Massen' m_s und deren Zuordnung zu den Lagen $\mathfrak{r}_s$.
4. Schließlich kann das Gewicht auch von den Translationen $\mathfrak{a}_i$ abhängen.

125

Wir schreiben die Gewichtsfunktion demnach ausführlich mit ihren Argumenten:

$$G(m_s, \mathfrak{r}_s, \mathfrak{h}, \mathfrak{a}_i). \tag{16}$$

Inwieweit läßt sich diese Funktion bestimmen aus der Forderung einer eindeutigen Beziehung zwischen Primärgitter und reziprokem?
1. Sei wie oben, Gl. (6),

$$\mathfrak{R}_l = \sum l_i \mathfrak{a}_i$$

ein Fahrstrahl im Translationsgitter. Statt die Basis durch die Angaben m_s, $\mathfrak{r}_s$ zu beschreiben, können wir ebensogut

$$m_s, \mathfrak{r}_s + \mathfrak{R}_l^{(s)}$$

dazu verwenden, d.h. wir können die S Basisatome in verschiedenen Gitterzellen wählen. Diese andere Beschreibung desselben Gitters darf an der Gewichtsfunktion nichts ändern und man entnimmt hieraus, daß die Koordinaten der Basis nur in der Form

$$\exp \pm 2\pi i(\mathfrak{h}\mathfrak{r}_s) \tag{17}$$

auftreten können, welche nach § 4 die verlangte Periodizität zum Ausdruck bringt.
2. Auch die Wahl der Translationen ist willkürlich. Statt der ursprünglichen Translation $\mathfrak{a}_1$ kann die doppelte, ... n-fache, eingeführt werden, wenn nur entsprechend die Anzahl der Basisatome verdoppelt, ... ver-n-facht, wird. Die n-fache Basis wird durch die $n.S$ Größen

$$m_s, \mathfrak{r}_s; m_s, \mathfrak{r}_s + \mathfrak{a}_1; \ldots m_s, \mathfrak{r}_s + (n-1)\mathfrak{a}_1 \tag{18}$$

geschildert. Der Wahl der Translationen $n\mathfrak{a}_1, \mathfrak{a}_2, \mathfrak{a}_3$ zur Darstellung des Primärgitters entsprechen die Achsen des reziproken: $\mathfrak{b}_1/n, \mathfrak{b}_2, \mathfrak{b}_3$, und der Fahrstrahl

$$\mathfrak{h} = h_1\mathfrak{b}_1/n + h_2\mathfrak{b}_2 + h_3\mathfrak{b}_3. \tag{15'}$$

In der $\mathfrak{b}_1$-Richtung würden die Punkte des reziproken Gitters also einen n-fach verkleinerten Abstand bekommen—was nicht sein darf, damit keine neuen Ebenenrichtungen angezeigt werden. Die Gewichtsfunktion muß also die Eigenschaft haben, daß bei der Basis (18) alle Punkte fortfallen, bei denen nicht h_1 ein ganzes Vielfaches von n ist. Da die Koordinaten nur in der unter 1. bestimmten Form auftreten dürfen, folgt, daß die Gewichtsfunktion wesentlich additiv sein muß:

$$G' = \sum_1^S m_s \exp 2\pi i(\mathfrak{h}\mathfrak{r}_s). \tag{16'}$$

Denn nur dann ist für die Basis (18)

$$G' = \sum_1^S m_s . \exp 2\pi i(\mathfrak{h}\mathfrak{r}_s)\{1 + \exp 2\pi i h_1/n + \exp 2\pi i . 2h_1/n + \dots$$
$$+ \exp 2\pi i . (n - 1)h_1/n\}$$

stets Null, wenn h_1/n keine ganze Zahl ist. (Potenzsumme von Einheitswurzeln!) Ist hingegen h_1/n ganzzahlig, so hat die geschweifte Klammer den Wert n. Um die alten Gewichte wieder zu erhalten, müßte noch durch n dividiert werden. Dies könnte geschehen, indem G' dividiert durch die Gesamtmasse der Basis als Gewicht eingeführt würde, doch wird im nächsten § aus anderen Gesichtspunkten $(1/v_a) . G'$ als Gewichtsfunktion angegeben werden, durch die das gleiche erreicht wird.

Die Periodizität des Gitters ließe es zu, auch eine homogene Funktion von G' als Gewicht zu benutzen, etwa das Quadrat; doch schließt die Forderung der Reziprozität im nächsten Paragraphen diese Kombinationen aus. Die Gewichte G_h sind nichts anderes als die in der Theorie der Röntgeninterferenzen wohlbekannten 'Strukturfaktoren'. Es ist sehr bemerkenswert, daß unsere mit rein geometrischen Absichten und von einem rein geometrischen Ausgangspunkt aus unternommene Untersuchung ganz genau auf den 'Strukturfaktor' führt, also auf diejenige Größe in der sich der Einfluß der Struktur auf die Intensität der Röntgenbilder zeigt. Hierin liegt die praktische Bedeutung des reziproken Gitters für die Darstellung und Verwertung der Ergebnisse der Röntgenaufnahmen.

Zusammenfassung

1. Es wird gezeigt, wie durch passende Normierung das in der Strukturtheorie schon von jeher gebrauchte polare Gitter (Bravais) an Einfachheit gewinnt und sich bequem vektoriell darstellen läßt.

2. Das durch diese Normierung erhaltene 'reziproke Gitter' stellt die Ebenenkoordinaten des 'Primärgitters' dar. Komponenten von Vektoren bezüglich der reziproken Achsen transformieren sich besonders einfach. Das reziproke Gitter bewährt sich bei der Darstellung von Funktionen, die im Primärgitter periodisch sind, z.B. Feldern von Licht- oder Röntgenwellen.

3. Dies gilt zunächst nur für 'einfache' Primärgitter, d.h. reine Translationsgitter. Es wird gezeigt, in welcher Art durch Beschwerung der Punkte des reziproken Gitters mit Gewichten eine Erweiterung vorgenommen werden kann, derart, daß auch 'zusammengesetzte' Primärgitter ('Gitterkomplexe' in Grothscher Bezeichnung) durch das reziproke völlig gekenn-

zeichnet werden. Dabei bleibt das reziproke eine Beschreibung des primären Gitters nach seinen Ebenen,—deren Richtungen, Abstandsfolgen,
Belastungen.

5. Auch für das zusammengesetzte Gitter besteht ein enger Zusammenhang zwischen Röntgeninterferenzen und reziprokem Gitter. Die Aufgabe
der Strukturerforschung kann dadurch mathematisch-algebraisch formu-
liert werden.

München, Institut f. theoret. Physik der Universität

*The mathematical analysis developed in Ewald's treatment of
the reciprocal lattice leads to the Fourier representation,
though he deals with a series of scattering points and not an
extended distribution of scattering matter.*

W. L. BRAGG,
Z. Krist. **70** (1929) 475

CHAPTER III

The Intensity Factors of the Kinematical Theory

POLARIZATION (OR THOMSON) FACTOR

28. P. P. EWALD (1913)

▬

29. Die Polarisierung von Röntgenstrahlen durch Reflexion an Kristallen, by H. MARK und L. SZILARD (1926)

▬

30. The Polarization Factor in X-ray Reflection, by P. KIRKPATRICK (1927)

▬

31. The Polarisation Factor in X-Ray Reflection, by R. W. JAMES (1928)

▬

28. Es ist anzunehmen, daß die Dipole senkrecht zum einfallenden Röntgenstrahl ($\mathfrak{s}$) schwingen, da dieser Strahl bei weitem die größte Intensität hat. Soll nun die Intensität eines Interferenzstrahls ($\mathfrak{s}'$) berechnet werden, so muß die Dipolamplitude $\mathfrak{a}$ in die in der Ebene ($\mathfrak{s}\mathfrak{s}'$) schwingende Komponente ($\mathfrak{a}_1$) und die andere $\perp(\mathfrak{s}, \mathfrak{s}')$ zerlegt werden ($\mathfrak{a}_2$). Die letztere kommt für $\mathfrak{s}'$ voll zur Wirkung, die erste mit dem Faktor $\cos(\mathfrak{s}'\mathfrak{s})$. Die Intensität des Strahls $\mathfrak{s}'$ ist also

$$\mathfrak{a}_1{}^2 + \mathfrak{a}_2{}^2 \cos^2(\mathfrak{s}'\mathfrak{s}).$$

Man sieht an den Interferenzbildern, daß die einfallenden Röntgenstrahlen (bzw. die Dipolschwingungen) nicht polarisiert sein können. Wären sie es nämlich, so müßten die Intensitäten zweier unter gleichem Winkel ($\mathfrak{s}'\mathfrak{s}$) gegen den Primärstrahl gelegener Interferenzstrahlen (korrespondierender Interferenzflecke in verschiedenen Quadranten) verschieden sein, weil die Zerlegung in die Komponenten $\mathfrak{a}_1$ und $\mathfrak{a}_2$ für beide Strahlen ungleich wäre.

Mit $\mathfrak{a}_1 = \mathfrak{a}_2$ ist die Intensität eines Strahls also proportional

$$1 + \cos^2(\mathfrak{s}'\mathfrak{s}). \tag{25}$$

29. Es wird in einigen Fällen gezeigt, daß an einem Kristall unter 90° nach der Braggschen Beziehung reflektierte Röntgenlicht praktisch vollständig polarisiert ist und daß bei Belichtung eines Kristalls mit linear polarisiertem Röntgenlicht keine Reflexion eintritt, falls die Richtung des reflektierten Strahles in die Schwingungsrichtung des polarisierten einfallenden Strahles fällt. Es lassen sich so Kristalle als Polarisatoren und Analysatoren für Röntgenstrahlen verwenden.

Die grundlegenden Versuche über die Polarisationserscheinungen an Röntgenstrahlen sind im Jahre 1905 von Barkla durchgeführt worden[1]. Er zerstreute ein Bündel von Röntgenstrahlen an einem Kohleblock und fand, daß die unter 90° zum Primärstrahl abgehenden sekundären—gestreuten—Strahlen sich insofern bemerkenswert verhalten, als die durch sie an einem zweiten Kohlestück ausgelösten Tertiärstrahlen sich bezüglich ihrer Intensität ungleichförmig um den Sekundärstrahl herum verteilen. Seine Beobachtung deutete er durch die Annahme, daß die unter 90° vom ersten Streustrahler ausgehenden gestreuten Strahlen vollständig polarisiert sind und daß dieses polarisierte Licht bei der Zerstreuung durch den zweiten Kohleblock in der Schwingungsrichtung des elektrischen Vektors keine und senkrecht hierzu die maximale Intensität ergibt. Das Ergebnis seiner Versuche läßt sich zusammenfassen in die Aussage: Bei der diffusen Zerstreuung von Röntgenstrahlen durch Kohle und andere leichte Elemente verlaufen die Erscheinungen so, als ob die Zerstreuung durch isotrop gebundene Elektronen nach den Gesetzen der klassischen Elektrodynamik erfolgte.

Es schien uns nun der Mühe wert, die Laueschen Kristallreflexionen mit Bezug auf die Polarisation zu untersuchen. Da die Reflexion am Kristall als eine Beugungserscheinung aufgefaßt werden muß, hat man auf Grund der Barklaschen Versuche mit diffus zerstreutem Lichte zu erwarten, daß das an einer Kristallfläche nach der Braggschen Beziehung unter dem Glanzwinkel reflektierte Röntgenlicht vollständig polarisiert ist, falls der reflektierte Strahl senkrecht zum Primärstrahl steht. Ebenso war zu erwarten, daß ein Kristall oder Kristallpulver linear polarisierte Röntgenstrahlen überhaupt nicht reflektiert, wenn der reflektierte Strahl in die Richtung des elektrischen Vektors des polarisierten Primärstrahles fallen würde.

Um zu sehen, ob dies tatsächlich zutrifft, wurde ein Versuch angestellt, welcher durch Fig. 1 schematisch dargestellt ist. Die monochromatische K-Strahlung einer Kupferantikathode wird an einem Steinsalzkristall (Polarisator P) so reflektiert, daß der Ablenkungswinkel nahezu 90° beträgt. Der reflektierte Strahl S fällt dann auf ein Kristallpulver A und erzeugt Debye-Scherrerkegel. Uns interessieren nun jene Kegel, deren

---

[1] Vgl. den zusammenfassenden Bericht von Ch. G. Barkla, *Jahrb. d. Radioakt. u. Elektronik* **5** (1908) 246.

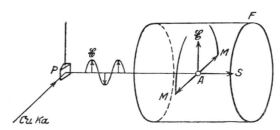

Fig. 1. Schematische Darstellung der Versuchsanordnung.

Erzeugende ungefähr einen Winkel von 90° mit dem Primärstrahl einschließen. Wenn nämlich die am Polarisator reflektierte Strahlung vollständig polarisiert ist, dann schwingt der elektrische Vektor des auf A treffenden Strahles S parallel der Richtung $\mathfrak{E}$, und die vom analysierenden Kristallpulver A unter 90° ausgehenden Debye-Scherrerkegel dürfen in der Richtung $\mathfrak{E}$ keine Intensität enthalten; senkrecht hierzu müssen sie hingegen die Maximalintensität besitzen.

Legt man um das Kristallpulver einen zylindrischen Film F, dessen Achse mit dem Strahl S zusammenfällt, so wird dieser durch die Debye-Scherrerkegel in Kreisen geschnitten, welche nach dem Ausbreiten des Zylinders in gerade Linien übergehen. Die Schwärzung entlang dieser geraden Linien wird nun keineswegs gleichförmig sein, wie dies bei einem Debye-Scherrerkreis der Fall wäre, welcher in der gebräuchlichen Weise mit unpolarisiertem Licht erzeugt ist; sie wird viel mehr einen charakteristischen Verlauf zeigen.

In Fig. 4 ist eine Aufnahme wiedergegeben, welche mit polarisierter Kupfer Strahlung an Platinfolie als Analysator erhalten wurde. Man sieht hier einen Schwärzungsverlauf, welcher einer praktisch vollständigen Polarisation entspricht.

Auch bei den schweren Elementen erfolgt also offenbar die Beugung so, als ob sie klassisch durch isotrop gebundene Elektronen bewirkt würde. Barkla fand bei seinen Versuchen an schwereren Elementen allerdings einen scheinbar geringeren Polarisationsgrad. Man muß aber bedenken, daß bei Polarisationsversuchen mit diffus zerstreuten Röntgenstrahlen die

Cu $K\alpha$-Strahlung an NaCl (422) polarisiert. ϑ 86°.

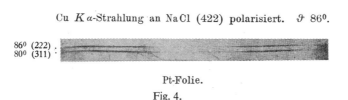

86° (222)
80° (311)

Pt-Folie.

Fig. 4.

Fluoreszenzstrahlung sich dem abgebeugten Lichte überlagert und so einen zu geringen Polarisationsgrad vortäuschen kann. Dies war auch die Deutung, die Barkla seinen Beobachtungen bei schwereren Elementen gab.

Berlin-Dahlem, Kaiser Wilhelm-Institut für Faserstoffchemie und Institut für theoretische Physik an der Universität Berlin.

30.

Introduction

The so-called polarization factor which appears in formulas expressing the intensity of x-rays reflected from crystals was first developed by Sir J. J. Thomson[1], and serves to account for the decrease of intensity which the change in direction incurs. The factor expresses the proportional reduction of intensity involved in this process, and is written $\frac{1}{2}(1 + \cos^2 2\theta)$. The factor may also be written $(\frac{1}{2} + \frac{1}{2}\cos^2 2\theta)$, thus exhibiting the fact that the intensity of the deviated portion of one-half of the incident (unpolarized) radiation is constant with the angle of deviation, while the intensity of the deviated portion of the other half varies as $\cos^2 2\theta$. The electric vectorial components of that half of the incident radiation which gives rise to the constant deviated portion lie in a direction at right angles to the plane of reflection while the components of the half which gives rise to the variable portion lie in the plane of reflection.

Although the polarization factor was designed to apply only to an unpolarized incident beam, those who have made use of it have not always been mindful of this limitation. Indeed the writer has not been able to discover a single case in the literature of crystal reflection where this restriction has been recognized, though the polarization factor has entered into the numerical computations of numerous papers[2]. The continuous spectral radiation from primary x-ray sources is never unpolarized, and Bishop's[3] results indicate that the characteristic radiations may not be assumed to be free from polarization either. It is desirable to develop a polarization factor which shall apply to reflection of x-radiation initially or completely polarized.

---

[1] Thomson, Conduction of Electricity Through Gases.
[2] A. H. Compton, *Phys. Rev.* **7** (1916) 658; Bragg, James, and Bosanquet, *Phil. Mag.* **41** (1921) 308, and later papers; Harris, Bates, and MacInnes, *Phys. Rev.* **28** (1926) 235. These papers are representative of a much larger number which might be cited.
[3] Bishop, *Phys. Rev.* **28** (1926) 625.

An Equivalence Theorem

As a preliminary step it will be well to simplify our method of representing the beam emitted from the x-ray tube. The beam as actually emitted is complex, and must be supposed to be constituted of a large number of elementary emissions having their planes of polarization oriented in many different directions. It will now be shown that this beam scatters identically with a much simpler beam, consisting of two components polarized in mutually perpendicular planes. (...) See Fig. 1.

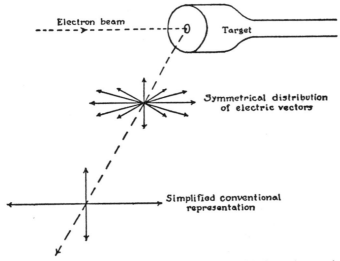

Fig. 1. Complex x-ray beam made up of a multiplicity of independent emissions. The electric vectors of the separate emissions are symmetrically disposed with respect to their prevailing direction, and in the present consideration may be replaced by two mutually perpendicular vectors.

Generalization of the Polarization Factor

In the beam of x-rays incident upon the reflecting crystal we need consider only such portion as is of the proper wave-length for reflection at the existing grazing angle, θ. Let this portion be regarded as consisting of two superposed plane polarized beams of the kind just discussed. The amplitudes may be designated by L and T, the greater one being L. The magnitudes of these amplitudes are governed by the requirements that $T^2 + L^2 =$ = total intensity, and $(T/L)^2 = P$.

For simple visualization let it be supposed that the plane of reflection is horizontal and that the x-ray tube is capable of rotation about the incident beam as axis. The orientation of the tube at any time may be specified by the angle α, between the plane of reflection and a plane defined by the incident beam and the cathode stream. Resolving the amplitudes T and L horizontally and vertically we have as vertical components $L \sin \alpha$ and $T \cos \alpha$, and as horizontal components $T \sin \alpha$ and $L \cos \alpha$. The reflected intensity due to the vertical components is constant with the angle of deviation, so that the intensity of this reflection portion is proportional to $(L \sin \alpha)^2 + (T \cos \alpha)^2$. The reflected intensity due to the horizontal components varies as $\cos^2 2\theta$, so that the intensity of this portion is proportional to $\{(T \sin \alpha)^2 + (L \cos \alpha)^2\} \cos^2 2\theta$. We therefore have

$$\text{Polarization factor} = \frac{\sin^2 \alpha + P \cos^2 \alpha + (P \sin^2 \alpha + \cos^2 \alpha) \cos^2 2\theta}{1 + P} \qquad (6)$$

Discussion

When the incident radiation is unpolarized P has the value unity, and Eq. (6) assumes the familiar form $\frac{1}{2}(1 + \cos^2 2\theta)$. The tube orientation most often employed is probably that defined by $\alpha = 0$. Investigators seldom if ever state the values of α employed in their work, but the diagrams accompanying all of the papers cited in footnote 2, indicate that the zero value was used in these cases. For this orientation we have

$$\text{Polarization factor } (\alpha = 0) = (P + \cos^2 2\theta)/(1 + P)$$

Uncertainty as to the correct values of P makes it impossible to apply exact corrections to work done in the past. A computation based upon values regarded as plausible has shown however that some of the numerical results given in the papers cited should be modified by as much as ten percent.

Lacking precise information as to the values of P it is by all means desirable that future investigations involving comparisons between theoretical and observed intensities of reflection should be carried out with the x-ray tube oriented so that $\alpha = 45°$, that is, with the plane determined by the cathode stream and the incident ray inclined at an angle of $45°$ with the plane of reflection. In this case the right member of Eq. (6) becomes $\frac{1}{2}(1 + \cos^2 2\theta)$, and P need not be known. Radiation received from a tube thus inclined will be reflected with the same intensity as unpolarized radiation, regardless of what its actual state of polarization may be.

Department of Physics, University of Hawaii, Honolulu, T.H.

31. Kirkpatrick suggests that it would be advisable in all such experiments to work with $\alpha = 45°$, since in this case the polarisation factor reduces to $\frac{1}{2}(1 + \cos^2 2\theta)$, and is independent of the degree of polarisation of the incident beam.

In view of the detailed comparison of the theory of atomic scattering with experiment which has been based on them, it is perhaps worth while to state that in the determinations of F recently published by the writer and Miss Firth (*Proc. Roy. Soc.* A **117** (1927) 62), α was in fact 45°, so that these results would appear to be unaffected by this source of error. It is, however, only fair to state that this value of α was used for reasons of practical convenience and not because of any particular foresight on our part.

Physical Laboratories, University of Manchester

STRUCTURE FACTOR

32. W. L. BRAGG (1913)

▄

33. The Reflexion of the X-rays, by H. G. J. MOSELEY and C. G. DARWIN (1913)

▄

34. M. LAUE (1913)

see also M. LAUE (1913), this Vol. p. 9, note[1]
C. G. DARWIN (1914), this Vol. p. 177
idem (1914), this Vol. p. 210

▄

35. W. L. BRAGG and J. WEST (1928)

▄

32. ... the element of the pattern is a cube with an atom at each corner and one at the centre of each cube face. Suppose the phase difference between vibrations from successive atoms along the three axes, when waves of wave-length λ fall on the crystal, to be $2\pi h_1$, $2\pi h_2$, $2\pi h_3$. Thus in order that vibrations from those atoms, which are arranged at the centres of the cube faces, should also be in phase, one must have

$$h_1/2 - h_2/2 = \text{an integer}, \quad h_2/2 - h_3/2 = \text{an integer}.$$

This condition is simply expressed by saying that h_1, h_2, h_3 must all be even or all odd integers.

33. In ferrocyanide the third order was enormously the most conspicuous. The sixth order was quite easily found, the fourth order not at all. These facts can be very simply explained. If the crystal structure completely repeats itself only every three layers, the distance between the first and fourth layers gives the fundamental distance d. It is possible either that the three layers are at nearly but not quite the same distance apart, or that every third layer is especially rich in the heavy atoms, iron for example, which most efficiently scatter the primary radiation. The two cases are shown diagrammatically in fig.3 In either case the different orders will all be present, but the third order and its multiples may well be

138

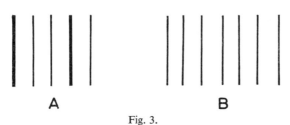

Fig. 3.

much stronger than the others, because in the third order all the layers cooperate, while in the first order only every third layer does so. If all the layers become both similar and similarly situated, the previous third order becomes the fundamental and the others disappear. This is the case with rocksalt, for which no subsidiary orders could be found. In this case d is presumably the distance between successive layers, and this happens to be almost exactly the same as the average distance in ferrocyanide. The behaviour of selenite is similar. Here, although the intensity of the first order was more than twice that of the second, the latter was the more conspicuous. The fourth order also was much more conspicuous than the third. In this case the crystal structure evidently repeats itself every second layer. This seems to offer a simple method of investigating the structure of crystals.

34. In den obigen Auseinandersetzungen wird stets nur von einem einfachen Raumgitter gesprochen. Treten nun aber außer den Atomen, deren Orte durch die Gleichungen (1)[1] bestimmt sind, andere, von den ersteren im allgemeinen verschiedene, auf, die in den Punkten

$$x' = (m + \delta')a_{1x} + (n + \varepsilon')a_{2x} + (p + \zeta')a_{3x}$$
$$y' = (m + \delta')a_{1y} + (n + \varepsilon')a_{2y} + (p + \zeta')a_{3y}$$
$$z' = (m + \delta')a_{1z} + (n + \varepsilon')a_{2z} + (p + \zeta')a_{3z}$$

liegen. Unter Umständen kommt noch eine dritte und vierte Art usw. hinzu, an den Orten:

$$x'' = (m + \delta'')a_{1x} + (n + \varepsilon'')a_{2x} + (p + \zeta'')a_{3x} \text{ usw.}$$
$$x''' = (m + \delta''')a_{1x} + (n + \varepsilon''')a_{2x} + (p + \zeta''')a_{3x} \text{ usw.}$$

usw. Die δ, ε, ζ sind dabei echte Brüche, deren Werte für das Punktsys-

[1] [This Vol. p. 8]

tem charakteristisch sind. Die Vektoren

$$
\begin{cases}
\mathfrak{r}' = \delta'\,\mathfrak{a}_1 + \varepsilon'\,\mathfrak{a}_2 + \zeta'\,\mathfrak{a}_3, \\
\mathfrak{r}'' = \delta''\mathfrak{a}_1 + \varepsilon''\mathfrak{a}_2 + \zeta''\mathfrak{a}_3, \\
\mathfrak{r}''' = \delta'''\mathfrak{a}_1 + \varepsilon'''\mathfrak{a}_2 + \zeta'''\mathfrak{a}_3
\end{cases}
\tag{15}
$$

usw. führen von einem ungestrichenen Atom zu den benachbarten ein-, zwei- und dreigestrichenen; ihre Komponenten nach den Koordinatenachsen sind deshalb gleich $x' - x, y' - y, z' - z$ usw. Da sich die durch die Striche unterschiedenen Atome i.A. verschieden verhalten, müssen wir ihnen auch verschiedene Funktionen Ψ, Ψ' usw. zuschreiben.

In diesem Fall tritt an die Stelle der Summe (4)[1]:

$$
\frac{\exp(-ikR)}{R}\,\{\Psi(\alpha,\beta)\,\textstyle\sum\exp[ik\{x(\alpha-\alpha_0)+y(\beta-\beta_0)+z(\gamma-\gamma_0)\}] +
$$

$$
+\,\Psi'(\alpha,\beta)\,\textstyle\sum\exp[ik\{x'(\alpha-\alpha_0)+y'(\beta-\beta_0)+z'(\gamma-\gamma_0)\}] + ...\} =
$$

$$
= \frac{\exp(-ikR)}{R}\,\{\Psi(\alpha,\beta)+\Psi'(\alpha,\beta)\exp(iR)+\Psi''(\alpha,\beta)\exp(iR')+...\}\cdot
$$

$$
\cdot\textstyle\sum_m\sum_n\sum_p\exp\{i(mA+nB+pC)\},
\tag{16}
$$

wo A, B, C die in (5)[1] angegebenen Werte haben, während analog

$$
\begin{aligned}
R' &= k(\mathfrak{r}_x'(\alpha-\alpha_0)+\mathfrak{r}_y'(\beta-\beta_0)+\mathfrak{r}_z'(\gamma-\gamma_0)), \\
R'' &= k(\mathfrak{r}_x''(\alpha-\alpha_0)+\mathfrak{r}_y''(\beta-\beta_0)+\mathfrak{r}_z''(\gamma-\gamma_0))
\end{aligned}
\tag{17}
$$

ist. Man sieht, daß der einzige Unterschied gegen früher in der Ersetzung der Funktion Ψ durch die Klammer besteht. Es werden eben eine ganze Schar benachbarter Atome als ein Gitterelement wirken.

35. Professor Ewald points out to us, in a private communication, the adventges of considering

$$
F = \textstyle\sum_i f_i \exp\left\{2\pi i\left(\rho_i\cdot\frac{\mathfrak{s}-\mathfrak{s}_0}{\lambda}\right)\right\}
$$

as a complex quantity, in which case it gives not only the amplitude of the scattered wave but also its phase defined with reference to a chosen origin in the unit cell. If F is defined in this sense, we should write $|F|$ for the quantity found by experimental measurement, and replace F^2 in the intensity formula by $F\bar{F}$, or by $|F|^2$.

---

[1] [this Vol. p. 9]

LORENTZ-FACTOR

For the first structure determinations by W. H. and W. L.
Bragg no accurate knowledge or interpretation of intensities
was necessary, the argument being based on enhancement,
weakening or absence of reflections. An empirical 'normal
decline' of intensity was constructed by W. H. Bragg with a
delicate feeling for what might be the normal amongst so many
deviations. This normal decline for the various orders on the
same face of reflection did invaluable service for a great
many years. Of course many attempts were made to account
for it on theoretical grounds. H. A. Lorentz was the first to
introduce the idea of an 'integrated reflexion' by considering
all contributions to a certain direction of observation, integra-
ting over wave-lengths and directions of incidence. Only as the
result of such an integration over the Laue function does the
total intensity become proportional to the total number N
of cells, i.e., to the volume of the crystal.

P. P. EWALD,
Current Sci. (1937) p. 11

36. Zur Diskussion des Verhaltens der Röntgenstrahlen in Kristallen, by J. STARK (1913)

37. Sur la diffraction des rayons Röntgen par les cristaux, by G. FRIEDEL (1913)
see also T. TAMARU, *this Vol. p.* 35 *note*[1]

The white *Lorentz-factor* $1/\sin\theta$
38. Nach brieflicher Bemerkung von H. A. LORENTZ, by P. DEBIJE (1914)
see also C. G. DARWIN (1914), *this Vol. p.* 175

39. Lorentz-Faktor, by M. v. LAUE (1926)

The monochromatic *Lorentz factor* $1/\sin\theta\cos\theta$
see C. G. DARWIN (1914), *this Vol. p.* 174 *and* 210
W. L. BRAGG, R. W. JAMES *and* C. H. BOSANQUET (1921), *this Vol. p.* 274

36. Die Intensität der Röntgenstrahlen, welche an den aufeinanderfolgenden parallelen zerstreuenden Kristallebenen einer bestimmten Art im Kristallinnern reflektiert werden, ist um so größer, je kleiner der Winkel zwischen dem primären Röntgenstrahlenbündel und der betrachteten Kristallebene ist, je schiefer also die primären Röntgenstrahlen die zerstreuende Kristallebene treffen. Desto kleiner erscheinen nämlich die nicht mit Atomen besetzten Löcher in der Ebene gesehen in der Achse des primären Röntgenstrahlenbündels. Es sind diese Verhältnisse analog der Reflexion gewöhnlicher Lichtstrahlen an einer rauhen Ebene, z.B. an einer Papier- oder Rußfläche; bei großem Einfallswinkel nähert sich nämlich die diffuse Reflexion mehr und mehr der Spiegelung.

Wie es für einen und denselben Kristall zerstreuende Ebenen verschiedener Art (verschiedener Intensität für den gleichen Einfallswinkel) geben wird, so ist auch ein großer Unterschied zwischen verschiedenen Kristallen hinsichtlich der selektiven Zerstreuung der Röntgenstrahlen zu erwarten. Solche Kristalle, deren Atomvolumen sehr klein ist, z.B. Diamant, dürften Ebenen besitzen, in welchen die Atome besonders dicht gelagert sind, welche darum die Röntgenstrahlen auch für kleine Einfallswinkel noch in erheblicher Intensität spiegelnd reflektieren. In der Tat konnten Friedrich, Knipping und Laue bei Diamant im Unterschied von der Zinkblende auch auf der Vorderseite der normal getroffenen Kristallplatte 'Interferenzfiguren' beobachten.

37. Si l'on recherche la raison pour laquelle l'intensité du rayon diffracté dépend de la densité réticulaire et croît avec elle, on est conduit presque nécessairement, je crois, à la trouver dans la très courte durée des émissions périodiques sans changement de phase.

Si, comme pour la lumière, l'interférence parfaite était possible entre deux rayons dont la différence de marche est d'un nombre immense de longueurs d'onde, on ne s'expliquerait nullement que la densité réticulaire intervînt. Pour une direction de rayon diffracté, quel que soit le plan réflecteur, tous les nœuds de la partie du cristal qui est traversée par le faisceau incident envoient dans cette direction des radiations d'égale intensité et qui doivent s'ajouter intégralement.

Il en est tout autrement si l'on suppose que les rayons ne puissent interférer qu'avec des différences de marche d'un petit nombre de longueurs d'onde.

Considérons P l'un des plans réticulaires ayant pour caractéristiques (p, q, r); soit S l'aire réticulaire de ce plan. Le nombre des nœuds par unité de surface dans ce plan (densité) est $1/S$. Les rayons issus de tous ces nœuds du même plan interfèrent entre eux sans différence de marche. Les nœuds du plan contigu P_1 fournissent des rayons qui interfèrent avec ceux issus du plan P avec une différence de marche $2e \cos u = \lambda$ (ou $n\lambda$ s'il s'agit d'une harmonique). Cette différence de marche est 2λ pour les nœuds du plan suivant P_2, et ainsi de suite. Si le régime périodique, sans changement de phase, ne dure que n périodes, il n'y aura que n plans successifs $P_1, P_2, ..., P_n$ dont les rayons pourront interférer régulièrement avec ceux issus du plan P. Par suite, l'intensité du rayon diffracté sera proportionnelle au nombre de noeuds contenus dans ces n plans, c'est-à-dire à n/S. *L'intensité sera donc proportionnelle à la densité réticulaire du plan réflecteur.*

L'hypothèse d'émissions périodiques très courtes, d'un petit nombre de périodes, séparées par de brusques changements de phase, explique ainsi d'une manière très satisfaisante le fait que les plans réflecteurs sont les plans réticulaires les plus denses et tend à faire penser que, toutes choses égales d'ailleurs, l'intensité des rayons diffractés doit non seulement croître avec la densité réticulaire, mais lui être exactement proportionnelle.

38. In Wirklichkeit operiert man weder mit absolut monochromatischer Strahlung, noch mit einer einzigen Einfallsrichtung. So kommt es, daß man in einer bestimmten Beobachtungsrichtung Energie von verschiedenen Wellenlängen und verschiedenen Einfallsrichtungen zusammenfassen wird.

Läßt man zunächst den Wärmeeinfluß unberücksichtigt, dann wird man zu Wellen, welche im räumlichen Winkelelement $d\Omega_0$ einfallen und das Spektralgebiet $d\kappa$ füllen eine sekundäre Intensität berechnen, welche dargestellt werden kann durch den Ausdruck

$$A^2 r^{-2} d\Omega_0 d\kappa \sum \sum \exp[i\kappa a\{(\alpha - \alpha_0)(n_1 - n_1')$$
$$+ (\beta - \beta_0)(n_2 - n_2') + (\gamma - \gamma_0)(n_3 - n_3')\}] \qquad (64)$$

wenn wir uns der Einfachheit halber auf den regulären Fall beschränken. Hat man $\alpha_0, \beta_0, \gamma_0, \alpha, \beta, \gamma$ und κ so gewählt, daß den Laueschen Bedingungen in einem Punkte mit den charakteristischen Zahlen h_1, h_2, h_3 Genüge geleistet wird und läßt dann nachträglich $\alpha_0, \beta_0, \gamma_0$ und κ etwas variieren, dann wird man diese Variationen messen können durch drei Zahlen $\varepsilon_1, \varepsilon_2, \varepsilon_3$, welche man einführen kann, mittels der Gleichungen:

$$\kappa a(\alpha - \alpha_0) = h_1 2\pi + \varepsilon_1, \qquad \kappa a(\beta - \beta_0) = h_2 2\pi + \varepsilon_2,$$
$$\kappa a(\gamma - \gamma_0) = h_3 2\pi + \varepsilon_3.$$

Die wirklich beobachtbare Intensität erhält man nun durch Summation nach $d\Omega_0 d\kappa$ über einen endlichen Bereich; bedenkt man, daß in den neuen

143

Koordinaten ε_1, ε_2, ε_3 das entsprechende Integrationselement den Wert

$$\frac{1}{\kappa^3 a^3} \frac{2}{[(\alpha - \alpha_0)^2 + (\beta - \beta_0)^2 + (\gamma - \gamma_0)^2]} d\varepsilon_1 d\varepsilon_2 d\varepsilon_3$$

hat, so erhält der integrierte Ausdruck die Form:

$$\frac{A^2}{r^2} \frac{1}{\kappa^2 a^3} \frac{2}{[(\alpha - \alpha_0)^2 + (\beta - \beta_0)^2 + (\gamma - \gamma_0)^2]} \qquad (64')$$

$$\sum \sum \int \int \int d\varepsilon_1 d\varepsilon_2 d\varepsilon_3 \exp[i\{\varepsilon_1(n_1 - n_1') + \varepsilon_2(n_2 - n_2') + \varepsilon_3(n_3 - n_3')\}].$$

Die Integration darf ausgeführt werden zwischen den Grenzen

$$- e_1 < \varepsilon_1 < + e_1, \quad - e_2 < \varepsilon_2 < + e_2, \quad - e_3 < \varepsilon_3 < + e_3,$$

wobei e_1, e_2, e_3 kleine, aber endliche Zahlen bedeuten. So erhält man

$$\frac{A^2}{r^2} \frac{8}{\kappa^2 a^3} \frac{2}{[(\alpha - \alpha_0)^2 + (\beta - \beta_0)^2 + (\gamma - \gamma_0)^2]}$$

$$\sum \sum \frac{\sin(n_1 - n_1')e_1}{n_1 - n_1'} \frac{\sin(n_2 - n_2')e_2}{n_2 - n_2'} \frac{\sin(n_3 - n_3')e_3}{n_3 - n_3'}. \qquad (64'')$$

Hält man zunächst n_1, n_2, n_3 fest und führt die Summation nach n_1', n_2', n_3' durch, dann kann für diese Teilsumme mit Rücksicht auf die Kleinheit von e_1, e_2, e_3 auch substituiert werden

$$\int_{-\infty}^{+\infty} \int_{-\infty}^{+\infty} \int_{-\infty}^{+\infty} \frac{\sin e_1 u_1}{u_1} \frac{\sin e_2 u_2}{u_2} \frac{\sin e_3 u_3}{u_3} du_1 du_2 du_3 = \pi^3.$$

Ist N die Anzahl bestrahlter Atome, dann hat man dieselbe Rechnung bei der Durchlaufung von n_1, n_2, n_3 im ganzes N mal zu wiederholen. Als Ausdruck für die beobachtbare Intensität in einem Interferenzpunkt erhält man also den Wert:

$$\frac{A^2}{r^2} \frac{8\pi^3}{\kappa^2 a^2} \frac{2N}{[(\alpha - \alpha_0)^2 + (\beta - \beta_0)^2 + (\gamma - \gamma_0)^2]} \qquad (65)$$

oder auch mit Rücksicht auf die Laueschen Bedingungen:

$$\frac{A^2}{r^2} \frac{4\pi}{a} \frac{N}{h_1^2 + h_2^2 + h_3^2}. \qquad (65')$$

Man sieht, daß infolge der experimentell stets ausgeführten Mittelung eine durch die Summe der Quadrate der charakteristischen ganzen Zahlen im Neuer von (65') gemessene Schwächung auftritt.

39. Über die Bedeutung des Lorentzschen Intensitätsfaktors in der Theorie der Röntgenstrahleninterferenzen bei einem einzelnen Kristall herrschen erfahrungsgemäß auch unter den Sachkundigen noch gewisse Zweifel. Diese haben die Veranlassung zu der nachfolgenden Untersuchung gegeben, in welcher die zum genannten Faktor führende und eine Reihe ähnlicher Integrationen in vereinfachter und übersichtlicher Art dargestellt werden sollen. Der erste Teil setzt dabei, wie seinerzeit Lorentz, die Interferenzmaxima, welche von einem einzelnen idealen Kristall bei streng monochromatischem Röntgenlicht geliefert werden, als unendlich scharf voraus; er bezweckt lediglich eine Klärung theoretischer Fragen. Man musz die einzelnen Kristalle so klein denken, daß die von Ewald berücksichtigte Wechselwirkung zwischen den Atomen ohne Einfluß bleibt.

Wir führen hier kurz die bekannten mathematischen Grundlagen aller solcher Rechnungen an. Es bezeichnen $\mathfrak{a}_1$, $\mathfrak{a}_2$, $\mathfrak{a}_3$ ein primitives Tripel von Translationen des Raumgitters, so gewählt, daß das skalare Produkt $(\mathfrak{a}_1\mathfrak{a}_2\mathfrak{a}_3)$ positiv ist; es bedeuten ferner

$$\mathfrak{b}_1 = \frac{[\mathfrak{a}_2\mathfrak{a}_3]}{(\mathfrak{a}_1\mathfrak{a}_2\mathfrak{a}_3)} \qquad \mathfrak{b}_2 = \frac{[\mathfrak{a}_3\mathfrak{a}_1]}{(\mathfrak{a}_1\mathfrak{a}_2\mathfrak{a}_3)} \qquad \mathfrak{b}_3 = \frac{[\mathfrak{a}_1\mathfrak{a}_2]}{(\mathfrak{a}_1\mathfrak{a}_2\mathfrak{a}_3)} \tag{1}$$

die Grundvektoren des reziproken Gitters, $\mathfrak{s}_0$ und $\mathfrak{s}$ sind Einheitsvektoren in der Richtung des einfallenden Strahls und der Richtung vom Kristall zum Aufpunkt; λ ist die Wellenlänge des Lichts, $k = 2\pi/\lambda$. Ferner definieren wir

$$\mathfrak{s} - \mathfrak{s}_0 = \mathfrak{H} \tag{2}$$

$$A_i = k(\mathfrak{a}_i\mathfrak{H}) \qquad i = 1, 2, 3. \tag{3}$$

Liegt zwischen $\mathfrak{s}$ und $\mathfrak{s}_0$ der Winkel χ, so folgt aus (2) durch Quadrieren:

$$4 \sin^2 \frac{\chi}{2} = \mathfrak{H}^2. \tag{3a}$$

Die Auflösung der Gleichungen (3) nach $\mathfrak{H}$ lautet, wie man durch skalare Multiplikation mit $\mathfrak{a}_i$ leicht bestätigt:

$$k\mathfrak{H} = \Sigma_{i=1}^3 A_i\mathfrak{b}_i. \tag{4}$$

Wegen (2) können wir dafür schreiben:

$$k(\mathfrak{s} - \mathfrak{s}_0) = \Sigma_{i=1}^3 A_i\mathfrak{b}_i. \tag{5}$$

Da ferner nach derselben Beziehung

$$\mathfrak{H}^2 = 2(\mathfrak{s}\mathfrak{H}) \tag{6}$$

145

ist, folgt aus (4):

$$k = \frac{(\sum A_i\mathfrak{b}_i)^2}{2(\mathfrak{s}, \sum A_i\mathfrak{b}_i)}. \tag{7}$$

Für den einzelnen Kristall bei monochromatischer Beleuchtung ist die Intensität eine Funktion $f(A_i)$. Interferenzmaxima liegen, wo

$$A_i = 2h_i\pi \quad (i = 1, 2, 3) \tag{8}$$

ist und wo die h_i ganze Zahlen sind. Wir nennen $f(A_i)$ die Interferenzfunktion. Da sie gleich dem Quadrat des absoluten Betrags einer Summe

$$\sum_{m_1} \sum_{m_2} \sum_{m_3} \exp\{i(m_1A_1 + m_2A_2 + m_3A_3)\}$$

ist (in der die Summationsgrenzen durch Größe und Gestalt des Kristalls gegeben sind), so ist sie, wie jeder einzelne Summand, in jedem A_i periodisch mit der Periode 2π. Ihr Verlauf in der Nähe eines Maximums ist somit unabhängig von den dieses Maximum kennzeichnenden Zahlen h_i. Struktur-, Atomform- und Wärmefaktor sind als Funktionen der A_i gegen $f(A_i)$ langsam veränderlich und lassen sich deshalb leicht nachträglich in die folgenden Betrachtungen einführen. Wir lassen sie zur Vereinfachung fort.

Die vorzunehmenden dreifachen Integrationen verwandeln wir stets in Integrationen nach den A_i. Zur geometrischen Veranschaulichung dient uns ein Raum, in welchem

$$\sum_{i=1}^{3} A_i\mathfrak{b}_i$$

den Radius-Vektor vom Nullpunkt zum Aufpunkt darstellt. Die A_i sind in ihm kartesische, im allgemeinen schiefwinklige Koordinaten, die $\mathfrak{b}_i$ geben die Richtungen der Koordinatenachsen an. Das Raumelement dV ist bestimmt durch

$$dV = (\mathfrak{b}_1\mathfrak{b}_2\mathfrak{b}_3)dA_1dA_2dA_3 = \frac{dA_1dA_2dA_3}{(\mathfrak{a}_1\mathfrak{a}_2\mathfrak{a}_3)}; \tag{9}$$

denn $(\mathfrak{b}_1\mathfrak{b}_2\mathfrak{b}_3)$ ist der Inhalt des von den Vektoren $\mathfrak{b}_i$ aufgespannten Parallelepipedes.

Die Gleichungen (8) bestimmen in diesem Raum die Punkte eines Gitters, das sich vom reziproken Raumgitter nur durch die Dehnung um den Faktor 2π unterscheidet. Wir nennen sie *ganzzahlige Punkte*. Zu jedem von ihnen gehört nach (3a), (4) und (8) der Winkel χ_h, der sich aus der Formel

$$\sin\frac{\chi_h}{2} = \frac{\pi}{k_h} |\sum h_i\mathfrak{b}_i| \tag{9a}$$

bestimmt; k_h ist der aus (7) und (8) folgende Wert von k.

TEIL I

DIE INTERFERENZFUNKTION HAT UNENDLICH SCHARFE MAXIMA

§ 1. *Der Lorentzfaktor. Einzelner Kristall, Wellenlänge und Richtung des einfallenden Strahls sind veränderlich*

Setzen wir die spektrale Intensität für den schmalen, in Betracht kommenden Bereich als konstant voraus, so können wir für die Intensität der abgebeugten Strahlung schreiben:

$$J_{\text{Lorentz}} = \int f(A_i) dk d\Omega. \tag{10}$$

Die Integration nach k ist zwischen festen Grenzen, k^0 und k', auszuführen; die nach dem Raumwinkel Ω über alle Richtungen, aus denen Strahlung auf den Kristall fällt.

Um diese Integrationen in solche nach den A_i zu verwandeln, fragen wir nach der Gestalt der Flächen $k = \text{const}$ im Raum der Koordinaten A_i. Nach (5) beschreibt der Endpunkt des Vektors $\sum A_i \mathfrak{b}_i$ bei veränderlichem $\mathfrak{s}_0$, aber festgehaltenem $\mathfrak{s}$, eine Kugelfläche vom Halbmesser k, deren Mittelpunkt das Ende des vom Nullpunkt aus gezogenen Vektors $k\mathfrak{s}$ ist. (Fig. 1.) Sie geht also durch den Nullpunkt O und berührt in ihm alle anderen Kugeln $k = \text{const}$. Ihre Gleichung erhält man aus (5), indem man das Glied $\mathfrak{s}_0$ auf eine Seite für sich bringt und quadriert, in der Form:

$$(\sum A_i \mathfrak{b}_i)^2 - 2k(\mathfrak{s}, \sum A_i \mathfrak{b}_i) = 0. \tag{11}$$

Sie ist 'Ausbreitungskugel' im Sinne Ewalds. Durchliefe $\mathfrak{s}_0$ alle Richtungen des Raums, so beschriebe der Endpunkt des Radiusvektors die ganze

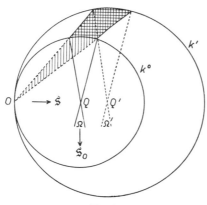

Fig. 1.

147

Kugelfläche k = const. Tatsächlich aber kommt nur ein sogar recht kleiner Winkel Ω für $\mathfrak{s}_0$ in Betracht, von jeder Kugel k = const also nur der Teil, der unter einem zu $\mathfrak{s}_0$ entgegengesetzt gerichteten Winkel von der Größe Ω erscheint. Verändert man k, so durchstreift dies Flächenstück den in Fig. 1 schraffierten Kegel mit dem Nullpunkt O als Spitze. Das geht entweder aus der Tatsache hervor, daß nach (3) die Verhältnisse $A_1 : A_2 : A_3$ von k unabhängig sind, oder aus Überlegung, daß O Ähnlichkeitspunkt für alle diese Flächen ist. Durch diesen Kegel und die Kugeln $k = k^0$ und $k = k'$ ist der Integrationsbereich vollständig begrenzt; er ist in Fig. 1 durch starke Schraffierung hervorgehoben.

Um $dk d\Omega$ durch $dA_1 . dA_2 . dA_3$ auszudrücken, berechnen wir das durch dk und $d\Omega$ bestimmte Raumelement dV. Wir zeichnen dazu in Fig. 2 den Punkt Q, welcher vom Nullpunkt O den Abstand $k\mathfrak{s}$ hat, und beschreiben um ihn die Kugeln mit den Halbmessern k und $k + dk$. Die letztere verrücken wir dann aus ihrer gestrichelten Lage um die durch $dk . \mathfrak{s}$ bestimmte Strecke; ihr Mittelpunkt gerät dabei nach Q' und sie selbst berührt nunmehr die Kugel O. Von Q aus ziehen wir in der zu $\mathfrak{s}_0$ entgegengesetzten Richtung alle dem Winkel $d\Omega$ angehörenden Geraden. Sie schneiden die Kugel k beim Punkt P in einem Flächenstück $k^2 d\Omega$. Das gesuchte Raumelement ist gleich diesem Flächenstück multipliziert mit der Dicke δ der Schale zwischen den ausgezogenen Kugeln k und $k + dk$. Nach der Fig. 2 und (3a) ist aber

$$\delta = dk - dk . \cos \chi = 2dk . \sin^2 \chi/2 = \tfrac{1}{2}\mathfrak{H}^2 . dk \qquad (11a)$$

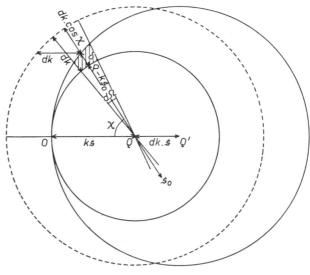

Fig. 2.

es folgt in Hinblick auf (4)

$$dV = \tfrac{1}{2}k^2\mathfrak{H}^2 dk d\Omega = \tfrac{1}{2}(\sum A_i \mathfrak{b}_i)^2 dk d\Omega.$$

Aus dem Vergleich mit (9) läßt sich also schließen:

$$dk d\Omega = 2 \, \frac{dA_1 dA_2 dA_3}{(\sum A_i \mathfrak{b}_i)^2 (\mathfrak{a}_1 \mathfrak{a}_2 \mathfrak{a}_3)}$$

und

$$J_{\text{Lorentz}} = \frac{2}{(\mathfrak{a}_1 \mathfrak{a}_2 \mathfrak{a}_3)} \int \int \int \frac{f(A_i)}{(\sum A_i \mathfrak{b}_i)^2} \, dA_1 dA_2 dA_3. \tag{12}$$

Der Integrationsbereich der Fig. 1 enthält einen ganzzahligen Punkt h_1, h_2, h_3 in seinem Inneren. Wegen unserer Voraussetzung des unendlich scharfen Interferenzmaximums bei ihm kommt es dann gar nicht mehr auf die Form des Integrationsbereichs an, sondern man kann über irgendeinen Teil des Raums der A_i integrieren, der diesen und nur diesen ganzzahligen Punkt enthält. Immer bekommt das Integral

$$\int \int \int f(A_i) dA_1 dA_2 dA_3 = F \tag{12a}$$

denselben, von h_1, h_2, h_3 nach der Einleitung unabhängigen Wert. Und es kommt nur auf dies Integral an, weil man die langsam veränderliche Funktion $(\sum A_i \mathfrak{b}_i)^2$ durch $4\pi^2 (\sum h_i \mathfrak{b}_i)^2$ ersetzen darf. Also folgt (vgl. (9a))

$$J_{\text{Lorentz}} = \frac{F}{2\pi^2 (\sum h_i \mathfrak{b}_i)^2 (\mathfrak{a}_1 \mathfrak{a}_2 \mathfrak{a}_3)} = \frac{F}{2k^2 \sin^2(\chi_h/2)(\mathfrak{a}_1 \mathfrak{a}_2 \mathfrak{a}_3)}. \tag{13}$$

Setzt man im besonderen, wie Lorentz es tat,

$$f(A_i) = \frac{\sin^2 M_1 A_1}{\sin^2 \tfrac{1}{2} A_1} \cdot \frac{\sin^2 M_2 A_2}{\sin^2 \tfrac{1}{2} A_2} \cdot \frac{\sin^2 M_3 A_3}{\sin^2 \tfrac{1}{2} A_3} \tag{14}$$

für große Zahlen M_i, so erstreckt man die Integrationen nach den A_i zweckmäßig von $(2h_i - 1)\pi$ bis $(2h_i + 1)\pi$ und findet[1]

$$J_{\text{Lorentz}} = \frac{32\pi M_1 M_2 M_3}{(\sum h_i \mathfrak{b}_i)^2 (\mathfrak{a}_1 \mathfrak{a}_2 \mathfrak{a}_3)}. \tag{15}$$

In (gg) findet man die bekannte Eigenschaft des Lorentzfaktors wieder, für denselben Interferenzpunkt, also konstantes χ, unter den verschiedenen in ihm möglichen Schwingungen die Grundschwingungen (mit dem kleinsten k) zu bevorzugen. Durchläuft man die Rechnung rückwärts, so findet man

---

[1] *Enzyklopädie d. Mathem. Wissenschaften*, Band V, Wellenoptik, Gleichung (193). Dort ist nur noch der Atomform-Faktor ψ hinzugesetzt.

als Ursache, daß in Fig. 2 die Grundfläche $k^2 d\Omega$ des schraffierten Raums zu k^2 proportional ist. Der Bereich hingegen, in welchem die Funktion $f(A_i)$ von Null wesentlich verschieden ist, ist bei jedem ganzzahligen Punkte gleich groß (vgl. die Einleitung). Also nimmt dieser Bereich von jenem Raum, und somit von der über alle Einfallsrichtungen nach Voraussetzung gleichmäßig verteilten Energie um so weniger in sich auf, je größer k ist. *Daran erkennt man die für die Oberschwingungen erhöhte Empfindlichkeit des Kristalls gegenüber der Einfallsrichtung und ihren Zusammenhang mit dem Lorentzfaktor.*

TEMPERATURE (OR DEBIJE-WALLER) FACTOR

Ein naheliegender Einwand gegen die Interferenztheorie liegt freilich in dem gegen alle Erwartung geringen Einfluß der Wärmebewegung; es wäre durchaus plausibel, wenn Interferenzerscheinungen nicht bei gewöhnlicher Temperatur, sondern erst bei sehr tiefen Temperaturen aufträten. Diesen Einwand, der übrigens alle anderen Deutungen ebenso trifft, kann man zurzeit wohl noch nicht völlig entkräften.

M. LAUE,
Physikal. Z. **14** (1913) p. 423

A further factor which was soon added by Debije in papers at the time, unequalled in daring, to tackle a question of seemingly unsurmountable difficulty: the temperature factor. The temperature displacements of the atoms in a lattice are of the order of magnitude of the atomic distances and therefore may produce any changes of phase whatsoever in the individual scattered waves. That an interference effect results in spite of this disorder is due (1) to the relative scarcity of large deviations from regularity and (2) to the greater efficiency of producing scattered intensity whenever a regular array holds good for a time in an element of volume. The result is a factor of exponential form whose exponent contains besides the temperature the order of the interference only. In later times Debye's original expression has been modified by Waller without altering essentially the physical assumptions.

P. P. EWALD,
Current Sci. (1937) p. 11

40. The Reflexion of the X-rays, by H. G. J. MOSELEY and C. G. DARWIN (1913)

▬

41. Über die Intensitätsverteilung in den mit Röntgenstrahlen erzeugten Interferenz-bildern, by P. DEBIJE (1913)

▬

42. Der Temperatureinfluss bei komplizierten Strukturen, by M. v. LAUE (1913)
see C. G. DARWIN (1914), *this Vol. p.* 176

▬

43. The Intensity of Reflexion of X-rays by Crystals, by W. H. BRAGG (1914)

▬

44. Interferenz von Röntgenstrahlen und Wärmebewegung, by P. DEBIJE (1914)

▬

45. Zur Frage der Einwirkung der Wärmebewegung auf die Interferenz von Röntgenstrahlen, by I. WALLER (1923)

▬

40. In the simple case of rocksalt the intensity falls off for the higher orders much more rapidly than theoretical considerations would suggest. This is doubtless due to the effect of the temperature oscillations of the atoms in the crystal. These oscillations will not affect the resolving power of the crystal, regarded for the moment as a grating, but will greatly reduce the intensity of the reflected beam. For suppose an atom displaced a distance b out of its plane. The wave scattered by this atom will have a phase difference from those of the other atoms in the plane of $2b \sin\theta \, 2\pi/\lambda$ or $2n\pi b/d$, where d is the distance between successive planes; so the phase deviations are more marked in the higher orders and the relative intensity greatly reduced.

41. Bekanntlich weisen die nach Friedrich-Knipping-Laue erhaltenen Interferenzbilder[1] im allgemeinen einen merkwürdigen seitlichen Intensitätsabfall der Interferenzflecke auf, welcher mit wachsendem Winkelabstand zwischen Sekundär- und Primärstrahl stark anwächst. Gewöhnlich beschränkt dieser Abfall die Beobachtung auf das Innere eines Kegels mit kleiner Öffnung, nur bei Diamant finden Friedrich und Knipping eine Ausnahme von dieser Regel. Der ganze Raum um den bestrahlten Diamanten enthält genügende Intensität der Interferenzstrahlung, um sogar noch in einem Winkelabstand von 180° die Interferenzflecke auf einer photographischen Platte hervorzubringen. Über die Ursache dieser Erscheinung hat man sich bis jetzt, wie es scheint, noch keine begründete Meinung gebildet. Laue selbst läßt die Frage im wesentlichen offen, indem er zwar bemerkt, man müsse wohl den Effekt auf eine für das die Sekundärstrah-

---

[1] *Sitzber. der Kgl. Bayer. Akad. d. Wiss.* 1912, S. 303 u. f.

lung erzeugende Atom charakteristische Richtungsfunktion Ψ zurückführen, dann aber gleich hinzufügt: 'doch ist es auch denkbar, daß die
Wärmebewegung zur Erklärung herangezogen werden muß'. Indem ich
die Überlegungen der vorigen Mitteilung[1] auf einen dreidimensionalen
wirklichen Kristall übertrage, möchte ich zeigen, daß der letztere Standpunkt tatsächlich der richtige ist. Die Theorie ergibt für den Richtungs-
effekt auf Grund der Wärmebewegung eine einfache Formel, welche die
Eigentümlichkeiten der Beobachtungsresultate durchaus zu erklären imstande ist. Darüber hinaus liefert sie eine neue, auf Intensitätsmessungen
gegründete Methode zur Bestimmung der Wellenlänge, wenn man die
Wärmebewegung des Kristalles als bekannt ansieht. Oder man kann umgekehrt z.B. die Intensitätsmessungen benutzen, um die Stärke der Wärmebewegung zu bestimmen und insbesondere die Frage nach der Nullpunktsenergie zu lösen.

§ 1. *Das Interferenzbild eines regulären Kristallgitters unter Berücksichtigung der Wärmebewegung*

In der Nähe des Nullpunktes eines rechtwinkeligen Koordinatensystems
x, y, z befinde sich das durchstrahlte parallelopipedische Stück eines
regulären Kristalles. Es enthalte N Atome und sei so orientiert, daß die
Hauptachsen des Kristallgitters den Koordinatenachsen x, y, z parallel
laufen. Die Gitterkonstante sei a, d.h. a sei der Abstand der Quellen der
Sekundärstrahlung (welche mit den Atomen fest verbunden sein mögen)
für den Fall, daß alle Atome sich in ihrer Ruhelage befinden. Irgend eine
Quelle habe in diesem Spezialfalle die Koordinaten:

$$x = ma, \quad y = na, \quad z = pa,$$

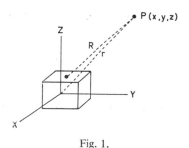

Fig. 1.

[1] *Verh. d. D. Phys. Ges.* **15** (1913) 678–689.

wobei m, n und p Ordnungszahlen des betreffenden Atoms in x-, y- und z-Richtung sind. Infolge der Wärmebewegung schwankt das Atom um seine Gleichgewichtslage; diese Schwankung werde für das betrachtete Atom gemessen durch die von der Ruhelage aus in Richtung der Hauptachsen gemessenen Koordinaten $\xi_{m, n, p}$, $\eta_{m, n, p}$, $\zeta_{m, n, p}$. In einem beliebigen Moment hat also die Strahlungsquelle die Koordinaten

$$ma + \xi_{m, n, p}, \quad na + \eta_{m, n, p}, \quad pa + \zeta_{m, n, p}.$$

Insofern gestatten wir uns eine Vereinfachung, als wir die Atome für die Berechnung der Wärmebewegung als unabhängig voneinander betrachten und für die potentielle Energie eines Atoms die Formel ansetzen:

$$f[\xi^2_{m, n, p} + \eta^2_{m, n, p} + \zeta^2_{m, n, p}]/2$$

wobei f die quasielastische Kraft im Abstand 1 bedeutet.

Die Anregung der Strahlung geschehe durch primäre Röntgenstrahlen, welche durch den Kristall in der positiven x-Richtung hindurchgehen. Pflanzen dieselben sich mit Lichtgeschwindigkeit fort, dann wird jedes Atom strahlen mit einer Anfangsphase, welche von seiner x-Koordinate abhängt und dann in üblicher Weise gemessen werden kann durch den Faktor $\exp\{- i\kappa(ma + \xi_{m, n, p})\}$, wobei κ gleich ist 2π, dividiert durch die Wellenlänge λ.

Um gleich von vornherein mit möglichst bestimmten Vorstellungen zu rechnen, nehmen wir weiterhin an, daß die Sekundärstrahlung ausgeht von Elektronen (z.B. ein Elektron für jedes Atom), welche in der z-Richtung schwingen. Nachträglich können wir dann leicht noch zu einer unpolarisierten Anregung übergehen. Nennen wir x, y, z die Koordinaten des Beobachtungspunktes, R seinen Abstand von dem gerade betrachteten Elektron und r seinen Abstand vom Nullpunkt des Koordinatensystems, dann gilt bekanntlich für große Abstände, auf welche wir uns beschränken:

$$R = r - [(ma + \xi_{m, n, p})x/r + (na + \eta_{m, n, p})y/r + (pa + \zeta_{m, n, p})z/r].$$

Die elektrische Feldstärke im Beobachtungspunkt P, herrührend von dem Elektron m, n, p, kann dann gesetzt werden[1] unter Weglassung der Indizes m, n, p:

$$Ar^{-1}(1 - z^2/r^2)^{-\frac{1}{2}} e^{-i\kappa r} e^{-i\kappa(ma + \xi)} e^{i\kappa[(ma + \xi)x/r + (na + \eta)y/r + (pa + \zeta)z/r]}. \quad (1)$$

---

[1] Wenn wir sagen, (1) stelle die elektrische Feldstärke dar, dann ist, wie üblich, gemeint, daß (1) nach Multiplikation mit $\exp(i\omega t)$ (ω = Schwingungszahl in 2π sec) und Übergang zum reellen Teil den endgültigen Ausdruck für diese Feldstärke liefert.

A ist proportional der unbekannten Amplitude des Elektrons; der Faktor $1/r$ mißt die Abnahme der Feldstärke mit wachsender Entfernung von der Quelle; die Wurzel $\sqrt{(1 - z^2/r^2)}$ trägt der bekannten Tatsache Rechnung, daß ein Elektron in seiner Bewegungsrichtung nicht strahlt, während schließlich der Faktor/$\exp\{- ix(ma + \xi)\}$ die Phase der Anregung mißt.

Aus (1) ergibt sich die Gesamtamplitude durch Summation über alle m, alle n und alle p zu

$$Ar^{-1}(1 - z^2/r^2)^{-\frac{1}{2}} e^{-i\kappa r} \sum_m \sum_n \sum_p e^{i\kappa a \left[m\left(\frac{x}{r}-1\right) + n\frac{y}{r} + p\frac{z}{r}\right]}$$

$$e^{i\kappa \left[\xi\left(\frac{x}{r}-1\right) + \eta\frac{y}{r} + \zeta\frac{z}{r}\right]} \quad (2)$$

und hieraus die Intensität J durch Multiplikation mit dem zu (2) konjugierten Wert. Letzterer kann also geschrieben werden in der Form

$$J = \frac{A^2}{r^2}\left(1 - \frac{z^2}{r^2}\right)$$

$$\sum_{m_1} \sum_{n_1} \sum_{p_1} \sum_m \sum_n \sum_p e^{i\kappa a \left[(m-m_1)\left(\frac{x}{r}-1\right) + (n-n_1)\frac{y}{r} + (p-p_1)\frac{z}{r}\right]}$$

$$e^{i\kappa \left[(\xi-\xi_1)\left(\frac{x}{r}-1\right) + (\eta-\eta_1)\frac{y}{r} + (\zeta-\zeta_1)\frac{z}{r}\right]} \quad (3)$$

wenn wir noch setzen ξ für $\xi_{m, n, p}$, ξ_1 für ξ_{m_1, n_1, p_1}, und ähnlich für η und ζ verfahren.

Die Formel (3) bestimmt die Intensität in einem beliebig herausgegriffenen, durch die Werte von ξ, η, ζ charakterisierten Moment. Beobachten können wir aber nur einen Mittelwert. Deshalb werden wir die Formel (3) noch zu multiplizieren haben mit der Wahrscheinlichkeit

$$wdS = wd\xi_{1,1,1}d\eta_{1,1,1}d\zeta_{1,1,1} \ldots d\xi_{m, n, p}d\eta_{m, n, p}d\zeta_{m, n, p} \cdots$$

für eine durch dS bestimmte Anordnung der Moleküle, um dann schließlich durch Summation über alle möglichen Anordnungen den gesuchten Mittelwert J_m der Intensität zu erhalten.

Nun gilt nach den Gesetzen der statischen Mechanik

$$w = C\, e^{- \frac{f}{2kT} \sum_m \sum_n \sum_p (\xi^2 + \eta^2 + \zeta^2)}$$

mit

$$1 = C(2\pi kT/f)^{\frac{3}{2}N}.$$

Weiterhin müssen wir auch hier bei der Ausrechnung des in dem Ausdrucke

155

für die mittlere Energie J_m auftretenden Integrals

$$J_m = \int\limits_{-\infty}^{+\infty} \int\limits_{-\infty}^{+\infty} J w \, dS$$

von der Form

$$K = C \int\limits_{-\infty}^{+\infty} \dots \int\limits_{-\infty}^{+\infty} e^{-\frac{f}{2kT} \Sigma_m \Sigma_n \Sigma_p (\xi^2 + \eta^2 + \zeta^2)}$$

$$e^{i\kappa \left[(\xi - \xi_1)\left(\frac{x}{r} - 1\right) + (\eta - \eta_1)\frac{y}{r} + (\zeta - \zeta_1)\frac{z}{r}\right]} \, dS \qquad (4)$$

unterscheiden zwischen einem Fall a) und einem Fall b).

a) Der Fall a) sei dadurch gekennzeichnet, daß die Verschiebungen ξ, η, ζ und ξ_1, η_1, ζ_1 zu verschiedenen Atomen gehören, daß also wenigstens einer der Indizes m, n, p im Exponenten der zweiten Exponentialfunktion des zu berechnenden Integrals verschieden ist von m_1, n_1, p_1. Ausgeschlossen ist also nur der Fall, in dem zugleich $m = m_1, n = n_1$, $p = p_1$. Dann berechnet man

$$K = e^{-\frac{kT}{f} \kappa^2 \left[\left(\frac{x}{r} - 1\right)^2 + \left(\frac{y}{r}\right)^2 + \left(\frac{z}{r}\right)^2 \right]}$$

oder, da

$$(x/r)^2 + (y/r)^2 + (z/r)^2 = 1$$

ist:

$$K = e^{-\frac{2kT}{f} \kappa^2 \left(1 - \frac{x}{r}\right)}. \qquad (5)$$

b) Im Falle b) sei von vornherein $m = m_1, n = n_1, p = p_1$, dann wird die zweite Exponentialfunktion unseres Integrals gleich 1 und damit auch

$$K = 1. \qquad (5')$$

Mit Rücksicht auf (5) und (5') erhält man nun aus (3) für die mittlere Energie die Darstellung

$$J_m = \frac{A^2}{r^2} \left(1 - \frac{z^2}{r^2} \right)$$

$$\Sigma_{m_1} \Sigma_{n_1} \Sigma_{p_1} \Sigma_m \Sigma_n \Sigma_p \, \varphi \, e^{i\kappa a \left[(m - m_1)\left(\frac{x}{r} - 1\right) + (n - n_1)\frac{y}{r} + (p - p_1)\frac{z}{r}\right]}. \qquad (6)$$

wenn φ eine Funktion der Indizes bedeutet, welche nur im Falle b) $m = m_1$, $n = n_1, p = p_1$ den Wert 1 hat und in allen anderen Fällen nach (5) gleich

$$e^{-\frac{2kT}{f} \kappa^2 \left(1 - \frac{x}{r}\right)}$$

ist.

Nehmen wir alle Glieder mit $m = m_1, n = n_1$ und $p = p_1$ aus der Summe heraus, addieren dann zu derselben wieder diese Glieder, aber jetzt multipliziert mit dem Faktor (5), und subtrahieren schließlich dasselbe, dann kann an Stelle von (6) Gleichung (6') geschrieben werden:

$$J_m = \frac{A^2}{r^2}\left(1 - \frac{z^2}{r^2}\right)\left\{\sum_{m_1}\sum_{n_1}\sum_{p_1} 1 - \sum_{m_1}\sum_{n_1}\sum_{p_1} e^{-\frac{2kT}{f}\kappa^2\left(1-\frac{x}{r}\right)}\right.$$

$$+ e^{-\frac{2kT}{f}\kappa^2)\,1-\frac{x}{r})}$$

$$\left.\sum_{m_1}\sum_{n_1}\sum_{p_1}\sum_{m}\sum_{n}\sum_{p} e^{i\kappa a\left[(m-m_1)\left(\frac{x}{r}-1\right) + (n-n_1)\frac{y}{r} + (p-p_1)\frac{z}{r}\right]}\right\} \quad (6')$$

Die sechsfache Summe geht nun ohne Unterbrechung über alle möglichen Werte der Indizes.

Die Ausrechnung hat keine Schwierigkeiten und liefert für J_m den endgültigen Ausdruck:

$$J_m = \frac{A^2}{r^2}\left(1 - \frac{z^2}{r^2}\right)\left\{N(1 - e^{-\frac{2kT}{f}\kappa^2\left(1-\frac{x}{r}\right)})\right.$$

$$\left. + e^{-\frac{2kT}{f}\kappa^2\left(1-\frac{x}{r}\right)}\,\frac{\sin^2 N_1\kappa a(1-x/r)/2.\sin^2 N_2\kappa ay/2r.\sin^2 N_3\kappa az/2r}{\sin^2 \kappa a(1-x/r)/2.\sin^2 \kappa ay/2r.\sin^2 \kappa az/2r}\right\} \quad (7)$$

denn die erste und zweite Summe der Klammer in (6') haben bzw. die Werte

$$N \text{ und } Ne^{-\frac{2kT}{f}\kappa^2\left(1-\frac{x}{r}\right)},$$

während die sechsfache Summe sich zerlegen läßt in ein sechsfaches Produkt einfacher Summen und jede dieser Summen in bekannter Weise als Potenzreihe summiert werden kann. N_1, N_2, N_3 stehen dann, wie leicht ersichtlich, in der endgültigen Formel für die Zahl der Atome auf Linien parallel der x-, y-, z-Richtung im durchstrahlten parallelopipedischen Kristallstück, so daß $N_1 N_2 N_3 = N$.

Schließlich haben wir noch die Annahme der Polarisation fallen zu lassen. Würden alle Elektronen in der y-Richtung statt in der z-Richtung schwingen, dann würde man für J_m einen Ausdruck bekommen haben, der nur dadurch von (7) abweicht, daß an Stelle des Faktors $(1 - z^2/r^2)$ jetzt der Faktor $(1 - y^2/r^2)$ auftritt. Für eine unpolarisierte Anregung wird man deshalb als Intensität den Mittelwert des Ausdruckes (7) und des neuen durch Vertauschung von $(1 - z^2/r^2)$ mit $(1 - y^2/r^2)$ entstandenen Ausdruckes bekommen, d.h. in diesem Fall wird

$$J_m = \frac{A^2}{2r^2}\left(1 + \frac{x^2}{r^2}\right)\left\{N(1 - e^{-\frac{2kT}{f}\kappa^2\left(1-\frac{x}{r}\right)})\right.$$

$$\left. + e^{-\frac{2kT}{f}\kappa^2\left(1-\frac{x}{r}\right)}\,\frac{\sin^2 N_1\kappa a(1-x/r)/2.\sin^2 N_2\kappa ay/2r.\sin^2 N_3\kappa az/2r}{\sin^2\kappa a(1-x/r)/2.\sin^2 \kappa ay/2r.\sin^2 \kappa az/2r}\right\} \quad (8)$$

157

§ 2. *Diskussion des Temperatureinflusses*

Obwohl wir zu der Formel (8) des vorigen Paragraphen für die Intensitätsverteilung gelangten unter Benutzung des Maxwell-Boltzmannschen Gesetzes für die Wahrscheinlichkeit einer bestimmten Anordnung der Atome und demnach mit Rücksicht auf die Quantentheorie keine numerische Übereinstimmung für tiefe Temperaturen mehr erwarten dürfen, so wollen wir doch zunächst unsere Diskussion an (8) anschließen.

Die Änderungen, welche die Anwendung der Quantentheorie an diesen Ausdruck hervorbringen wird, werden das Bild der Erscheinungen nur mehr in quantitativer, nicht in qualitativer Hinsicht ändern. Deshalb möge die Berücksichtigung der Quantenhypothese für den § 3 reserviert werden. Dazu berechtigt außerdem noch der Umstand, daß die Unterschiede zwischen dem Verhalten des Diamantes und der anderen Körper zu einem wesentlichen Teil schon ohne Rücksicht auf die Abweichungen vom Dulong-Petitschen Gesetz ihre Erklärung finden.

Das erste, was an dem Ausdruck (8) auffällt, ist die Tatsache, daß die Wärmebewegung durchaus keinen Einfluß auf die Schärfe der Interferenzpunkte hat. Ähnlich wie in der vorhergehenden Mitteilung besteht nämlich die Klammer aus einem ersten Teil:

$$I = N\left(1 - e^{-\frac{2kT}{f}\kappa^2\left(1-\frac{x}{r}\right)}\right),\tag{9}$$

der nur einer Zerstreuung der Strahlung entspricht, und aus einem zweiten Teil:

$$II = e^{-\frac{2kT}{f}\kappa^2\left(1-\frac{x}{r}\right)}\frac{\sin^2 N_1\kappa a(1 - x/r)/2.\sin^2 N_2\kappa ay/2r.\sin^2 N_3\kappa az/2r}{\sin^2 \kappa a(1 - x/r)/2.\sin^2 \kappa ay/2r.\sin^2 \kappa az/2r}\tag{9'}$$

der sich von dem Laueschen Ausdruck für die Energieverteilung nur durch den Exponentialfaktor unterscheidet.

Wir wollen die dem ersten Teile entsprechende Strahlung die 'zerstreute Strahlung' und die dem zweiten Teil entprechende die 'Interferenzstrahlung' nennen. Was dann durch die Temperaturbewegung geändert wird, ist nur die relative Intensität dieser beiden Strahlungen.

Vergleichen wir jetzt die beiden Strahlungen in einem richtig ausgebildeten Interferenzpunkt. Derselbe ist bekanntlich gekennzeichnet durch ein gleichzeitiges Verschwinden der drei Nenner im Ausdrucke II. In diesem Falle wird also

$$II = e^{-\frac{2kT}{f}\kappa^2\left(1-\frac{x}{r}\right)}N_1^2N_2^2N_3^2 = N^2\, e^{-\frac{2kT}{f}\kappa^2\left(1-\frac{x}{r}\right)}.$$

Wir setzen die reine Zahl $kT\kappa^2/f = \varepsilon$ und substituieren für x/r die Funktion cos θ. Dann ist θ der Winkel, den der Sekundärstrahl mit der Richtung der primären Strahlen macht, und wir erhalten für das Verhältnis der Intensität von Interferenzstrahlung und zerstreuter Strahlung im Interferenzpunkt den Wert:

$$\frac{N^2\, e^{-2\varepsilon(1-\cos\theta)}}{N(1 - e^{-2\varepsilon(1-\cos\theta)})} = N\,\frac{1}{e^{2\varepsilon(1-\cos\theta)} - 1}. \tag{10}$$

Für $\theta = 0$ ist $1 - \cos\theta = 0$ und das Verhältnis wird ∞; mit wachsendem Winkelabstand wächst aber $1 - \cos\theta$ stetig von 0 bis 2, wobei der letztere Wert für $\theta = 180°$ erreicht wird, so daß für Werte von ε, welche einigermaßen größer als 1 sind, die Interferenzstrahlung auf das Innere eines Kegels mit kleiner Öffnung um den primären Strahl beschränkt bleibt.

Bemerkenswert ist insbesondere der außerordentlich große Einfluß einer Wellenlängenänderung. Betrachten wir den Bau von ε:

$$\varepsilon = kT\kappa^2/f = 4\pi^2 kT/\lambda^2 f, \tag{11}$$

dann finden wir auch sofort die Erklärung für das beobachtete abnormale Verhalten von Diamant. Nach (11) ist nämlich ε umgekehrt proportional der quasielastischen Kraft für den Abstand 1, welche wir mit f bezeichnet haben, und diese ist gerade bei dem äußerst wenig kompressiblen Diamant verhältnismäßig groß.

Andererseits ist aber ε auch direkt proportional der absoluten Temperatur; wir werden also zu erwarten haben, daß Diamant keine Ausnahme bildet, sondern nur Erscheinungen gibt, die auch jeder genügend tief abgekühlte Kristall hervorzubringen imstande ist. Zahlenmäßig folgt aus der für den Verlauf der spezifischen Wärme charakteristischen Temperatur $\Theta = 1890°$, für f der Wert $1,17.10^6$ dyne/cm. Bei einer Temperatur von $290°$ absolut wird demnach für $\lambda = 10^{-9}$ cm $\varepsilon = 1,32$ und für $\lambda = 10^{-8}$ cm $\varepsilon = 0,0132$, so daß auch zahlenmäßig der experimentelle Befund durchaus theoretisch begründet ist. Im übrigen darf nicht vergessen werden, daß wir noch zu unseren Ungunsten gerechnet haben, indem wir Formel (11) benutzten, da dieselbe der Äquipartition der Energie auf alle Freiheitsgrade entspricht und bekanntlich gerade bei Diamant das Dulong-Petitsche Gesetz bei $T = 290°$ schon nicht mehr erfüllt ist.

42. Der Unterschied gegen früher besteht allein darin, daß *jede* der Richtungsfunktionen Ψ noch mit dem *derselben Atomart zugehörigen* Debijeschen Temperaturfaktor

$$\exp\left\{-\frac{\kappa T}{2f}\, k^2[(\alpha - \alpha_0)^2 + \beta - \beta_0)^2 + (\gamma - \gamma_0)^2]\right\}$$

multipliziert auftritt.

43. The effects of temperature upon the intensity of reflexion have been investigated by surrounding the rocksalt crystal by a small electric oven. Mica windows permitted the passage of the X-rays and stopped convection currents. The results are most conveniently expressed in terms of the ratio of the intensity I at the temperature of the room to the intensity I' at the temperature of the furnace. The temperature was measured with sufficient accuracy by inserting into the oven a thermometer the bulb of which was nearly in contact with the crystal.

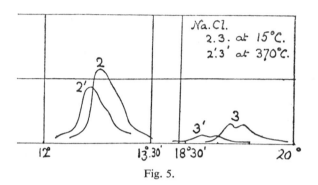

Fig. 5.

The ionization currents were observed for each separate position of the crystal. The figure shows the second and third spectra of the rhodium line at each of the two temperatures. The diminution of intensity with temperature is very obvious; and the spectrum of higher order is more affected than that of lower order. As the crystal expands, the spacing of the planes increases and the glancing angle diminishes. This effect is also clearly seen.

The table shows the variation of the effect with the magnitude of the sine of the glancing angle. The latter is expressed in terms of θ, the glancing angle of the first order reflexion by the (100) plane: the value of $\sin \theta$ is 0.1097.

Face	Glancing angle	I/I'
(100)	$1 \times \sin \theta$	1.07
(110)	$\sqrt{2} \times$,,	1.20
(100)	$2 \times$,,	1.26
(110)	$2\sqrt{2} \times$,,	2.07
(100)	$3 \times$,,	1.94

The effects of temperature have been foreseen and calculated by Debije, and the figures of the table may be looked on as measurements of the Debije effect.

160

It is interesting to compare the results given above with the corresponding figures calculated from Debije's formula. The latter may be written in the form

$$I_\theta = (A/\sin^2 \theta) \exp(- B \sin^2 \theta)$$

where A and B are constants, given the crystal, the wavelength, and the temperature, and θ is the glancing angle at which the pencil is reflected. I_θ is the intensity of the reflected pencil.

The constant B contains a quantity which Debije calls the characteristic temperature of the crystal. Its value for rocksalt is not known with certainty, but is believed to be about 240°. In the following table the observed values are set against calculated values. The principal reflexion from the (100) face is always put equal to 100.

The calculated values are slightly modified (become smaller) if we take account of the possible existence of 'nullpunkt energie' and of an obliquity factor $(1 + \cos^2 2\theta)$, where θ is the glancing angle. The two possibilities are considered by Debije. But the figures are hardly accurate enough as yet to bear discussion in respect to these questions.

Sine of glancing angle	Observed values at 15°C	Calculated, taking $\Theta = 200$	Calculated, taking $\Theta = 280$	Proportional change on raising to 370°C	Calculated change
1×0.1097	100	100	100	1.07	1.075
$\sqrt{2} \times 0.1097$	41	46.3	47.6	1.20	1.16
$\sqrt{3} \times 0.1097$	24.4	28.5	30.2	–	–
2×0.1097	18.7	19.8	21.6	1.26	1.35
$2\sqrt{2} \times 0.1097$	7.05	7.2	8.9	2.07	1.90
3×0.1097	6.25	6.0	7.5	1.94	1.92
$3\sqrt{3} \times 0.1097$	4.2	3.6	4.9	–	–

On the whole there is certainly a surprising agreement. I find also that fluorspar shows a small temperature effect: this is also in agreement with Debije's theory, for the characteristic temperature is large and the constant B is small.

44. In einigen Notizen habe ich versucht, Belege dafür beizubringen[1], daß die Wärmebewegung der Kristallatome einen wesentlichen Einfluß hat auf die von Friedrich-Knipping-Laue entdeckten und von Laue[2] schon theoretisch behandelten Interferenzen von Röntgenstrahlen. Ebenso wie das bei der ursprünglichen Einsteinschen Theorie der spezifischen Wärme der Fall war, wurden bei dieser Berechnung alle Atome als voneinander unabhängig betrachtet und jedes derselben als einfach schwingendes Gebilde in die Rechnung eingeführt. Außerdem aber wurde noch die weitere Beschränkung gemacht, daß die Beobachtungstemperatur so hoch sei, daß von einer Abweichung von der Äquipartition der Energie noch keine Anzeichen zu bemerken sind. Die Summation der Wirkung des jetzt nicht mehr wie bei Laue starren Atomgerüstes auf den einfallenden Strahl ergab dann das Fehlen einer Wirkung auf die Schärfe der Interferenzmaxima und die Existenz eines Intensitätseffektes. Es wurde so ein Grund dafür gefunden, daß merkbare Interferenzintensität meistens nur in Richtungen auftritt, die kleine Winkel mit dem einfallenden Strahl bilden und damit zugleich, daß die sogenannte Reflexion von Röntgenstrahlen unter gewöhnlichen Umständen nur bei nicht zu steilem Einfall beobachtet wird. Ferner lehrt die Rechnung, wie infolge der Wärmebewegung die Interferenzintensität immer begleitet sein muß von einer zerstreuten Strahlung, welche maximal dort auftritt, wo die Interferenzintensität am schwächsten ist. Außerdem zeigten die Formeln, wie die kleine, im wesentlichen von der geringen Kompressibilität herrührende Amplitude der Wärmebewegung von Diamantatomen Ursache wird von der Sonderstellung, welche dieser Körper auch hier wieder einnimmt.

Wegen der oben angezeigten Beschränkungen konnte die Theorie nur als ein erster Schritt auf dem Wege nach einer vollständigen theoretischen Beschreibung gelten. Beobachtet ist bis jetzt nur das abnormale Verhalten des Diamanten, aber selbst die Frage, ob die Interferenzerscheinungen durch Temperaturänderungen in ihrem Aussehen beeinflußt werden, ist bisher experimentell noch nicht in Angriff genommen. Unter diesen Umständen mag es voreilig scheinen, die Theorie über das schon durch die Näherungsrechnungen Erreichte ausbauen zu wollen. Dennoch haben wir das im folgenden ausgeführt, von dem Gedanken ausgehend, daß es für die experimentelle Prüfung bequemer sein muß, über die Richtigkeit unserer Vorstellungen zu entscheiden, wenn man sich einer bis zu gewissem Grade abgeschlossenen Theorie gegenüber befindet.

[1] P. Debije, *Verh. d. Deutsch. Phys. Ges.* **15** (1913) 678, 738 [this Vol. p. 152] u. 857.
[2] M. v. Laue, *Sitzungsber. d. Kgl. Bayer. Akad. d. Wiss.*, p. 303, 1912 [this Vol. p. 7]. Man vergleiche außerdem die Zusammenstellung im 'Rapport du deuxième Conseil de physique Solvay'.

Die Erweiterung der Theorie haben wir ausgeführt in den beiden obengenannten Richtungen.

Erstens haben wir die Annahme der gegenseitigen Unabhängigkeit der Atome fallen gelassen. Die Bewegung derselben ist in dieser Notiz zusammengesetzt aus übereinander gelagerten elastischen Wellen, deren Schwingungszahlen das elastische Spektrum des Körpers durchlaufen, ein Verfahren, das sich ja bei der Theorie der spezifischen Wärme bewährt hat.

Zweitens haben wir uns dadurch die Gelegenheit geschaffen, die Quantenhypothese in unzweideutiger Weise auch in diesem Falle zur Anwendung zu bringen. Für oder gegen die Nullpunktsenergie haben wir uns nicht entschieden. Der einzig berechtigte Standpunkt ist vorläufig wohl der, beide Hypothesen vollständig auf ihre Folgen zu prüfen, wenn auch verschiedene neuere Arbeiten von A. Einstein und O. Stern, H. Kamerling-Onnes, W. H. Keesom, E. Oosterhuis schwerwiegende Gründe für die Annahme einer Nullpunktsenergie bringen. Das war in unserem Falle um so angebrachter, da es sich zeigt, daß man durch Beobachtung der Interferenzen von Röntgenstrahlen eine wahrscheinlich nicht schwer zu handhabende Methode erhält, die Frage zu entscheiden. Tatsächlich ist es von vornherein klar, daß, wenn überhaupt die vorgeschlagene Theorie in ihren Grundlagen richtig ist, das mittlere Quadrat der Amplitude der Atombewegungen und nicht der Differentialquotient dieser Größe nach der Temperatur (wie bei der spezifischen Wärme) maßgebend sein muß. Gerade mit Rücksicht auf diese experimentell beizubringende Entscheidung haben wir die Theorie bis zu einer numerisch brauchbaren Formel durchgeführt und eine numerische und graphische Erläuterung daran angeknüpft. Freilich konnte letzteres wieder nur erreicht werden, indem wir die allgemeine Formel durch näherungsweise Auswertung des elastischen Spektrums auf eine handlichere Gestalt brachten, aber diese Näherungsmethode hat sich schon einmal bei der Berechnung der spezifischen Wärme bewährt und dürfte voraussichtlich auch hier nicht zu wesentlich fehlerhaften Resultaten führen, wenigstens, soweit man sich beschränkt auf einatomige Körper oder solche, welche wie Sylvin z.B. als einatomig behandelt werden dürfen.

Dann findet man für M, den Exponenten des Wärmefaktors, den Ausdruck

$$- M = \frac{3}{4\pi^2} \frac{\kappa^2 h^2}{\mu k \Theta} (1 - \cos \theta) \frac{1}{x^2} \int_0^x \frac{\xi d\xi}{e^\xi - 1}, \qquad (56')$$

wenn μ die Masse eines Atoms der betreffenden Substanz bedeutet, $\kappa = 2\pi/\lambda$, $h = $ Wirkungsquantum, $x = h\nu_{\max}/kT = \Theta/T$.

Damit ist die gesuchte Darstellung von M für das ganze Temperaturgebiet gefunden.

Im nächsten Paragraphen werden wir eine eingehendere, numerische Diskussion an diese Formel anschließen, hier mögen nur die zwei Grenzfälle $T \ll \Theta$ und $T \gg \Theta$ eine besondere Erwähnung finden.

a) $T \ll \Theta$.

In diesem Falle ist $x = \Theta/T \gg 1$, die obere Grenze im Integral kann dann gleich ∞ gesetzt werden und man findet:

$$\int_0^x \frac{\xi d\xi}{e^\xi - 1} = \int_0^\infty \frac{\xi d\xi}{e^\xi - 1} = \int_0^\infty \xi(e^{-\xi} + e^{-2\xi} + e^{-3\xi} + \ldots)d\xi$$

$$= 1 + \frac{1}{4} + \frac{1}{9} + \frac{1}{16} + \ldots = \frac{\pi^2}{6}.$$

Ersetzt man nun noch $1/x^2$ durch T^2/Θ^2, dann wird z.B. (56'):

$$- M = \frac{1}{8} \frac{\kappa^2 h^2}{\mu k \Theta^3} (1 - \cos \theta) T^2. \tag{57}$$

Wir finden also das $- M$ proportional dem Quadrate der absoluten Temperatur wird.

b) $T \gg \Theta$.

In diesem Falle ist $x = \Theta/T \ll 1$ und kann man das Integral in (56') näherungsweise berechnen zu

$$\int_0^x \frac{\xi d\xi}{e^\xi - 1} = \int_0^x \frac{\xi d\xi}{\xi} = x.$$

Damit wird (56'):

$$- M = \frac{3}{4\pi^2} \frac{\kappa^2 h^2}{\mu k \Theta^2} (1 - \cos \theta) T. \tag{58}$$

Dieselbe Temperaturabhängigkeit gab auch die frühere Näherungstheorie. Der einzige Unterschied besteht darin, daß wir jetzt nicht mehr eine nur angenähert bekannte 'quasielastische Kraft' f für das Atom einzuführen haben. Man kann das auch so ausdrücken: durch (58) werde die früher eingeführte quasielastische Kraft f bestimmt. In der Näherungstheorie fanden wir nämlich

$$- M = 2 \frac{\kappa^2 k}{f} (1 - \cos \theta) T,$$

ein Vergleich mit (58) liefert also für f die Bestimmungsgleichung:

$$f = \frac{4\pi^2}{3} \frac{\mu k^2 \Theta^2}{h^2}.$$

Mit Rücksicht auf die Definition von Θ:

$$\Theta = \frac{h\nu_{\max}}{k}$$

mittels der Grenzschwingungszahl des elastischen Spektrums kann man auch noch schreiben

$$\frac{f}{\mu} = \frac{2}{3} 4\pi^2 \nu^2{}_{\max}$$

und deshalb das Schlußresultat folgendermaßen aussprechen:

Die jetzige, verbesserte Theorie liefert im Grenzfall für hohe Temperaturen dasselbe Resultat, wie die frühere, ohne Rücksicht auf die gegenseitige Bindung der Atome, entworfene; als 'Schwingungszahl der Atome' hat man in letztere einen Wert einzusetzen, der $\sqrt{(2/3)}$ Mal der Schwingungszahl des elastischen Spektrums ist.

Im Fall, daß eine Nullpunktsenergie existiert, findet man jetzt

$$- M = \frac{3}{4\pi^2} \frac{\kappa^2 h^2}{\mu k \Theta} (1 - \cos \theta) \left\{ \frac{1}{4} + \frac{1}{x^2} \int_0^x \frac{\xi d\xi}{e^\xi - 1} \right\} \tag{59}$$

an Stelle von (56′), womit auch hier eine Darstellung für das ganze Temperaturgebiet erhalten ist. An dem obigen Satz ist nichts zu ändern, nur liegen die Temperaturen, welche als 'hoch' zu bezeichnen sind, erheblich höher, wie bei verschwindender Nullpunktsenergie.

Zusammenfassung

1. Die Wärmebewegung der Atome hat einen wesentlichen Einfluſs auf die bei Röntgenstrahlen beobachtbaren Interferenzerscheinungen.

2. Die Schärfe der Interferenzmaxima wird nicht, ihre Intensität, ebenso wie die räumliche Intensitätsverteilung aber wohl beeinflußt.

3. Die Interferenzintensität nimmt wegen der Wärmebewegung exponentiell ab

a) mit zunehmendem Winkelabstand zwischen Einfalls- und Beobachtungsrichtung,

b) mit zunehmender Temperatur,

c) mit abnehmender Wellenlänge.

165

4. Der Exponent der ebengenannten Exponentialfunktion verschwindet bei $T = 0$ bei fehlender Nullpunktsenergie und behält einen endlichen, wesentlich in Betracht kommenden Wert, wenn eine Nullpunktsenergie existiert.

5. Der Exponent ist stets umgekehrt proportional dem Quadrate der Wellenlänge.

6. Die Interferenzintensität ist stets begleitet von einer zerstreuten Intensität, welche dort am intensivsten ist, wo die Interferenzintensität am meisten geschwächt erscheint und umgekehrt.

7. Der Verlauf der Erscheinungen läßt sich annäherungsweise vorausberechnen, wenn Daten über den Verlauf der spezifischen Wärme als Funktion der Temperatur vorliegen.

8. In der betreffenden Näherung gilt ein Ähnlichkeitsgesetz wie bei den spezifischen Wärmen einatomiger Körper, wonach auch hier der Temperaturverlauf nur Funktion von dem Verhältnis der charakteristischen Temperatur Θ zur Beobachtungstemperatur ist.

Utrecht, 29. September 1913

Zusätze bei der Korrektur (*26. November 1913*):

1. Inzwischen teilte mir A. Sommerfeld eine Fassung der obigen Resultate mit, welche die räumliche Verteilung der Wärmewirkung auf die Interferenzpunkte in sehr einfacher Weise allgemein zu übersehen gestattet.

Wir fanden, daß z.B. bei fehlender Nullpunktsenergie der Wärmeeffekt gemessen wird durch eine Exponentialfunktion mit einem Exponenten M, welcher unter Wiedereinführung der Richtungscos. $\alpha_0, \beta_0, \gamma_0$, α, β, γ auf die Form:

$$M = - \frac{3h^2}{2\mu k\Theta\lambda^2} \frac{\Phi(x)}{x} \{(\alpha - \alpha_0)^2 + (\beta - \beta_0)^2 + (\gamma - \gamma_0)^2\} \quad (63)$$

gebracht werden kann. In einem Interferenzpunkt aber kann dafür nach den Grundformeln

$$\alpha - \alpha_0 = h_1\lambda/a, \quad \beta - \beta_0 = h_2\lambda/a, \quad \gamma - \gamma_0 = h_3\lambda/a \quad (64)$$

der Laueschen Theorie (für das reguläre System bei beliebiger Incidenz gültig) auch geschrieben werden

$$M = - \frac{3h^2}{2\mu k\Theta a^2} \frac{\Phi(x)}{x} (h_1^2 + h_2^2 + h_3^2) \quad (63')$$

166

ein Ausdruck, aus dem nun die Wellenlänge als solche verschwunden ist und nur mehr die für den Interferenzpunkt charakteristischen ganzen Zahlen h_1, h_2, h_3 übriggeblieben sind.

Unser ursprünglicher Ausdruck (63) für M bezog sich, wie mehrfach hervorgehoben, auf eine bestimmte Wellenlänge und verglich den Temperatureinfluß auf die verschiedenen Richtungen θ, in denen dieselbe Wellenlänge auftreten kann. In den Laueschen Photogrammen ist die Wellenlänge von Punkt zu Punkt verschieden; der Ausdruck (63') indessen gestattet eben Punkte verschiedener Wellenlänge in einfacher Weise miteinander zu vergleichen.

45. Die ersten Berechnungen der Einwirkung der Wärmebewegung der Kristallatome auf die Interferenz von Röntgenstrahlen hat bekanntlich Debye ausgeführt. Eine ausführliche Behandlung des Problems hat er in seiner Abhandlung 'Interferenz von Röntgenstrahlen und Wärmebewegung'[1] gegeben. Als Ausgangspunkt seiner Berechnungen benutzt Debye Vorstellungen, welche der Laueschen Theorie der Interferenz von Röntgenstrahlen in einem starren Atomgitter zugrunde liegen. Debye vervollständigt diese Theorie durch die Berücksichtigung der Wärmebewegung. Dabei wird mit einer Modifikation, über welche wir Bedenken anführen müssen, die von Born und v. Kármán angegebene Methode, Normalkoordinaten bei einem Gitter einzuführen, benutzt. Die Rechnung von Debye gibt als Resultat erstens ein Herabsetzen der Intensität der Strahlung in den Lauemaxima, zweitens eine zerstreute Strahlung, deren Intensität durch einen sehr einfachen Ausdruck dargestellt wird. Die Schärfe der Lauemaxima wird nach Debye von der Wärmebewegung nicht beeinflußt.

Den einfachen Ausdruck für die zerstreute Strahlung hat Debey erhalten auf Kosten einer in der Rechnung begangenen Inkonsequenz, die von ihm auch hervorgehoben wird. Wie die Rechnung auszuführen ist, wenn diese Inkonsequenz vermieden werden soll, das hat Faxén[2] gezeigt. Nach ihm ist die zerstreute Strahlung von kompliziertem Bau. Faxén hebt das interessante Resultat hervor, daß eine große Intensität der zerstreuten Strahlung in der Nähe der Lauemaxima zu erwarten ist.

Schrödinger[3] hat im Jahre 1913 unter strenger Benutzung der Born- und v. Kármánschen Theorie eine Behandlung des vorliegenden Problems gegeben. Leider bezieht sich seine Berechnung nur auf ein lineares Gitter, d.h. eine Reihe äquidistanter Atome, und es ist nicht ganz einleuchtend,

---

[1] P. Debije, *Ann. d. Phys.* **43** (1914) 49 [this Vol. p. 162].
[2] H. Faxén, *ebenda* **54** (1918) 615.
[3] E. Schrödinger, *Phys. Zs.* **15** (1914) 79 u. 497.

inwieweit sich seine Schlüsse auf das dreidimensionale Gitter erweitern lassen können. Außerdem wird von Schrödinger die Quantentheorie nicht berücksichtigt. Schrödinger zieht aus seinen Berechnungen den Schluß, daß mit wachsender Temperatur die Schärfe der Lauemaxima allmählich verschwindet.

Das Problem wird hier aufs neue behandelt, weil es mir, wie oben erwähnt, scheint, daß Debye die Born- und v. Kármánsche Methode in unrichtiger Weise benutzt hat. Außerdem ist eine Erweiterung der Theorie auf andere Gittertypen erwünscht. Das Ergebnis der Untersuchung in letzterer Hinsicht werde ich später mitteilen.

Der Gang der vorliegenden Untersuchung gestaltet sich folgendermaßen:

In § 1 wird gezeigt, wie es in einfacher Weise möglich ist, unter Benutzung der Normalkoordinaten von Born und v. Kármán die Interferenzintensität zu berechnen. Es zeigt sich dann, daß sich diese in der Form einer Summe $J = J_1 + J_2$ darstellen läßt. J_1 entspricht dem von Debye für die Intensität der Lauemaxima gegebenen Ausdruck und hat dieselbe Form. Doch ist der Exponent M in der Debyeschen Formel hier durch seinen doppelten Wert ersetzt, was einen stärkeren Temperatureinfluß zur Folge hat. J_2 ist ein Ausdruck, welcher dem von Faxén für die zerstreute Strahlung gegebenen ähnlich ist. Es wird weiter die Frage erörtert, welcher Beitrag von J_2 zur Strahlungsintensität in einem Lauefleck und dessen Umgebung zu erwarten ist. Es scheint, als könnte bei der Anwendung kontinuierlicher Röntgenstrahlung dieser Beitrag ziemlich bedeutend sein. Die Voraussetzungen, welche hier gemacht werden, sind im wesentlichen die gleichen, die schon Debye gemacht hat.

In § 2 gehen wir dann etwas näher auf den Debyeschen Ansatz ein. Es wird erwähnt, daß dieser Ansatz bei richtiger Durchführung der Rechnung zu dem in § 1 erhaltenen Ergebnis führen kann.

In § 3 wird hervorgehoben, daß bei der Ableitung viele Vernachlässigungen gemacht worden sind. Doch scheint es, als würden die experimentellen Ergebnisse von Backhurst[1] ziemlich gut mit den Forderungen der Theorie übereinstimmen.

(...)

---

[1] I. Backhurst, *Proc. Royal Soc.* (A) **102** (1922) 340.

*Still the decrease of intensity with higher order was not suffi-
cient. In fact, neither the Lorentz factor nor Debye's temperature factor accounted for the rapid decrease of intensity and
the great and pressing question was how to explain it.*

*By this time a sound theory for the diffracted intensity had
not only become increasingly desirable for general theoretical
reasons but even worse than that, all practical progress in
crystal structure work towards the determination of more
complex structures was hampered by the impossibility of
evaluating the measured intensities.*

*C. G. Darwin was the first to attack the problem of inten-
sities by an utterly new method. His pioneer papers of 1913–14
are truly remarkable for the intrepidness and skill with which
he approaches the problem. He was the first to concern him-
self about absolute intensities—i.e., the ratios of diffracted
beams not to another but to the primary beam.*

P. P. EWALD,
Current Sci. 1937, p. 12

46. THE THEORY OF X-RAY REFLEXION

by C. G. Darwin, M.A.

Lectures in Mathematical Physics in the University of Manchester [1]

1. The formulae developed by Prof. Laue [2] in connexion with the interference of X-rays in crystals are competent to show the positions in which
the interference maxima occur, but do not give the intensities at the maxima.
For it is readily calculated that it is impossible experimentally to get a crystal
so small that the spherical waves coming from a source at any manageable
distance can be regarded as plane. If, following Bragg [3], we regard the
phenomenon as due to reflexion in a set of parallel planes of atoms, the
extreme shortness of the waves makes the Fresnel zones in these planes
very small (in Friedrich and Knipping's [4] experiments they would be about
2×10^{-7} sq. cm.), and this vitiates the application of Laue's formula for

---

[1] Communicated by Sir Ernest Rutherford, F.R.S.
[2] M. Laue, *Kön. Bay. Ak.* 1912, p. 303 [this Vol. p. 7].
[3] W. L. Bragg, *Proc. Camb. Phil. Soc.* vol. xvii. i. p. 43 [this Vol. p. 38].
[4] W. Friedrich & P. Knipping, *Kön. Bay. Ak.* 1912, p. 311 [this Vol. p. 13].

the intensity. In a later paper Laue[1] has made use of the Fresnel diffraction principles to account for the shapes of the spots on the interference photographs, but a complete theory must regard the whole problem as one of spherical waves.

In working out such a theory there is great advantage in taking as model that experimental arrangement which has in fact proved most fruitful, reflexion from the planes parallel to an external face of a crystal. This gets rid, both for theory and experiment, of a great deal of rather complicated geometry, which is useful in investigating the structure of crystals, but has nothing to do with the nature of the reflexion.

2. *Assumptions*

We shall assume simply that X-ray phenomena are a branch of optics. The optical theories of diffraction, and also of dispersion, etc., work out correctly on principles depending on a simple vibration theory, although some of the phenomena of light can only be reconciled with this theory with difficulty. Thus the photoelectric effect depends on Planckian considerations which seem contradictory to the wave theory. In the same way we shall suppose that X-rays obey the ordinary laws of the electromagnetic theory, in spite of the well-known fact that their absorption occurs by means of the emission of high-speed electrons. It should be said at once that part of the quantitative discussion in the present paper is inadequate and can only be regarded as a first approximation, but several points of interest have emerged. It is hoped to treat of a more complete theory in a future paper.

(...)

It is convenient here to anticipate a future result (§ 6). We shall see that the X-rays must be held to have a refractive index which differs from unity by about a millionth. On account of the refraction the position of the line on the photograph is slightly shifted. Let λ, θ be the external wave-length and glancing angle, λ', θ' the internal. Let $1 + p$ be the refractive index. Then $\lambda = (1 + p)\lambda'$ and $\cos \theta = (1 + p) \cos \theta'$ or $\theta - \theta' = - p \cot \theta$. The observed position of the line corresponds to $n\lambda' = 2a \sin \theta'$, while that which would be expected is given by $n\lambda = 2a \sin \theta_0$. So $(1 + p) \sin \theta' = \sin \theta_0$, and so $\theta_0 - \theta' = p \tan \theta$. Thus the shift is

$$\theta - \theta_0 = - p \operatorname{cosec} \theta \sec \theta.$$

This result will be proved later *ab initio*.

[1] M. Laue, *Annal. d. Phys.* **41** (1913) 1003.

4. *Quantitative Method*

We next consider the case where the reflexion is measured electrically. For this, the information required is quantitative. We shall first find the total energy reflected into the electroscope when monochromatic radiation falls on a crystal without any slits. As would be the case in most experiments, we shall suppose the electroscope to be so wide that all the reflected radiation is included; it is then unnecessary to allow for the fact that the distance of the electroscope is finite, and complicated operations with Fresnel integrals are avoided.

It is not necessary to carry through all the details strictly according to the electromagnetic theory. These can be introduced later. Let us suppose that when a wave of length $2\pi/k$ falls on an atom, the amplitude of the scattered radiation at unit distance bears to that of the incident a ratio $f(\psi, k)$, where ψ is the angle between the direction of observation and the incident beam. f is of the dimensions of a length. In accordance with §§ 11–13 it will be taken to be real, involving no change of phase. In addition to ψ and k it will depend on the direction of polarization of the incident beam. We shall suppose f so small that the wave scattered by one atom does not influence the amplitude of vibration of the radiating system in any other. As we shall see, there is an effect on the phase which can still be included. It will appear that there is definite experimental evidence that the scattering of one atom does affect that of others, because we shall find reason to believe that over a narrow range of angles of incidence the reflexion is nearly perfect; so we can only regard the present process as a first approximation. For simplicity we shall take a crystal composed of atoms of a single element, arranged in a single lattice, but this lattice may be cubic or parallelopipedal. We also neglect the temperature vibrations of the atoms. These omissions are very easily set right later.

5. *Reflexion from a Single Plane*

We first find the reflexion from one plane of atoms. Let the incident beam be $R^{-1} \exp\{ik(Ct - R)\}$, where R is the distance from O (see fig. p. 172).

Taking C as origin, O is the point $(0, 0, h)$. To find the reflexion at angle θ we take as point of observation $(\rho \cos \theta, 0, \rho \sin \theta - h)$, so that ρ is the distance from I_1. Then the point of geometrical reflexion A is $(R \cos \theta, 0, 0)$ where $h = R \sin \theta$. Let there be an atom at $(R \cos \theta + \xi, \eta, 0)$. This atom

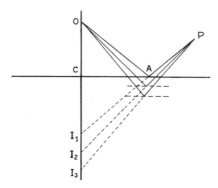

will contribute a component

$$\frac{f(2\theta, k)}{R(\rho - R)} \exp\{ik(Ct - R_{\xi\eta} - r_{\xi\eta})\},$$

where the quantities that do not vary rapidly have been replaced by their values at A, and $R_{\xi\eta}$, $r_{\xi\eta}$ are the distances of ξ, η from O and P respectively. By expansion we find that

$$R_{\xi\eta} + r_{\xi\eta} = \rho + \frac{1}{2} \frac{\rho}{R(\rho - R)} (\xi^2 \sin^2 \theta + \eta^2),$$

so that the whole effect is

$$\frac{f(2\theta, k)}{\rho} e^{ik(Ct-\rho)} \frac{\rho}{R(\rho - R)} \Sigma \exp\left\{-\frac{ik}{2} \frac{\rho}{R(\rho - R)} (\xi^2 \sin^2 \theta + \eta^2)\right\}.$$

Let M be the number of atoms per unit area. Then the number in an area $d\xi d\eta$ is $M d\xi d\eta$. Since the phase variation between neighbouring atoms is small we can replace the sum by an integral, and get as the reflected wave

$$\frac{f(2\theta, k)}{\rho} e^{ik(Ct-\rho)} M \frac{\rho}{R(\rho - R)}$$

$$\cdot \int\int_{-\infty}^{\infty} \exp\left\{-\frac{ik}{2} \frac{\rho}{R(\rho - R)} (\xi^2 \sin^2 \theta + \eta^2)\right\} d\xi d\eta$$

$$= \frac{f(2\theta, k)}{\rho} e^{ik(Ct-\rho)} \frac{M.2\pi e^{-i\pi/2}}{k \sin \theta}.$$

If N be the number of atoms per unit volume and a the distance between successive planes of the crystal, $M = Na$, and we have as reflexion coefficient,

$$f(2\theta, k) \frac{Na2\pi e^{-i\pi/2}}{k \sin \theta} = - iq \tag{1}$$

This expression is not perfectly general since q might be made greater than unity by increasing N. This would violate the conservation of energy. In actual matter this would be prevented, because the vibration of each atom would diminish those of its neighbours, so that we should have to regard f as dependent on N. Numerical calculation shows that q is of the order 10^{-4}, so that the simple form probably stands. The factor $\exp(-i\pi/2)$ is the converse of the quarter wave which has to be introduced into diffraction problems.

6. *The Refractive Index*

If the factor $f(2\theta, k)$ is replaced by $f(0, k)$ the same radiation, represented by $-iq_0$, is scattered on the other side of the plane, so that the wave there is of the form

$$R^{-1}(1 - iq_0) \exp\{ik(Ct - R)\} \quad \text{or} \quad R^{-1} \exp\{ik(Ct - R) - iq_0\},$$

since q_0 is small. This neglects the absorption in the plane which cuts down the amplitude by a real factor b, so that the transmitted wave is

$$R^{-1}b \exp\{ik(Ct - R) - iq_0\}.$$

The effect in the second plane is due to the incident wave and to the wavelets scattered by the atoms of the first. We have above seen that these reconstruct themselves and produce a component in the primary wave. This reconstruction will not really be very perfect until four or five layers have been passed, but no great error is introduced by supposing that it happens at once. Taking into account the effect of the first plane on the emerging wave, we find that the second plane gives a reflexion

$$- iqb^2 \, \frac{\exp\{ik(Ct - \rho_2) - 2iq_0\}}{\rho_2},$$

where ρ_2 is the distance from I_2. Proceeding in this way, we find that the sth plane gives an emerging wave

$$- iqb^{2s} \, \frac{\exp\{ik(Ct - \rho_s) - 2iq_0 s\}}{\rho_s}$$

and that beyond it the transmitted beam is

$$b^s \, \frac{\exp\{ik(Ct - R) - iq_0 s\}}{R}.$$

The intensity corresponding to this is b^{2s}/R^2. But the rays have traversed a thickness $sa \operatorname{cosec} \theta$, so we take

$$b^2 = \exp\{- \mu a \operatorname{cosec} \theta\}.$$

The presence of the term iq_0s implies a refractive index. For $s = z/a$, so that the wave is propagated in a new direction with a velocity different from that of light. The refractive index is

$$1 + q_0(\sin \theta)/ka \quad \text{or} \quad 1 + 2\pi N f(0, k)/k^2. \tag{2}$$

It should be observed that in the forward direction the wavelets scattered by the atoms are in phase together, whether the latter are arranged regularly or not. So this refractive index applies equally well to amorphous substances.

7. Reflexion of Monochromatic Radiation

Returning to the reflexion we get as the whole reflected amplitude

$$- iq \; \frac{e^{ik(Ct-\rho_1)}}{\rho_1} \; (1 + \exp\{- \mu a \, \mathrm{cosec} \, \theta + ik(\rho_1 - \rho_2) - 2iq_0\}$$
$$+ \exp\{- 2\mu a \, \mathrm{cosec} \, \theta + ik(\rho_1 - \rho_3) - 4iq_0\} + \ldots),$$

where the slowly varying quantities have been replaced by their values for the first plane. As has been indicated, the whole radiation at a finite distance is the same as at an infinite, so that we may take the ρ's as large as we please. Thus $\rho_s = \rho_1 + 2as \sin \theta$ and the whole expression is

$$- iq \; \frac{e^{ik(Ct-\rho)}}{\rho} \; (1 + \Sigma_1^\infty \exp - s.\mu a \, \mathrm{cosec} \, \theta - sika2 \sin \theta - s2iq_0) =$$

$$= - iq \, e^{ik(Ct-\rho)}/\rho\{1 - \exp - (\mu a \, \mathrm{cosec} \, \theta + ika2 \sin \theta + 2iq_0)\}.$$

If $ka \sin \theta$ is near $n\pi$ this has a strong maximum. Let $ka \sin \phi = n\pi$. Then $ka \sin \theta = n\pi + ka \cos \phi(\theta - \phi)$ and the amplitude is

$$- iq \, e^{ik(Ct-\rho)}/\rho\{\mu a \, \mathrm{cosec} \, \phi + i(2ka \cos \phi(\theta - \phi) + 2q_0)\}.$$

Corresponding to this we have an intensity

$$q^2/\rho^2\{(\mu a \, \mathrm{cosec} \, \phi)^2 + (2ka \cos \phi(\theta - \phi) + 2q_0)^2\}. \tag{3}$$

This has its maximum at $ka \cos \phi(\theta - \phi) + q_0 = 0$. If q_0 is replaced by its value in terms of the refractive index, the expression at the end of § 3 can be recovered.

Suppose now that we measure the ionization in an electroscope of length l and sufficient breadth to include the whole beam. The effect then is

$$\frac{Il}{\rho} \, q^2 \int \frac{d\theta}{(\mu a \, \mathrm{cosec} \, \phi)^2 + 4(ka \cos \phi(\theta - \phi) + q_0)^2},$$

where I is the intensity of the incident beam

$$= I \frac{l}{\rho} q^2 \frac{\pi}{\mu a \operatorname{cosec} \phi . 2ka \cos \phi},$$

which reduces to

$$I \frac{l}{\rho} \frac{f^2(2\theta, k)}{\mu} N^2 . \tfrac{1}{2}\lambda^3 \operatorname{cosec} 2\phi. \tag{4}$$

This expression, like that for reflexion from one plane, is not general because N may be so large that the reflexion would be greater than the incident beam and the energy would not be conserved. In reality, this would be avoided by the atoms influencing one another's scattering. (...)

We can now deduce an upper limit to the reflexion. Taking $r = 30$ cm. and $k = 10^9$ for medium X-rays, we find that all the reflexion occurs within an angular breadth of about 5″. If the observed reflexion is more than the whole amount included within 5″, it is a sign that the simple theory will not hold, and that in an improved theory which takes account of the influence between atoms, the reflexion must be spread out in a broader pattern than indicated above.

9. Heterogenous Radiation

The transition from monochromatic radiation to the general 'white' radiation is simple. Let the amplitude be represented by

$$\int_0^\infty \{\phi(k) + i\psi(k)\} \frac{e^{ik(Ct-R)}}{R} \, dk.$$

The intensity corresponding to this will be proportional to

$$\frac{1}{R^2} \int_0^\infty (\phi^2 + \psi^2) dk \quad \text{or} \quad \frac{1}{R^2} \int_0^\infty u_k dk.$$

The reflected amplitude is

$$\int_0^\infty \{\phi(k) + i\psi(k)\} \cdot$$

$$(-iq) \frac{e^{ik(Ct-\rho)}}{\rho} \frac{dk}{1 - \exp - (\mu a \operatorname{cosec} \theta + i . 2ka \sin \theta + 2iq_0)}$$

175

corresponding to which there is an intensity

$$\frac{1}{\rho^2} \int_0^\infty u_k q^2 \frac{dk}{|1 - \exp - (\mu a \operatorname{cosec} \theta + i.2ka \sin \theta + 2iq_0)|^2} .$$

We suppose that u_k only varies slowly. As k varies the integrand has strong maxima when $ka \sin \theta + q_0 = n\pi$. Denote this value of k by k_n and near k_n put $k = k_n(1 + x)$.

Then the expression is approximately

$$\frac{1}{\rho^2} \Sigma_n u_n(q^2)_n \int_{-\infty}^\infty \frac{k_n dx}{(\mu_n a \operatorname{cosec} \theta)^2 + (2n\pi x)^2},$$

where the n subscript denotes that the quantity has reference to k_n. Performing the integration and putting in the value of q, we have

$$\frac{1}{\rho^2} N^2 a^2 2\pi \Sigma_n \frac{f^2(2\theta, k_n)}{\mu_n} \frac{1}{n^2} u_n,$$

or in terms of the more usual E_λ where $E_\lambda d\lambda = u_k dk$,

$$\frac{1}{\rho^2} N^2 a^2 \Sigma \frac{1}{n^2} f^2(2\theta, k_n) \left(\frac{E_\lambda \lambda^2}{\mu} \right)_n . \tag{5}$$

10. Temperature Effect and Compound Crystal

We will next introduce an effect so far disregarded, the temperature correction. This, due to the fact that the atoms are at no time all in their planes, affects the reflexion from a single plane, but makes no further change. Of the displacements of the atoms, those in the plane produce no change of phase, and we only have to consider displacements out of the plane. The treatment here is rather different in detail from that of Debye [1]. Let us suppose that the potential energy for a displacement ζ is $\frac{1}{2}\sigma\zeta^2$. By the principle of equipartition out of the M atoms per sq. cm. a number

$$M(\sigma/2\pi kT)^{\frac{1}{2}} \exp \left\{ - \frac{\sigma\zeta^2}{2kT} \right\} d\zeta \quad [2]$$

are displaced a distance between ζ and $\zeta + d\zeta$. These atoms are wrong in phase to an extent expressed by $\exp\{- ik2\zeta \sin \theta\}$. There are a great many atoms in any region over which the phases of the undisturbed atoms are

---

[1] Debije, *Ber. d. Deut. Phys. Ges.* (1913) 671.
[2] k is used in two different senses, but the difference will be clear.

sensibly constant. The temperature effect can be thus expressed as a factor in the value of q, and this factor is

$$(\sigma/2\pi kT)^{\frac{1}{2}} \int_{-\infty}^{+\infty} \exp\left\{-\frac{\sigma\zeta^2}{2kT} - ik2\zeta \sin\theta\right\} d\zeta$$

or

$$\exp\{- kT(2k \sin\theta)^2/2\sigma\} \quad \text{or} \quad \exp\{- kT(2n\pi)^2/2\sigma a^2\}$$

This is for the amplitude, and so for the intensity the temperature vibrations introduce a factor

$$\exp\{- kT(2n\pi)^2/\sigma a^2\}. \tag{6}$$

It is the same for a given order of reflexion, but diminishes rapidly with the higher orders.

We next deduce the reflexion for a crystal composed of several similar interpenetrating lattices. Let N_r be the number of atoms per c.c. of the rth lattice, f_r their scattering effect, and let the planes of this lattice be at distance $\alpha_r a$ from those of the first, let σ_r give the restraining force on the atoms. Then the expression

$$N^2 f^2 \exp\{- kT(2n\pi)^2/\sigma a^2\}$$

must be replaced by

$$| \Sigma_r N_r f_r \exp\{- i2n\pi\alpha_r - kT(2n\pi)^2/2\sigma_r a^2\}|^2. \tag{7}$$

This applies to both monochromatic and white radiation.

11. *The Scattering of a Single Atom [Electron]*

We must now discuss the form of the function f. In $f^2(2\theta, k)$ there will be a factor $(1 + \cos^2 2\theta)/2$ due to the two polarized components of the incident beam. This gets rid of the polarization, and we need only consider the form of f in a plane perpendicular to the electric vector.

The atom consists of a positive charge and of electrons, but the former is much too heavy to scatter radiation and may be neglected. Though there can be little doubt that it does not represent the reality of the case, we shall proceed according to the ordinary electromagnetic theory, as applied to dispersion. In optics this gives satisfactory results, and it should do so here as well. Let e, m be charge and mass of an electron, and let the forces which hold it in equilibrium have a 'stiffness' $mk_0^2 C^2$, so that the emission wave-length is $2\pi/k_0$. Under the action of an electric force X

X the electron moves according to the equation

$$m\ddot{\xi} + mk_0^2C^2\xi - 2e^2\dddot{\xi}/3C^3 = eX.$$

Then if $X = \exp\{ik(Ct - x)\}$ we have

$$\xi = \frac{eX}{m(k_0^2 - k^2)C^2 + 2e^2k^3i/3}.$$

At a great distance r in the plane of yz this gives a wave of amplitude

$$\frac{k^2e^2X \exp(-ikr)}{r\{m(k_0^2 - k^2)C^2 + 2e^2k^3i/3\}}$$

If we take this expression and add together the terms for each electron in the atom, and substitute in (2) for the refractive index, we get the Selmeyer dispersion formula. Since it is quite possible that k should be greater than k_0 for all the electrons, the refractive index may quite well be less than unity.

12. *Mutual Action of the Electrons in an Atom* *

For the electrons which contribute the light spectrum k_0 is very much smaller than k and may be neglected. Sir J. J. Thomson [1] assumes this for all the electrons. The imaginary term is very much smaller than the real, so he puts $f = -e^2/mC^2$ for each electron, and uses this expression to estimate the number of electrons in the atom, from the known scattering of an amorphous substance.

But without further discussion this is not legitimate, even assuming that all the k_0's are negligible. For some of the electrons are crowded very close together, probably within a distance of about 5×10^{-10} cm. [2], which is fairly small compared with the wave-length of the radiation. Now it is well known that a small body scatters light of short wave-length much more completely than long. We must make certain that this will not be the case here. Suppose we have ν electrons crowded together at points $x_1y_1z_1$, the scale of their distances being measured by a length ρ. Let the external radiation be $X = \exp(ikCt)$. This sets all the electrons in vibration, and the motion of each influences the others. Let ξ_1 be the displacement of the first electron. Then ξ_1 is of the form $\{A_1 \exp(ikCt)\}/e$. At a near

---

* [For historical approach to the atomic scattering factor, see this Vol. p. 182.]
[1] J. J. Thomson, 'Conduction of Electricity through Gases,' p. 326.
[2] Calculated on Bohr's theory for a ring of 4 electrons in a sodium atom.

point this electron exerts a force

$$\frac{3(x - x_1)^2 - r^2}{r^5} \, A_1 \exp{(ikCt)}.$$

Similarly for the others. The whole electric force on the first electron then is

$$\left(1 + \Sigma_2^\nu \frac{3(x_s - x_1)^2 - r_{1s}^2}{r_{1s}^5} \, A_s \right) \exp{(ikCt)} =$$

$$= \frac{m\ddot{\xi}_1}{e} = - \frac{mk^2C^2}{e^2} \, A_1 \exp{(ikCt)}.$$

We are neglecting the restraining forces on the electrons, and also the reaction of their radiation on their motion. We thus get a set of equations

$$- A_1 = (e^2/mk^2C^2)(1 + \Sigma_2^\nu \beta_{1s} A_s/\rho^3),$$

where β_{1s} is a quantity depending on the arrangement and is of the order of unity. The whole amplitude of the radiation scattered to a distant point in the yz plane is

$$(k^2/r) \exp{\{ik(Ct - r)\}} \, \Sigma \, A_s.$$

The character of the solution of the simultaneous equations depends on the magnitude of $e^2/mk^2C^2\rho^3$. If it is small we get $A_1 = - e^2/mk^2C^2$, so that the scattered radiation is proportional to $\nu e^2/mC^2$. For our inner ring of electrons we take $\rho = 5 \times 10^{-10}$ and for soft X-rays $2\pi/k = 10^{-8}$. Then $e^2/mk^2C^2\rho^3 = 6 \times 10^{-3}$. This is small enough, so that we may assume that an [electron in the] atom scatters long waves to the same extent as short.

13. The 'Excess' Scattering

The waves scattered by the electrons in an atom combine to a certain extent so as to give a scattered radiation greater in intensity than is simply proportional to their number. For example, the electrons at distances 5×10^{-10} cm. apart would exert an effect almost proportional to the square of their number. Consider the effect of an atom in a direction inclined to the incident beam at angle 2θ.*

* [For a difference between the effect of a single atom and its cooperative effect in the crystal lattice, see this Vol. p. 186, line 10 from bottom, and in particular W. L. Bragg, James and Bosanquet, Z. Physik 9 (1921) 77. Ed.].

Of the ν electrons, all in any plane at angle θ give waves in phase together. Let p_s be the distance of an electron from some plane drawn in this direction. The whole resultant amplitude is then proportional to $\Sigma \exp\{-ik.2p_s \sin \theta\}$. To find the corresponding intensity we multiply by the conjugate imaginary and get

$$\nu + 2 \Sigma \Sigma \cos 2k \sin \theta(p_s - p_t). \tag{9}$$

This expression accounts for the phenomenon of the 'excess radiation' which is observed in the scattering at small angles by an amorphous substance [1]. For k is of the order 10^9 for medium rays and $p_s - p_t$ is at most 10^{-8}, so if θ is less than $5°$ every single electron in the atom contributes to the excess. At broader angles a few of the outermost electrons fail to help, but there will be still a number of contributors. Finally, when $\theta = \pi/2$ only those contribute which are less than a quarter wave apart. Moreover, the same excess will be exhibited at a broader angle for the softer rays [2].

When we come to consider the reflexion of a crystal we get the formula

$$\nu + 2 \Sigma \Sigma \cos 2n\pi(p_s - p_t)/a.$$

We may probably assume that the interiors of the atoms are oriented in all directions, since any forces which were strong enough to turn them into one direction, would probably show some optical effect, and this would mean that a cubic crystal should show double refraction. So we may suppose that the average of $p_s - p_t$ is independent of θ. Then the excess radiation contributes a constant factor to the reflexion in each order, but that factor is greater for the lower than for the higher orders.

Using the value of f as above, we arrive at the following formula for the reflexion of white radiation from a crystal composed of one lattice

$$\frac{N^2a^2(1 + \cos^2 2\theta)}{\rho^2 2} \Sigma_n \frac{1}{n^2} \left(\frac{e^2}{mC^2}\right)^2$$

$$\left(\nu + 2 \Sigma \Sigma \cos \frac{2n\pi}{a} (p_s - p_t)\right) e^{-\frac{kT}{\sigma a^2}(2n\pi)^2} \left(\frac{E_\lambda \lambda^2}{\mu}\right)_n. \tag{10}$$

[1] Barkla, *Phil. Mag.* vol. **21** (1911) 270; Crowther, *Proc. Roy. Soc.* A. vol. **85** (1911) 29.
[2] Various hypotheses have been put forward to account for the excess radiation, by J. A. Crowther (*Proc. Camb. Phil. Soc.* **16** (1913) 534) and by D. L. Webster (*Phil. Mag.* **25** (1913) 234). The last assumes it due to the cooperation between electrons.

14. *Comparison with Experiment*

We will now compare this result with experiment, and shall find that our formula gives more reflexion than is possible. The comparison is with the experiments on rocksalt in Moseley and Darwin [1]. Using the experimental value 0.0035 for the efficiency of the rocksalt reflexion at $4°$, we can estimate the value of $v + 2 \sum \sum \cos 2n\pi(p_s - p_t)/a$. It is 26 [*]. But there is strong reason to believe that the efficiency was overestimated. We have seen that, assuming the independence of scattering from separate atoms, the whole reflexion really only takes place within a breadth of about $5''$. If we assume that the radiation in this breadth is completely reflected, we arrive at an efficiency amounting to 0.0004. It is possible that when the reflexion becomes strong it is spread over a broader angle, so that we cannot conclude that the overestimate of efficiency is as great as suggested by this figure.

Unfortunately the fact that the reflexion must be regarded as nearly perfect vitiates the formulae for reflexion. The wave scattered by one atom disturbs the vibrations of the others. It is hoped to discuss this aspect of the matter in a future paper [2].

15. *The Absence of Resonance*

A very interesting question arises with regard to the natural periods of the electrons. If there are such periods in the X-ray region it should be possible to observe a marked change in the refractive index in their neighbourhood. It should also be found that a substance scatters a particular wave-length much more efficiently than any other. The early work on refraction was all with heterogeneous rays and so cannot be taken as evidence, and no one has worked at the scattering of characteristic radiation. (...) With regard to there being some real resonance effect, we can only hold that it seems rather improbable that it exists.

[1] *Loc. cit.*
[*] [Note that only here the *formula* is directly tested with experiment where the result is found to be satisfactory. The following considerations concern the *model* on which equations (4) or (10) are based. In *Darwin* II § 8, this Vol. p. 212, it is argued that a mosaic model of the crystal too results in these equations—see also the straightforward derivations of the intensity of reflection by a mosaic crystal, Bragg, James and Bosanquet, this Vol. p. 276. Ed.].
[2] [This Vol. paper 53.]

ATOMIC SCATTERING FACTOR (EARLY DEVELOPMENT)

47. 1. Für die Schwingung eines einzelnen Atoms wollen wir zunächst einmal die Annahme machen, dass sie rein sinusförmig verläuft. Die von einen Atom ausgehende Welle können wir dann in grosser Entfernung vom Atom darstellen durch den Ausdruck

$$\Psi e^{-ikr}/r \tag{2}$$

wo r den Betrag des Radiusvektors von Atom zum Aufpunkt bedeutet, Ψ eine Funktion seiner Richtung und $k = 2\pi/\lambda$ ist, wo λ die Wellenlänge der später interferierenden Röntgenstrahlen darstellt. Wäre, wie man es in der Optik gewohnt ist, das Atom klein gegen die Wellenlänge, so wäre

Ψ eine Konstante. Hier aber muss man mit der Möglichkeit rechnen, und die Versuchsergebnissen legen die Vermutung nahe, dass infolge der mit der Wellenlänge vergleichbaren Abmessung des Atoms Richtungsunterschiede auftreten.

48. Der Verfasser dieses Berichtes hat anfangs versucht, dieser Funktion in Hinblick auf die charakteristische Strahlung der Elementen stark selektive Eigenschaften zu zuschreiben, in dem Sinn, dass das Atom nur auf eine oder auf einige Wellenlängen anspricht. Diese Ansicht wird jedoch durch die Tatsache der allgemeinen Spiegelung widerlegt. Näher der Wahrheit scheint schon die Annahme von Ewald zu kommen—P. Debye, *Ann. Physik* **43** (1914) 49—, dass Ψ für alle Röntgenstrahlewellenlängen den gleichen Wert hat.

49. In a recent paper by Mr. J. A. Crowther [1], are described some experiments on the scattering of Röntgen rays by disks of aluminium or paraffin paper, made to test the formula that gives the intensity of the rays scattered to an angle θ as proportional to $(1 + \cos^2 \theta)$. This formula may readily be obtained from the expressions for the radiated electric and magnetic vectors given by Prof. Sir J. J. Thomson in his book, 'The Conduction of Electricity through Gases,' with the assumption that each electron in the radiator scatters the same amount of energy that it would scatter if it were alone.

The observed radiation is found to fit the formula well at angles greater than about 60°, but to be much in excess of the calculated value at small angles.

The purpose of the present paper is to revise the original formula without the hypothesis that each electron scatters energy exactly as if it were alone, and to show how the re-enforcement of the radiation from one electron by that from another may produce the 'excess radiation' that Mr. Crowther has observed.

50. It is very important to know the exact nature of the law connecting the atomic weight with the amount of scattering. The experiments show that there are not the same abnormal variations in the amount of scattering as we proceed from lower to higher atomic weights as there are in the case

---

[1] *Proc. Roy. Soc.* A. **86**. pp. 472–494.

of the absorption coefficients. Certain experiments which have been made by my son and myself indicate that the law is one of simple proportionality; that is to say, the amplitude of the scattered wave is proportional to the weight of the scattering atom. At any rate, certain results, to which I will now refer briefly, are very simply explained on this hypothesis.

A structure of the diamond, founded on measurements made with the X-ray spectrometer, has been explained in a recent paper [1]. It was pointed out that the second-order spectrum given by the (111) plane disappeared in consequence of the peculiar spacing of the planes. Zinc blende has the same construction as the diamond, except that the two interpenetrating lattices are composed of zinc and sulphur atoms respectively, and are therefore of different weight, while the two lattices of the diamond are both composed of carbon atoms, and are therefore of equal weight. The disappearance of the second-order spectrum referred to may be considered as due to an interference between the effects of the two lattices. When these two lattices are no longer of equal weight, the interference is incomplete, and accordingly the (111) spectrum of zinc blende gives a small second-order spectrum.

In the case of fluorspar, the first order spectrum of the (100) planes and the second order spectrum of the (111) planes have again disappeared, or very nearly so. In this case there are three lattices. The two fluorine lattices can be derived from the calcium lattice by equal simple translations in opposite directions along a cube diagonal; the amount of translation being a quarter of the length of the diagonal. The result is that the (100) planes contain calcium atoms and fluorine atoms alternately. There are two fluorine atoms to one calcium atom and therefore the weights in the planes are approximately equal, as in the case of the diamond. The disappearance of the first order spectrum indicates, therefore, that the conditions for mutual interference are satisfied when the weights are nearly equal, independently of the fact that in the one case the weight is due to calcium atoms and in the other to twice as many fluorine atoms. Weight alone and not atomic nature has determined the amount of scattering. The disappearance of the second order (111) spectrum is explained in the same way.

> *Gibt man die Wahrscheinlichkeit der folgenden Überlegungen zu, dann scheint mir der exp. Untersuchung der zerstreuten Strahlung, insbesondere bei leichten Atomen, ein erhöhtes Interesse zu zukommen, denn auf diesem Wege muss es dann gelingen, die besondere Anordnung der Elektronen im Atom*

[1] *Roy. Soc. Proc.*, A vol. 89, p. 277.

exp. festzustellen. Eine solche Untersuchung hat also die Bedeutung einer Ultramikroskopie des Atominnern.

P. DEBIJE,

Ann. d. Phys. **46** (1915) 811

51. In the study of the spectra of X-rays as analyzed by crystal gratings, the remarkably low intensity of the higher orders of reflection has from the first attracted a considerable amount of attention. Preliminary measurements by Mr. W. L. Bragg[1] showed that, when corrected for temperature effects [?Ed.], the intensities of the different orders of reflection of a given X-ray spectrum line are approximately proportional to the inverse square of the order. A more detailed experimental investigation by Professor W. H. Bragg[2] showed that if X-rays of a definite wavelength are reflected at a glancing angle θ by a crystal in which the successive layers of atoms are similar and are similarly spaced, the energy in the reflected beam can be expressed with considerable accuracy by the formula

$$E_r = \frac{C(1 + \cos^2 2\theta)}{\sin^2 \theta} e^{-B \sin^2 \theta}. \tag{1}$$

Since the sine of the glancing angle is proportional to the order of reflection, this formula includes the result found by W. L. Bragg, but is more general, as it expresses the intensity of the reflection from all possible planes in the crystal.

The theory of the intensity of X-ray reflection has been examined in considerable detail by Mr. C. G. Darwin[3], who finds that if all the electrons which are effective in scattering the X-rays are close to the centers of the atoms, the energy in the beam reflected at an angle θ should be proportional to

$$\frac{(1 + \cos^2 2\theta) e^{-B \sin^2 \theta}}{\sin \theta \cos \theta}.$$

This expression differs from Bragg's experimental formula by the factor $\tan \theta$, which must be explained, as Darwin pointed out, by the fact that the electrons are not all concentrated near the centers of the atoms, but that at least some of the electrons are at distances from the atomic centers which are of the same order of magnitude as the distance between the

---

[1] W. L. Bragg, *Proc. Roy. Soc.* A. vol. **89** (1914) 468 [this Vol. p. 76].
[2] W. H. Bragg, *Phil. Mag.* **27** (1914) 881 [this Vol. p. 160], also W. H. Bragg and W. L. Bragg, *X-rays and Crystal Structure*, p. 195.
[3] C. G. Darwin, *Phil. Mag.* **27** (1914) 675 [this Vol. p. 203].

185

atoms. Since the relative intensity of the different orders of X-ray reflection is thus a function of the distribution of the electrons in the atoms of the crystal, it should be possible, knowing the relative intensity of the different orders, to obtain some definite idea of the manner in which these electrons are arranged.

The possibility of finding an arrangement of the electrons which will account in a satisfactory manner for the observed intensity of X-ray reflection at different angles was suggested first by Professor Bragg[1] and independently soon after by the writer[2]. Both of us were able to show the nature of the effect on the intensity of reflection due to certain different distributions of the electrons in the atoms of a crystal grating, but we both neglected to consider certain important factors that must seriously modify the conclusions at which we arrived. We based our arguments on the assumption that the reflected energy would be the same for all orders if all the scattering occurred at the centers of the atoms. This is indeed true for the intensity in the middle of the reflected line, if the crystal acts as a perfect grating, but since the effective width of the spectrum line can be shown to be proportional to $1/\sin \theta \cos \theta$, the reflected energy is reduced in the same ratio. Thus instead of a factor $1/\sin^2 \theta$ there is really, as pointed out above, a factor of only $1/\tan \theta$ to be accounted for by the assumed structure of the atom.

Atoms with a Finite Number of Electrons

If each atom of a certain kind has an electron at a distance a from its center, the average effect from a large number of such atoms will be the same as that due to a uniform distribution of the electrons over the surface of a sphere of radius a. The center of this equivalent spherical shell will be in the mid-plane of the atomic layer, and the probability that a given electron in the shell will be at a distance z from the middle of the layer may be shown to be

$$F(z) = c \qquad [- a < z < a],$$

or, in virtue of the relation

$$\int_{-a}^{a} c\,dz = 1,$$

$$F(z) = \frac{1}{2a} \qquad [- a < z < a].$$

[1] W. H. Bragg, Bakerian Lecture, March 18, 1915; *Phil. Trans.* A **215**, 253 (July 13, 1915).
[2] A. H. Compton, *Nature*, May 27, 1915.

The value of Ψ' due to an electron in such a shell is therefore

$$\Psi' = \frac{1}{2a} \cos\left(\frac{4\pi z \sin\theta}{\lambda}\right) dz = \frac{\sin\left(\dfrac{4\pi a \sin\theta}{\lambda}\right)}{\dfrac{4\pi a \sin\theta}{\lambda}}, \qquad (17)$$

and the value of Ψ for a whole atom is

$$\Psi = \frac{1}{\nu} \Sigma_r \Psi_r' = \frac{1}{\nu} \Sigma_r \sin\left(\frac{4\pi a_r \sin\theta}{\lambda}\right) \Big/ \left(\frac{4\pi a_r \sin\theta}{\lambda}\right), \qquad (18)$$

where ν is the number of electrons in the atom, and the summation extends over all the r's from 1 to ν. (...)

The values of Ψ obtained by thus adding the effects of a number of electrons placed at arbitrary distances a from the centers of the atoms soon convince one that the form of the resulting curve is very sensitive to changes in the assumed values of a. The results obtained above indicate that there must be a rather strong concentration of the electrons near the centers of the atoms, but it is difficult to select a distribution of the outer electrons which will give a reflection formula that agree with the experimental data.

Bearing on Theories of Atomic Structure

While it is difficult by any 'cut and try' method to find the only possible arrangement of the electrons in atoms, it is evident that a study of the intensity of X-ray spectra thus affords an extremely sensitive test of any theory which assigns a definite distribution to the electrons in atoms. From the experimental data now available it may be said, for example, that unless some important factor has been neglected in our formula for X-ray reflection, it seems impossible to account for the rapid diminution of the intensity of the higher orders on any theory, such as Crehore's[1], which would confine the electrons of an atom within a distance less than 10^{-10} cm. from its center. On the other hand, it seems possible to explain all the X-ray intensities on the basis of the type of atom suggested by Bohr[2].

52. Gerade bei Kristallen aber sind wir in der glücklichen Lage, die Grundidee der Elektronenringe auf ihre Richtigkeit direkt experimentell zu

[1] A. C. Crehore, *Phil. Mag.* **26** (1913) 25 and elsewhere.
[2] N. Bohr, *Phil. Mag.* **26** (1913) pp. 1, 476, 857; **27** (1914) 506.

prüfen; eine Tatsache, welche in unmittelbarem Zusammenhange steht mit dem einzigen Punkte in der v. Laueschen Interferenztheorie[1], der dort nur formell gefaßt wird. Diese Theorie nämlich geht von dem Ansatze aus, daß ein von Strahlung getroffenes Atom eine Sekundärstrahlung in den Raum hinausschickt, welche in fester Phasenbeziehung zur auffallenden Welle steht, und deren Amplitude und Raumverteilung ebenfalls bestimmt ist. Über die Art dieser letztgenannten Größen wird indessen keine Annahme gemacht. Es wird das alles nur phänomenologisch gefaßt durch Einführung der unbestimmten v. Laueschen Strahlenkoeffizienten Ψ, deren spezielle Eigenschaften im übrigen für den unmittelbaren Zweck der v. Laueschen Theorie ja auch nicht herangezogen zu werden brauchen. Indessen zeigte sich bald die Wichtigkeit einer näheren Bestimmung jener Größen Ψ. Bekanntlich wurden ja die Braggschen Fortschritte zu einem wesentlichen Teile erst dadurch ermöglicht, daß über diese Koeffizienten die Annahme gemacht wurde, sie seien dem Atomgewicht des betreffenden zerstreuenden Atoms (wenigstens annähernd) proportional. Es scheint Bragg selbst nicht aufgefallen zu sein und wurde auch sonst wenig beachtet, daß diese Annahme im Widerspruche zu den Erfahrungen steht, welche man schon vorher über die Zerstreuung von Röntgenstrahlung gesammelt hat und als gesichert anzusehen hatte. Barkla[2] hatte schon seine Resultate über den in üblicher Weise gemessenen Zerstreuungskoeffizienten s in Materie von der Dichte ρ (wenigstens für Substanzen von kleinem Atomgewicht) zusammengefaßt in der Formel

$$s/\rho = 0{,}2. \tag{1}$$

Nun bedeutet s die gesamte von 1 cm^3 der Substanz pro Sekunde zerstreute Strahlung, wenn eine Primärstrahlung von der (überall gleichen) Intensität 1 die Zerstreuung anregt. Nennt man den Zerstreuungskoeffizienten des Atoms σ (so daß also ein Atom, bestrahlt mit der Intensität J pro Sekunde im ganzen die Energie σJ zerstreut), dann wird

$$s = \sigma\rho/Am_H,$$

wobei A das Atomgewicht und m_H die Masse eines Wasserstoffatoms bedeutet. Das Barklasche Gesetz besagt also

$$\sigma = 0{,}2m_H A, \tag{2}$$

d.h. die von einem Atom zerstreute *Intensität* ist dem Atomgewicht proportional. Der Braggsche Ansatz indessen behauptet dieselbe Proportiona-

[1] Siehe z.B. den Enzyklopädie-Artikel (V, 24) Wellenoptik von M. v. Laue, S. 459.
[2] C. G. Barkla, *Phil. Mag.* **7** (1904) 543; **21** (1911) 648.

lität von der zerstreuten *Amplitude*, und doch bewähren sich beide An-
sätze. Das kann natürlich nur so verstanden werden, daß beide Ansätze
Näherungen sind für das richtige Gesetz unter verschiedenen äußeren
Bedingungen.

Das Barklasche Gesetzt hatte zur Zeit seiner Entstehung den Umstand
für sich, daß auch die theoretische Begründung nicht ausstand. Befindet
sich nämlich ein einziges völlig freies Elektron in einem Röntgenstrahlenbündel von der Intensität J und berechnet man nach der klassischen Elektrodynamik die Streustrahlung, die von diesem Elektron infolge der von
der Primärstrahlung aufgezwungenen Bewegung ausgesandt wird, so
findet man dafür den Betrag:

$$\frac{8\pi}{3} \frac{\varepsilon^4}{\mu^2 c^4} J^1$$

wobei ε die Ladung, μ die Masse des Elektrons und c die Lichtgeschwindigkeit bedeutet. Eine wesentliche Eigenschaft der Streustrahlung eines
Elektrons besteht nach dem angegebenen Ausdruck darin, daß dieselbe
ihrem Betrage nach von der Wellenlänge der Primärstrahlung völlig unabhängig ist. Sind nun pro Atom Z Elektronen vorhanden, dann wird
man für dessen Zerstreuungskoeffizienten σ annehmen:

$$\sigma = \frac{8\pi}{3} \frac{\varepsilon^4}{\mu^2 c^4} Z. \tag{3}$$

Nun erübrigt es nur noch, im Zusammenhange mit der durch die Röntgen-
strahlenuntersuchungen vermittelten Bedeutung des periodischen Systems
der Elemente, für Z den Wert $A/2$ zu substituieren, um das Barklasche
Gesetz in der Form:

$$\sigma = \frac{4\pi}{3} \frac{\varepsilon^4}{\mu^2 c^4} A$$

zu bekommen. Auch der Zahlenfaktor hat den richtigen Wert, denn mit

$$\varepsilon = 4{,}77 . 10^{-10}, \quad \varepsilon/\mu = 5{,}30 . 10^{-17}$$

und

$$c = 3{,}00 . 10^{10}$$

wird

$$\frac{4\pi}{3} \frac{\varepsilon^4}{\mu^2 c^4} = 0{,}27 . 10^{-24},$$

---

[1] J. J. Thomson, *Conduction of Electricity through Gases*. Cambridge 1903, p. 271.

während man für den in (2) vorkommendem Faktor 0,2 m_H den Wert

$$0,2 m_H = 0,33 \cdot 10^{-24}$$

findet. Die Brücke von hier zum Braggschen Gesetz wird unserer Meinung nach durch eine Bemerkung geschlagen, welche der eine von uns 1915 veröffentlicht hat[1], und welche den Ausgangspunkt unserer inzwischen angestellten Untersuchungen bildete. Dort wurde nämlich gezeigt, daß man festhalten darf an der Grundidee der Erzeugung der Streustrahlung durch die Elektronen. Denn, hat man lange Röntgenwellen (lang im Verhältnis zu den Elektronenabständen), dann werden im Atom die Elektronen alle in Phase schwingen und deshalb nicht ihre Streuintensitäten, sondern ihre Streuamplituden addieren. Das bedeutet, daß σ nicht nach (3), sondern nach der Formel

$$\sigma = \frac{8\pi}{3} \frac{\varepsilon^4}{\mu^2 c^4} Z^2 \qquad (4)$$

zu rechnen ist. Dieses aber wäre mit $Z = A/2$ das Braggsche Gesetz.

Die quantitative Durchführung der Aufgabe (die im wesentlichen eine Interferenzrechnung ist), zeigt, daß man bei jeder genügend kleinen Wellenlänge um den Primärstrahl einen Winkelraum abgrenzen kann, in dem das Braggsche Gesetz $\sigma \sim A^2$ gilt. Die Öffnung desselben indessen wird mit abnehmender Wellenlänge der Primärstrahlung immer kleiner. Außerhalb dieses Winkelraums bekommt man bald das Barklasche Gesetz $\sigma \sim A$.

So versteht man, wie bei den Braggschen Versuchen, bei denen der Hauptsache nach nur kleine Glanzwinkel verwendet wurden, die Proportionalität der Amplitude mit dem Atomgewicht eine gute Näherung sein konnte.

Gibt man die Stichhaltigkeit dieser Überlegung zu, dann ist das wesentliche Resultat derselben, auf das es uns für das folgende hauptsächlich ankommt, dieses: *Die Streuung der Röntgenstrahlen wird nur von den Elektronen erzeugt. Intensitätsmessungen haben die Bedeutung von Messungen eines Interferenzeffektes der Elektronen, müssen also über Zahl und Lagerung der Elektronen Aufschluß erteilen können.*

Darin, daß sowohl das Braggsche, wie das Barklasche Gesetz je nach Umständen aus den Versuchen hervorgeht, liegt zugleich der Nachweis, daß das Wellenlängengebiet, in dem die fraglichen Interferenzen eine wesentliche Rolle spielen, innerhalb experimentell zugänglicher Grenzen liegt.

[1] P. Debije, *Ber. d. Königl. Ges. d. Wiss.* Göttingen, 27. Febr. 1915.

§ 2. Zählung der den Atomen zukommenden Elektronenzahlen

Nach den Ausführungen der Einleitung ist für genügend lange Wellen die von einem als Elektronenkomplex mit z-Elektronen aufgefaßten Atom zerstreute Amplitude proportional mit z. Die Braggsche Annahme war die rohe Form dieses Gesetzes. Bei beliebiger Wellenlänge können wir dieselbe Proportionalität erwarten für genügend kleine Streuwinkel, oder ganz präzis: Die Proportionalität der Amplitude mit z ist das für verschwindenden Streuwinkel geltende Grenzgesetz bei beliebiger Wellenlänge. Der Faktor in diesem Gesetze ist theoretisch bekannt. Eine absolute Bestimmung der Elektronenzahl bedingt also eine absolute Messung der Streuintensität. Hat man es indessen mit mehratomigen Kristallen zu tun, dann kann an Stelle der absoluten die relative Bestimmung der Elektronenzahlen von den beteiligten Atomen mit sehr viel geringerem Arbeitsaufwand auf Grund von relativen Intensitätsmessungen ausgeführt werden.

Stellen wir uns auf den Standpunkt, daß die eben besprochene Proportionalität mit z für alle Streuwinkel genau richtig ist, dann kann man leicht einige Fälle ausfindig machen, in denen dieses Gesetz ohne viel Mühe zur Entscheidung über die Frage der Elektronenzuordnung zu den Atomen herangezogen werden kann.

Jetzt soll über Intensitätsmessungen berichtet werden, welche die relativen Elektronenzahlen bei *LiF* nunmehr einwandfrei bestimmen. *LiF* kristallisiert wieder ähnlich wie *NaCl*, *KCl*, *NaF* usw. Nur insofern ist gegen *NaF* und *KCl* ein Unterschied vorhanden, als im freien Zustande $Li = 3$ und $F = 9$ ist, so daß auch dann, wenn die 'Gitterpunkte' Ionen sind, ein Verschwinden der Reflexion an Ebenen mit ungerader Indizessumme nicht zu erwarten ist. Nach wie vor sind nur Ebenen mit ungemischten Indizes vorhanden. Bei Ebenen mit gerader Indizessumme ist der Strukturfaktor proportional $(Li + F)$, bei Ebenen mit ungerader Summe ist derselbe proportional $(Li - F)$.

Es wurde eine neue Aufnahme mit *LiF*-Pulver als strahlender Substanz nach unserer Methode hergestellt, und zwar wurde dafür gesorgt, daß die Schwärzungen den Wert 1 nicht überstiegen[1]. Hat man diese Vorsorge getroffen, dann ist, wie Friedrich und Koch nachgewiesen haben[2], einfache Proportionalität zwischen Schwärzung und Intensität vorhanden, sofern die Schwärzung von Röntgenstrahlung herrührt. Wesentlich ist natürlich darüber hinaus, daß die Linien, die man vergleichen will, von Rönt-

---

[1] Bekanntlich versteht man unter der Schwärzung einer Stelle des Films den gewöhnlichen Logarithmus des Verhältnisses der auffallenden zur durchgelassenen Intensität.

[2] W. Friedrich und P. P. Koch, *Ann. d. Phys.* **45** (1914) 399.

genstrahlung einheitlicher Wellenlänge erzeugt wurden, und das ist bei unserer Aufnahme ja von selbst erfüllt. Alle verglichenen Linien rühren von der K_α-Strahlung von Kupfer her. Mit einem Hartmannschen Mikrophotometer, bei dem ähnlich wie beim Kochschen selbstregistrierenden, mit Hilfe von Kaliumzellen die zu beobachtende Intensität in den Ausschlag eines Elektrometers umgesetzt wurde, haben wir dann die zu den verschiedenen Indizes gehörigen Linien photometriert. Zunächst erhalten wir also als Maß der Schwärzung der betreffenden Stelle in der Linie den Ausschlag des Elektrometers. Von Herrn Hartmann bezogen wir aber eine Schwärzungsskala, das ist eine photographische Platte mit Feldern bekannter, mittels direkter Messung bestimmter Schwärzungen. Mit Hilfe dieser Skala war es möglich, die beobachteten Elektrometerausschläge in absolute Schwärzungen und damit nach dem Friedrich-Kochschen Gesetz in Intensität der Röntgenstrahlung umzusetzen. Für jede Linie wurde in dieser Weise eine Intensitätskurve gezeichnet, deren Flächeninhalt nach Abzug der Schleierschwärzung der Intensität der Linie direkt proportional zu setzen ist.

Um nun von der Intensität zum beobachteten Strukturfaktor zu kommen, bedarf es noch einer (theoretisch begründeten) Reduktion, welche im folgenden § 3 auseinandergesetzt wird. Ist dieselbe ausgeführt, dann entstehen im vorliegenden Falle schließlich Zahlen, welche in unserer Bezeichnungsweise proportional den Größen

$$(Li + F)^2, \text{ bzw. } (Li - F)^2$$

sind, jedesmal für den betreffenden Streuwinkel unter dem die Linie auftritt. Den Streuwinkel selbst kann man am einfachsten messen durch die Summe der Indizesquadrate

$$h_1{}^2 + h_2{}^2 + h_3{}^2 = H^2$$

der betreffenden Linie, denn bekanntlich gilt,

$$\sin^2 \frac{\theta}{2} = \frac{\lambda^2}{4a^2} (h_1{}^2 + h_2{}^2 + h_3{}^2),$$

wenn λ die benutzte Wellenlänge und a die Gitterkonstante ist. Tabelle III enthält das Resultat der Messungen.

Durch einen Stern sind die Intensitätszahlen, welche zu Ebenen mit ungerader Indizessumme gehören, hervorgehoben. Dieselben sind also proportional $(Li - F)^2$. Alle anderen Zahlen gehören zu Ebenen mit gerader Indizessumme und sind demnach proportional $(Li + F)^2$. Trägt man die $(Li + F)^2$ proportionalen Zahlen der Tabelle als Funktion von $H^2 =$ $= h_1{}^2 + h_2{}^2 + h_3{}^2$ auf, dann kann man durch dieselbe eine glatte Kurve legen. Das wurde getan. Die drei $(Li - F)^2$ proportionalen Zahlen liegen,

Tabelle III

h_1, h_2, h_3	$H^2 = h_1{}^2 + h_2{}^2 + h_3{}^2$	$(Li + F)^2$, bzw. $(Li - F)^2$
111	3	*107
002	4	239
022	8	112
113	11	*17,6
222	12	63,8
004	16	46,6
133	19	*7,65
024	20	28,8
224	24	17,2

wie schon die Tabelle zeigt, weit unterhalb dieser Kurve. Nun kann man schließlich die letzteren Zahlen vergleichen mit den Ordinaten der Kurve an derselben Stelle und so jedesmal für einen bestimmten Winkel, d.h. also für einen bestimmten Wert von H^2, in unserer Darstellung das Verhältnis

$$\left(\frac{Li + F}{Li - F} \right)^2$$

bilden. Die folgende kleine Tabelle enthält das Resultat; durch Fig. 2 wird der Inhalt der Tabelle veranschaulicht.

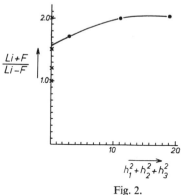

Fig. 2.

Tabelle IV

$H^2 = h_1{}^2 + h_2{}^2 + h_3{}^2$	$\dfrac{F + Li}{F - Li}$
3	1,72
11	2,04
19	2,06

193

Jenes Verhältnis ist, wie man sieht, nicht konstant; uns interessiert der für $H^2 = 0$ und damit für $\theta = 0$ zu erwartende Grenzwert. Um diesen Grenzwert von Willkür möglichst frei zu bestimmen, legen wir durch die drei Punkte eine quadratische Kurve, deren Gleichung man leicht zu

$$\frac{F + Li}{F - Li} = 1{,}523 + 0{,}0728H^2 - 0{,}00234H^4$$

bestimmt. Damit haben wir gefunden, daß als Grenzwert für verschwindenden Streuwinkel der Wert

$$\frac{F + Li}{F - Li} = 1{,}52$$

experimentell zu erwarten steht.

Nach der Theorie hat man folgendes zu erwarten:

a) Atome ungeladen

$$\frac{F + Li}{F - Li} = \frac{9 + 3}{9 - 3} = 2$$

b) Li einfach positiv geladen

$$\frac{F + Li}{F - Li} = \frac{10 + 2}{10 - 2} = 1{,}5 \quad \text{oder}$$

c) Li zweifach positiv geladen

$$\frac{F + Li}{F - Li} = \frac{11 + 1}{11 - 1} = 1{,}2 \quad \text{oder}$$

usw.

Diese Zahlen sind in der Figur durch Sterne auf der Ordinatenachse hervorgehoben. Man sieht, daß das Experiment innerhalb der Genauigkeitsgrenzen für den Fall b) entscheidet. * Somit ist experimentell gezeigt, daß im LiF-Kristall das Li einfach positiv, und das F einfach negativ geladen ist, so wie uns das von der Elektrolyse her geläufig ist.

---

* [Criticized by W. L. Bragg, James and Bosanquet, *Phil. Mag.* **44** (1922) 435: 'In view of the difficulties ... and of the large extrapolation which they had to make in order to get the limiting value of $(F + Li)/(F - Li)$, we feel that their results cannot be regarded as proving that the transference of the valency electron has taken place. The fact of the transference is supported by much indirect evidence and their conclusion is probably correct'. Ed.]

Es sollte der *LiF*-Fall hier nur mehr als Beispiel für das experimentelle Vorgehen besprochen werden.

§ 3. *Größe des Elektronensystems der Atome*

Schon eine oberflächliche Betrachtung der Tabelle III macht auf einen Umstand aufmerksam, der als allgemeines Merkmal allen Interferenzbeobachtungen zukommt. Während H^2 von $4 - 24$ geht, nimmt die $(Li + F)^2$ proportionale Intensität ab von 239 auf 17,2, d.h. sie sinkt auf etwa den 14ten Teil. Nun kennen wir zwar den Temperatureffekt als Ursache für eine in H^2 exponentielle Abnahme der für die Interferenzen verantwortlichen Streuamplitude der Atome. Ein Eingehen auf die Zahlenverhältnisse zeigt aber, daß eine so starke Abnahme, wie sie das Experiment ergibt, auf Grund der thermischen Bewegung nicht zu erwarten ist, auch wenn man berücksichtigt, daß die erforderlichen Daten für *LiF* nur schätzungsweise bekannt sind.

Eine Entscheidung über die Frage, ob außer der Temperaturbewegung noch ein anderer Grund vorhanden ist, der ebenfalls eine Abnahme der Streuamplitude mit zunehmendem Winkel bedingt, wird man am besten erhalten durch Untersuchung einer Substanz, deren Temperaturbewegung möglichst gering ist. Bei Diamant nun sind wir in dieser Lage und können, da die spezifische Wärme in ihrem Verlaufe genau bekannt ist, außerdem noch quantitativ angeben, welchen Betrag jener Einfluß hat.

Das Diamantpulver, mit dem eine Aufnahme nach unserm Verfahren hergestellt wurde, war uns von Professor Keesom in Utrecht zur Verfügung gestellt. Demselben möchten wir auch hier für seine Hilfe danken. Das Pulver war nicht ganz so fein, als es zur Erlangung einer gut photometrierbaren Aufnahme mit nicht gepünktelten Linien nötig ist. Wir konnten aber dieser Schwierigkeit einfach dadurch Herr werden, daß wir das aus dem Pulver bestehende Stäbchen während der Aufnahme von Zeit zu Zeit um einen kleinen Winkel drehten und gelegentlich ein wenig hoben und senkten.

Die fertige Aufnahme wurde dann photometriert, so wie das im § 2 beschrieben ist. Die erhaltenen Resultate stellen somit die wirklichen Intensitäten der Linie dar; dieselben sind in Spalte 3 der Tabelle V eingetragen, Spalten 1 und 2 enthalten die Indizes der Linien und deren Quadratsumme H^2.

Nun gilt es aus den Intensitäten J den Zerstreuungskoeffizienten des C-Atoms zu bestimmen.

Zunächst haben wir zu diesem Zwecke eine mehr äußerliche Korrektur

Tabelle V

Indizes	H^2	Intensität	Θ	J/Θ	R	$C^2 = J/R\Theta$
111	3	406	0,780	521	4,38	119
022	8	158	0,860	184	2,04	46
113	11	94	0,982	96	3,20	30
004	16	55	1,20	46	2,00	23
133	19	171	1,20	142	11,26	13

vorzunehmen. Wegen der Absorption der Strahlung im Stäbchen wird nicht jedes Volumelement desselben von derselben Primärintensität getroffen, außerdem wird die von einem Volumelement ausgehende Streustrahlung auf ihrem Wege innerhalb des Stäbchens zum Teil absorbiert. Im idealen Falle wäre die Absorption verschwindend, die wirklich beobachtete Intensität entsteht aus der idealen durch Multiplikation mit einem Faktor Θ, der noch Funktion der Beobachtungsrichtung ist. Derselbe wird dargestellt durch ein nicht ohne weiteres auswertbares Doppelintegral. Wir haben deshalb Θ als Funktion von θ durch graphische Ausführung der vorgeschriebenen Integration bestimmt; ein Verfahren, das zwar ziemlich mühsam ist, aber gut zum Ziele führt. Die Zahlen, welche bis auf einen gemeinsamen (für alles Folgende) unwesentlichen Zahlenfaktor diesen Koeffizienten Θ für diejenigen Richtungen, in denen die Linien auftraten, darstellen, sind in Tabelle V in Spalte 4 enthalten. Spalte 5 gibt daraufhin die auf Absorption im Stäbchen korrigierte ideale Intensität.

Nunmehr haben wir zu überlegen, wie diese ideale Intensität mit der Streuamplitude C des Atoms verknüpft ist.

1. Aus der v. Laueschen Theorie folgt bekanntlich, daß jene Intensität proportional ist dem Quadrate des absoluten Betrages des *Strukturfaktors S*. Derselbe hat für Diamant unter Zugrundlegung der Braggschen Atomanordnung den Wert:

$$S = C\{1 + \exp\{i\pi(h_1 + h_2)\} + \exp\{i\pi(h_2 + h_3)\} + \exp\{i\pi(h_3 + h_1)\}\}$$

$$(1 + \exp\{i(\pi/2)(h_1 + h_2 + h_3)\}).$$

2. Die Streustrahlung ist nach bekannten Versuchen polarisiert bei unpolarisierter Primärstrahlung. Das bedingt nach üblicher Rechnung, daß ein zweiter Faktor, der *Polarisationsfaktor*, in der Intensität auftritt mit dem Werte

$$(1 + \cos^2 \theta)/2.$$

196

3. Bei unserem Verfahren wird nicht jeder eflektierende Ebene gleich stark berücksichtigt. Vielmehr kommt bei ungeordneter Anordnung der Teilchen des Pulvers jede Fläche proportional der Anzahl verschiedener Stellungen, in denen sie eine Kristallform begrenzen kann, zur Reflexion. Die Hexaederebene 001 z.B. 6mal, die Oktaederebene 111 dagegen 8mal, usw. Dem durch diese Zahlen 6, 8, usw. definierten *Häufigkeitsfaktor Z* ist die zu beobachtende Intensität ebenfall proportional.

4. Schließlich tritt noch ein Faktor hinzu, der ganz analog dem von H. A. Lorentz für die v. Lauesche Anordnung berechneten ist.

Ein Parallelstrahlenbündel von genau passend gewählter Wellenlänge und Einfallsrichtung erzeugt in der Richtung, für die die Reflexionsbedingung[1] streng erfüllt ist, eine Intensität, welche proportional dem Quadrate der bestrahlten Atomzahl ist. In Nachbarrichtungen ist indessen ebenfalls noch Intensität vorhanden, die um so schneller klein wird, je größer die Atomzahl ist. Außerdem aber reflektiert nicht nur der genau passend eingestellte Kristall, sondern auch in Nachbarlagen verdreht, gibt er immer noch merkliche Reflexionsintensität. Was wir beobachten, ist die Summe aller Wirkungen. Die Summation ergibt ein der Atomzahl selbst proportionales Resultat mit einem '*Summationsfaktor*', der von Lorentz für die Lauesche Anordnung zu $1/H^2$ bestimmt wurde, der aber in unserem Falle den Wert

$$1/H^2 \cdot 1/\cos(\theta/2)$$

hat *.

Indem wir noch den von der Wärmebewegung erzeugten Temperaturfaktor unter den Zeichen C im Strukturfaktor aufgenommen denken, kommen wir also zum Resultat, daß die Intensität proportional ist der Größe

$$|S|^2 \frac{1 + \cos^2\theta}{2} Z \frac{1}{H^2 \cos(\theta/2)}.$$

Wir bezeichnen dieselbe mit RC^2; Zahlen für den Reduktionsfaktor R sind in Tabelle V in Spalte 6 eingetragen. Dividieren wir schließlich die ideale Intensität J/Θ durch den Reduktionsfaktor R, dann bekommen wir

---

[1] $\sin\dfrac{\theta}{2} = \dfrac{\lambda}{2a}\sqrt{(h_1{}^2 + h_2{}^2 + h_3{}^2)}.$

* [For several more years the factor $1/\cos(\theta/2)$—which was missing in Debije's original paper on the powder method—did not reappear in the literature. The above powder factor $1/\sin^2(\theta/2) \cdot 1/\cos(\theta/2)$ is made up of the following factors—note that in the present paper θ denotes *twice* the glancing angle—: (1) the monochromatic Lorentz factor $1/\sin(\theta/2) \cdot 1/\cos(\theta/2)$; (2) the extension of the cone of normals of reflecting planes, amounting to $\sin(\pi/2 - \theta/2)$; (3) the reciprocal, $1/\sin\theta$, of the extension of the cone of reflected rays. Ed.]

die in Spalte 7 angegebenen Werte von

$$C^2 = J/R\Theta,$$

welche also proportional der vom Einzelatom zerstreuten Intensität sind.

Man bemerkt, wie diese Zahlen verhältnismäßig rasch mit zunehmendem Winkel abnehmen.

Läßt man die Überlegungen der Einleitung außer acht, dann kann für diese Abnahme nur die Temperaturbewegung des Atoms verantwortlich gemacht werden. Eine kurze Rechnung zeigt indessen sofort, daß dieser Ausweg nicht gangbar ist. Betrachtet man, wie in der ursprünglichen Einsteinschen Theorie der spezifischen Wärme das Atom als an eine Ruhelage quasi-elastisch gebunden, dann ist die Wahrscheinlichkeit dafür, daß eine Verschiebung desselben in ein durch die Koordinaten

$$\xi, \eta, \zeta, \xi + d\xi, \eta + d\eta, \zeta + d\zeta$$

charakterisiertes Raumelement stattgefunden hat, dargestellt durch die Formel

$$(2\pi)^{-3/2} r^{-3} \exp\left(-\frac{\xi^2 + \eta^2 + \zeta^2}{2r^2}\right) d\xi\, d\eta\, d\zeta$$

wobei r ein Maß für die mittlere Verschiebung ist. Mit diesem Ansatz bekommt man für die im Strukturfaktor auftretende Größe C den Wert

$$C = C_0 \exp\left(-\frac{4\pi^2 r^2}{a^2} H^2\right), \tag{7}$$

wenn a die Gitterkonstante bedeutet und C_0 eine nur mehr für das Atom selbst charakteristische Größe ist. Ist weiter m die Masse des Atoms und ν seine Schwingungszahl im Einsteinschen Sinne und nimmt man an, daß keine Nullpunktsenergie existiert, dann wird bei $T = 290°$ absolut

$$4\pi^2 r^2 = \frac{h}{m\nu} \frac{1}{\exp(h\nu/kT) - 1} = 7,55 . 10^{-20}.$$

Bei Anwesenheit einer Nullpunktsenergie wird

$$4\pi^2 r^2 = \frac{h}{m\nu}\left(\frac{1}{\exp(h\nu/kT) - 1} + \frac{1}{2}\right) = 562 . 10^{-20}.$$

Die erste Annahme ergibt somit

$$4\pi^2 r^2/a^2 = 0,60 . 10^{-4},$$

die zweite

$$4\pi^2 r^2/a^2 = 4,5 . 10^{-3},$$

198

da bei Diamant

$$a = 3{,}54 \cdot 10^{-8}\ \text{cm}$$

ist.

Auch die zweite Annahme genügt also bei weitem nicht, den starken beobachteten Abfall von C^2 zu erklären, denn nach (7) erhielten wir:

$$C^2 = C_0{}^2 \exp\{-2(4\pi^2 r^2/a^2)H^2\} = C_0{}^2 \exp(-9{,}0 \cdot 10^{-3}H^2).$$

Für die letzte Linie der Tabelle V wäre also infolge der Temperaturbewegung $C^2 = 102$ zu erwarten, wenn für die erste Linie $C^2 = 119$ ist; statt dessen ist $C^2 = 13$ beobachtet.

Die Temperaturbewegung spielt also hier eine untergeordnete Rolle. Es muß ein anderer inneratomischer Grund für den beobachteten Abfall vorhanden sein.

Als Grund vermuten wir nun die endliche Größe des zum Atom gehörigen Elektronensystems. (...)

Somit hatten wir eine Methode, um die wirkliche Größe des zum Atom gehörigen aus Elektronen bestehenden Planetensystems zu bestimmen.

Göttingen, Physikal. Institut

CHAPTER IV

The Dynamical Theory

Darwin was also the first to treat reflexion on a crystal face as a to and fro reflexion in the interior of the crystal—a point later taken up by the writer from a more general point of view and leading to the 'dynamical theory of X-ray diffraction'.

P. P. EWALD,
Current Sci. 1937, p. 12

53.   THE THEORY OF X-RAY REFLEXION, PART II

by

C. G. Darwin

1. In the First Part of this paper [1] formulae were obtained giving the intensity of reflexion of X-rays by a crystal, and by a discussion of the results of experiment it was concluded that a factor had been neglected which in fact must be of some importance, and that to represent the case at all accurately an improved theory was necessary. It was indicated that the factor to be included is the influence of the vibration of each atom on that of the others. If this is not done, cases will present themselves in which the conservation of energy is apparently violated. The experiment which was discussed is one of these cases. In the present paper this mutual influence is allowed for and a revised formula is found for the reflexion from a crystal. Comparison with experiment shows that the new formula is no better able than the old to account for the observed strength of reflexion. It appears, however, that this may be attributed to the fact that in all crystals there is a considerable amount of distortion, so that there are a great many separate small regions in which reflexion takes place. As a consequence of this fact it will be deduced that, constant factors apart, the old reflexion formulae may be allowed to stand. We shall first of all deal with the reflexion from a perfect crystal.

2. *Reflexion from one Plane*

In the earlier work the procedure was first to calculate the reflexion from a single plane of atoms and then to combine the effects of the different

---

[1] Darwin, *Phil. Mag.* vol. **27** (1914) 315 [this Vol. p. 169].

planes. The amplitude of the reflexion from one plane was represented by a coefficient $-iq$, where q is made up in the following way. A wave of unit amplitude and length $2\pi/k$ falls on an atom. Let $f(\psi, k) \exp(-ikr)/r$ be the amplitude of the wave it scatters, measured at a distance r in a direction inclined at angle ψ to the direction of the incident wave. In addition to ψ and k, f will depend on the direction of polarization of the incident wave. Let N be the number of atoms per c.c. (for the present we shall suppose them all identical) and a the distance between successive planes; then Na is the areal density of atoms in a plane. Let θ be the glancing angle between the direction of incidence and the plane. Then [1]

$$q = \frac{2\pi Naf(2\theta, k)}{k \sin \theta}.$$ (1)

As long as the atoms are supposed not to influence one another's motion, every plane however deep in the crystal scatters the same amount of radiation, and if no allowance were made for the absorption of the transmitted wave the reflexion would become indefinitely large. Now an atom in rocksalt may be supposed to have about 10 electrons, and so f is probably about $10(e^2/mc^2)$.[2] Taking $N = 4.50 \times 10^{22}$, $a = 2.81 \times 10^{-8}$ and reflexion in the first order so that $k \sin \theta = \pi/a$, we find that q is about 2×10^{-4}. According to the assumptions of the earlier paper, the amplitude of the wave is reduced by absorption in passing through one plane by an amount $\frac{1}{2}\mu a$ cosec θ, and for soft X-rays this is 4×10^{-6}. Thus we should expect reflexion to be much more efficient than absorption in extinguishing the transmitted wave. Indeed, we shall find that over a certain small range of angles of incidence the reflexion is practically complete and does not depend on the absorption coefficient.

In the earlier paper the coefficient of reflexion q was calculated by considering a spherical wave coming from a point source. In view of the greater complexity of the present problem it is more convenient to deal with plane waves, and we must therefore first observe that the evaluation of q could have been done equally well with these. It is only necessary fo find the amplitude of reflexion at a point so distant from the crystal, that in the principal part of the field the phases of waves from adjacent atoms are sensibly the same—this permits the summation to be replaced by an integration—while yet the point is not so distant that the crystal has to be regarded as finite—this introduces the Fresnel factors in the integral and

[1] *Loc. cit.* eq. (1).
[2] *Loc. cit.* §§ 11–13.

makes it converge. There can be littele doubt that the procedure gives the right value, though it is not of course mathematically rigorous. It has the great advantage that the formulae do not involve the exact number of atoms in the whole plane, which is obviously quite irrelevant to the final results.

The formula for q cannot be quite general, if f is supposed to depend only on the atom itself. For we might then make Na, the areal density of atoms, so large that the conservation of energy would be violated. In nature this is of course obviated by the fact if the atoms are too closely crowded together, the wave from each will influence the others. We have seen that for rocksalt q is only of the order 10^{-4}, so that the conservation of energy is in no danger, and we shall continue to use q as it stands. The direct calculation of the influence of all the atoms on one of their number leads to a double series of some complexity. I am informed by a friend [1] to whom I referred the matter, that the series does in general converge (which was not at all obivous at first sight), but that the question is quite a difficult problem in pure mathematics. I do not give the form of the series as no use is to be made of it. It will be found that the forces from the other atoms exert an effect like an addition to the radiation term in the vibration of an electron. The radiation term hardly influences the amplitude of vibration of an electron under the influence of X-rays (except in the case of resonance), and so we may conclude that the mutual influence of the atoms in a plane may be neglected.

When a wave falls on a single plane of atoms, besides the directly reflected wave there are others scattered. Thus there will be a wave given off in any direction for which a line of atoms are in phase together, while the next parallel line is a phase 2π behind. These diffracted waves are destroyed by the operation of the other planes of the crystal; but there remains a wave scattered in the same direction as the transmitted beam. The amplitude of this wave is given by $-iq_0$, where q_0 is obtained from q by replacing $f(2\theta, k)$ by $f(0, k)$. As was shown in the earlier work, it is the wave $-iq_0$ which gives rise to the refractive index [2].

[1] Mr. G. H. Hardy, F.R.S., of Trinity College, Cambridge, to whom I must express my thanks for his kind interest in the question.
[2] *Loc. cit.* § 6.

205

DARWIN

3. *Combination of Planes*

The difficulty of the problem of allowing for the mutual influence of the atoms in one plane is the complete absence of phase relations between the waves arriving at one atom from the rest, but this is also the reason why it is justifiable to neglect it. For the combination of all the planes the matter is quite otherwise. Here, when the radiation is at the angle of reflexion, all the waves reflected from the successive planes are in phase together, and they must be supposed to give rise to a secondary reflexion, which contributes a component in the direction of the transmitted wave. It was this secondary reflexion that was neglected in the earlier work, on the assumption that the radiation scattered by one atom had no effect on the others. The recombination into a single wave of the wavelets from the atoms in one plane will not be very complete in the short distance between adjacent planes, but the error in assuming it complete will not be systematic. Moreover, the mutual influence of two planes alone is very small; it is only the cumulative effect that is important. We thus have a problem very smilar to that of the Fabry-Perrot étalon, only with an infinite number of parallel equidistant plates.

We shall suppose that independently of the scattering of the atoms there is also a small absorption. Thus if a plane wave $\exp\{ik(Ct - x\cos\theta + z\sin\theta)\}$ falls on a single plane of atoms, the reflected wave is $-iq\exp\{ik(Ct - x\cos\theta - z\sin\theta)\}$ and the transmitted wave is $(1 - h - iq)\exp\{ik(Ct - x\cos\theta + z\sin\theta)\}$. The term h represents the absorption and may be taken as $\frac{1}{2}\mu a \csc\theta$.

We consider a crystal composed of atoms of a single substance arranged in planes at distance a. Let T_r represent in amplitude and phase the total transmitted wave just above the $(r + 1)$th plane, S_r the total reflected wave in the same position. Then T_0 is the incident wave, and S_0 the reflected wave. S_r is derived from two components, the part of T_r reflected by the $(r + 1)$th plane and the part of S_{r+1} transmitted through it. The latter must be multiplied by a phase factor $\exp(-ika\sin\theta)$ to give its value just below the $(r + 1)$th plane instead of just above the $(r + 2)$th. Thus

$$S_r = -iqT_r + (1 - h - iq_0)\exp(-ika\sin\theta)\,S_{r+1}.$$

Again T_{r+1} is made up of the part of T_r transmitted through the $(r + 1)$th plane and the part of S_{r+1} reflected by it. Putting in the proper phase factors we have

$$T_{r+1}\exp(ika\sin\theta) = (1 - h - iq_0)T_r - iq\exp(-ika\sin\theta)\,S_{r+1}.$$

206

If we eliminate the S's from these difference equations we obtain

$$(1 - h - iq_0) \exp(- ika \sin \theta)(T_{r-1} + T_{r+1}) = \{1 + q^2 \exp(- 2ika \sin \theta)$$
$$+ (1 - h - iq_0)^2 \exp(- 2ika \sin \theta)\}T_r,$$

and the solution is given by $T_r = T_0 x^r$, where x is the root of

$$(1 - h - iq_0) \exp(- ika \sin \theta)(x + 1/x) =$$
$$= 1 + q^2 \exp(- 2ika \sin \theta) + (1 - h - iq_0)^2 \exp(- 2ika \sin \theta). \quad (2)$$

The product of the roots of this equation is unity and that one is to be taken which makes $|x| < 1$. Otherwise the intensity would increase with r. If we substitute back with this solution we find

$$S_r = T_0 \frac{-iqx^r}{1 - x \exp(- ika \sin \theta)(1 - h - iq_0)},$$

and in particular

$$\frac{S_0}{T_0} = \frac{-iq}{1 - x \exp(- ika \sin \theta)(1 - h - iq_0)}. \quad (3)$$

This expression holds for any angle of incidence.

We shall now approximate by allowing for the fact that q, q_0, h are small and by supposing that the incident wave is very nearly at the angle of best reflexion. Then θ is very near ϕ, where $ka \sin \phi = n\pi - q_0$. The presence here of q_0 represents the shift in the angle of best reflexion due to the refractive index, as explained in the former paper. We have then

$$ka \sin \theta = n\pi - q_0 + v,$$

where

$$v = ka \cos \phi(\theta - \phi). \quad (4)$$

To the degree of approximation needful we have

$$\exp(- ika \sin \theta) = (-)^n(1 + iq_0 - iv),$$

so that

$$\frac{S_0}{T_0} = \frac{-iq}{1 - (-)^n x(1 - h - iv)}$$

and x is that root of

$$(-)^n(1 - h - iv)\left(x + \frac{1}{x}\right) = 1 + q^2 + (1 - h - iv)^2,$$

for which $|x| < 1$.

207

The roots of this equation are very nearly $(-1)^n$, so to solve it we put $x = (-)^n(1 - \varepsilon)$.

Substituting in the equation we have

$$(1 - h - iv)(2 + \varepsilon^2) = 1 + q^2 + (1 - h - iv)^2,$$

so that

$$\varepsilon = \sqrt{\{q^2 + (h + iv)^2\}}.$$

The ambiguity is to be determined so that the real part is positive. Thus

$$\frac{S_0}{T_0} = \frac{-iq}{h + iv + \sqrt{\{q^2 + (h + iv)^2\}}}. \tag{5}$$

The earlier paper was written under an assumption which may be seen to be equivalent to taking q much smaller than h, so that $S_0/T_0 = -iq/2(h+iv)$. [1] It is quite possible to evaluate the expressions required with any values of h and q, but the formulae involve elliptic functions, so that their numerical values are not easy to see. Now as we saw q is probably about 2×10^{-4} while h is only 4×10^{-6}, so that not much error is introduced by supposing h/q negligible. It would not, however, have been permissible to have supposed that h vanished at the beginning of the work, because if this were done it would be found that for some angles the reflexion tends to no definite value as the number of planes tends to infinity.

In discussing the ambiguity of $\sqrt{\{q^2 + (h + iv)^2\}}$ when h vanishes it will be convenient to suppose q positive. We do not know whether this is true, but if q is really negative the modification is very simple. When $-q < v < q$ we have simply $\sqrt{(q^2 - v^2)}$, the positive square root being taken. When $v > q$ we must write the expression in the form $\pm i\sqrt{(v^2 - q^2 - 2ivh)}$, and if the radicle is expanded it will be seen that the proper value is $+i\sqrt{(v^2 - q^2)}$. Without the presence of h this could not have been determined. Similarly when $v < -q$ we have to take $-i\sqrt{(v^2 - q^2)}$. Thus the amplitude of reflexion is

$$\left. \begin{array}{ll} -\dfrac{q}{v - \sqrt{(v^2 - q^2)}} & \text{for } v < -q \\[3mm] -\dfrac{q}{v - i\sqrt{(q^2 - v^2)}} & \text{for } -q < v < q \\[3mm] -\dfrac{q}{v + \sqrt{(v^2 - q^2)}} & \text{for } q < v \end{array} \right\}. \tag{6}$$

[1] This is equivalent to one of the equations in § 7 of the earlier paper.

208

To express the intensity of reflexion we take the moduli of the squares of these quantities. In the middle region this is unity and reflexion is perfect. Now $v = ka \cos \phi(\theta - \phi)$, so this is the region

$$\theta = \phi \pm s, \text{ where } s = q/ka \cos \phi.$$

If we take the reflexion in the first order of rocksalt for the platinum radiation β ($\lambda = 1.11 \times 10^{-8}$ cm.) we find $s = 3''$. For the second order it is about half this.

On account of the perfect reflexion the transmitted wave is rapidly extinguished. Since $T_r/T_0 = x^r = (-)^{nr} \exp\{-r\sqrt{(q^2 - v^2)}\}$ it follows that at a depth z in the crystal the intensity is only $\exp\{-(2z/a)\sqrt{(q^2 - v^2)}\}$ of its value at the surface, and so we may speak of an extinction coefficient

$$(2/a)\sqrt{(q^2 - v^2)}. \tag{7}$$

Averaged across the whole region of perfect reflexion this gives a coefficient

$$4q/\pi a \ *. \tag{8}$$

For the value of q which we have been using, this gives about 8000, whereas the absorption coefficient, taken as $\mu \cosec \phi$, is for the platinum rays only 300. Thus the extinction is complete long before the rays going in a slightly different direction are appreciably absorbed. This fact is important in explaining the reflexion from an ordinary imperfect crystal.

4. *Spherical Wave*

We have so far only dealt with plane waves. A spherical wave can be made by compounding together in an integral a set of equal plane waves going in all different directions. If we put in the reflexion factor for each of these plane waves, we obtain an integral representing the diffraction pattern of the reflected beam. At the distances at which experiments are usually made this pattern would be of some complexity. Since it would never be observed in practice on account of the finite area of any actual source and the imperfection of the crystal, it is unnecessary to discuss it. To find the whole intensity of reflexion we may examine the effect at infinity. Here the waves are all plane, so that we can apply the formulae (6) direct. If we take the intensity at a point at glancing angle $\phi + \varepsilon$, we have $v = ka \cos \phi.\varepsilon.$ ** So, making use of the abbreviation $s = q/ka \cos \phi$,

---

* $[\pi q/2a.$ Ed.]

** [Darwin, *Phil. Mag.* **43** (1922) 813: 'I am afraid that ɪn Part II ε was used in two senses on p. 679 and p. 681 resp.'; this Vol. p. 208 and 209. Ed.]

we find as the intensity at a great distance ρ

$$
\left.
\begin{array}{ll}
\dfrac{1}{\rho^2} \cdot \dfrac{s^2}{\{\varepsilon - \sqrt{(\varepsilon^2 - s^2)}\}^2} & \text{when } \varepsilon < -s \\[3ex]
\dfrac{1}{\rho^2} \cdot \qquad 1 & \text{when } -s < \varepsilon < s \\[3ex]
\dfrac{1}{\rho^2} \cdot \dfrac{s^2}{\{\varepsilon + \sqrt{(\varepsilon^2 - s^2)}\}^2} & \text{when } s < \varepsilon
\end{array}
\right\}. \qquad (9)
$$

Suppose that the intensity of the monochromatic incident beam at a distance R is I/R^2, and that the whole effect is observed in an instrument having a slit of length l and sufficient breadth to include the whole beam. Then the instrument will measure

$$
I \frac{l}{\rho} \left\{ \int_{-\infty}^{-s} \frac{s^2 d\varepsilon}{\{\varepsilon - \sqrt{(\varepsilon^2 - s^2)}\}^2} + 2s + \int_{s}^{\infty} \frac{s^2 d\varepsilon}{\{\varepsilon + \sqrt{(\varepsilon^2 - s^2)}\}^2} \right\},
$$

which reduces to

$$
I \frac{l}{\rho} \frac{8}{3} s.
$$

If we put in the value of s this reduces to

$$
I \frac{l}{\rho} \frac{8}{3\pi} \, N \, |f(2\phi, k)| \, \lambda^2 \, \text{cosec } 2\phi. \qquad (10)
$$

Of the two polarized components that for which the electric vibration is in the plane of incidence has in its f a factor $\cos \phi$. Introducing this and also the temperature factor we have

$$
I \frac{l}{\rho} \frac{8}{3\pi} \frac{1 + |\cos 2\phi|}{2} \, N|f| \exp\left\{ -\tfrac{1}{2} \frac{kT}{\sigma a^2} (2n\pi)^2 \right\} \lambda^2 \, \text{cosec } 2\phi. \qquad (11)
$$

(...)

6. Composite Crystal

When the crystal is composite the complete discussion of any special case is rather more complicated. If, for example, the alternate planes are different in character, we obtain a set of four difference equations involving two different types of T's and S's. If three of these are eliminated we obtain a single difference equation for the fourth, the solution of which depends on a quadratic equation rather more complicated than (2). The subsequent procedure follows the same course as in § 3. The general problem, though straightforward, might be rather complicated, but by the following argument is made unnecessary. The influence of a single atom on another is always very minute, and the effect only becomes important by its repeated recurrence. Consequently no error will be introduced by regarding as the unit of scattering, not the atom, but the group of atoms in a single unit of the crystal lattice. Let f_r be the scattering of an atom of type r, of which there are N_r per c.c., and let this atom occur at distance $\alpha_r a$ from the first plane, a being the distance in which the structure of the crystal repeats itself. Then in the reflexion formulae the expression

$$N|f| \exp\left\{ -\tfrac{1}{2} \frac{kT}{\sigma a^2} (2n\pi)^2 \right\}$$

must be replaced by

$$\left| \Sigma_r\, N_r f_r \exp(-i2n\pi a_r) \exp\left\{ -\tfrac{1}{2} \frac{kT}{\sigma_r a^2} (2n\pi)^2 \right\} \right|.$$

7. Comparison with Experiment

We now compare our result with experiment, and to do so shall take the same experiment as was discussed in the former paper. (...)

The calculated value of the efficiency is no better than the old one.

In spite of their failure to account for the amount of reflexion, the formulae developed here are to be preferred to the earlier ones, since they include an effect which has been shown to have been unjustifiably disregarded in the former paper. The new formulae make the reflexion independant of the absorption coefficient of the crystal. Now the work of W. H. Bragg[1] has proved that absorption does play an important part in the reflexion, and this suggests a way out from the discrepancy. If a crystal is not perfect, so that the planes are not everywhere absolutely parallel, it may happen that some part of the beam which has not been extinguished by reflexion at the surface will find a piece of the inside of the crystal at the proper angle, and so will give rise to a second reflexion. Such an effect will obviously involve the absorption coefficient of the rays in the crystal.

[1] W. H. Bragg, *Proc. Roy. Soc.* A vol. **89** (1914) 430.

8. *Imperfect Crystal*

The irregularity of a crystal is of necessity a rather indefinite matter, which it would be perhaps difficult to discuss with rigour. We shall only attempt to see the general type of change to be expected. We will first study the effect of supposing that the surface is irregular, without taking into account the possibility of interior reflexions. Suppose that the surface is divided up into a number of plates whose normals all point in slightly different directions. It is clear that in some cases there might be no reflexion or there might be several. Now the rays reflected from two different plates of the crystal will travel in slightly different directions, and if a photographic plate is put in their path they will strike it at different points. But if the distance of the photographic plate from the crystal is the same as that of the source, they will strike it at the same point; for on account of the constancy of the angle of reflexion, the locus of points which can reflect rays from a given source to a given point is a circle, and only when source and point are equidistant from it does this circle touch the crystal. In this case only is there any considerable area on the crystal which can all reflect to the same point. Moreover, as we shall see later, a very important fraction of the reflected radiation comes from reflexions inside the crystal, and these will be focussed to points only very slightly different from those coming from the surface. The accuracy with which Moseley[1] could determine his X-ray spectra is probably partly due to this focussing, since (though for a different reason) his photographic plate and source were at the same distance from the crystal.

It is quite possible that a given crystal surface should systematically reflect more than its due share of radiation. For example, if it were of a wavy form, each separate wave would reflect a ray. But we can show that on the average there is no improvement in the reflexion when the surface is supposed divided into small plates, the normals of which deviate from their mean direction in a random manner. In such an indefinite question as the present it is useless to proceed with any great rigour, and we shall be content with a rather general argument. In the first place, there is no need to allow for the fact that the normals of the plates deviate from the plane of incidence of the rays. The only effect of this is to shift the ray to a different part of the line of reflected rays. In considering the reflexion from a set of plates, the normals of which all lie in the plane of incidence, it will be sufficient to take it that a ray is reflected to the full extent given

[1] Moseley, *Phil. Mag.* vol. **26** (1913) 1024.

in (11), when a line can be drawn from the source to the plate, making exactly an angle ϕ, the reflexion angle, with its plane. For a plate in any fixed position on the crystal there will be a certain small range of directions of the normal such that a line can be drawn from a given source to make angle ϕ with the plate. This range is limited by the two positions when the line cuts the plate at either of its two edges, and therefore the range of inclinations of the plate which can give a reflexion is proportional to its breadth. The chance of a reflexion is thus not altered by cutting the plate in half, for if this is done either of the halves must be aimed in the proper direction with just twice the accuracy, that is to say each half is just half as likely to give a reflexion. Thus there is on the average the same probable number of reflexions when the crystal is broken into many plates as when it is broken into few, or finally as when it is perfect. We conclude that there is no average improvement or deterioration of reflexion when the surface of the crystal is broken up.

When we come to consider the inside of the crystal the matter is quite different. We saw in § 3 that if the crystal is perfect all the radiation that can be reflected, is so, long before the depth at which rays at a different angle are appreciably absorbed. Now if the crystal is twisted internally these unabsorbed rays may come on a part of it at the right angle, and so give rise to a second reflexion. We must estimate how this will affect the matter. Suppose d to be a depth such that the crystal is twisted through an amount sufficient to allow of a new reflexion. Roughly speaking, then, at every successive d we shall get a reflexion, and the intensities of these reflexions will be 1, $\exp(-2\mu d \operatorname{cosec} \phi)$, $\exp(-4\mu d \operatorname{cosec} \phi)$, etc. The whole reflexion formula should then be multiplied by $1/\{1 - \exp(-2\mu d \operatorname{cosec} \phi)\}$, or $1/\{2\mu d \operatorname{cosec} \phi\}$ if the crystal is so badly twisted that there are a number of reflexions. It appears that as it describes a property of the crystal, d ought to be taken constant. For a not very great distortion this might be justifiable, but we have strong experimental reason to believe that the crystals are even more imperfect than this. For when the reflexion is evaluated with this factor it will be found that the second order of re-flexion is as strong as the first, a result known to be untrue. This must be taken to indicate that crystals are so badly twisted that their planes do not remain parallel even long enough to produce a single perfect reflexion.

Suppose, therefore, that the crystal is composed of pieces each of depth d small compared with the amount necessary to produce a perfect re-flexion. At the depth d the transmitted wave has on the average an intensity $\exp(-4qd/\pi a)$ (see (8)), and the wave reflected by the thickness d has intensity $1 - \exp(-4qd/\pi a)$ or $4qd/\pi a$. Suppose one of the reflecting pieces is at depth z. Then the amount reflected from it is proportional to $(4qd/\pi a)\exp(-2\mu z\,\text{cosec}\,\phi)$. The number of such pieces in a length dz is dz/d, so that the reflexion formula is to be multiplied by a factor

$$\frac{4qd}{\pi a}\int_0^\infty \exp(-2\mu z\,\text{cosec}\,\phi)\,dz/d \quad \text{or by} \quad \frac{2}{\pi a}\,\frac{q\sin\phi}{\mu}.$$

If we multiply (11) by this we see that apart from a numerical factor they lead to the old expressions for the reflexion[1]. That this should be so is not remarkable, since each reflecting piece of the crystal consists only of a few planes, so that the mutual influence of the atoms becomes unimportant. The chief difference is that the whole reflexion now no longer takes place in a band 5″ broad, so that the argument[2] which pointed to the insufficiency of the earlier formulae loses its validity. The displacement of the reflexion due to refraction remains, since the distortion of the crystal does not influence the phase relations of the waves scattered in the direction of the transmitted beam.

For convenience I repeat the reflexion formula.

The effect of monochromatic radiation measured in an instrument at distance ρ from the image of the source with a slit of length l and sufficient breadth is

$$I\frac{l}{\rho}A\,\frac{1+\cos^2 2\phi}{2}\,N^2\,\frac{f^2}{\mu}\exp\left\{-\frac{kT}{\sigma a^2}(2n\pi)^2\right\}\tfrac{1}{2}\lambda^3\,\text{cosec}\,2\phi. \quad (13)$$

The factor A will probably vary from crystal to crystal according to the amount of contortion, but we should not expect it to depart widely from unity, its value in the earlier paper. As we are now free from the argument about the limitation of reflexion to a breadth of 5″, we may use the experimental value of the efficiency to determine f^2. When A was unity it was found to be $26(e^2/mC^2)^2$, and this is of the order to be expected from atoms with about 10 electrons, of which some, but not all, are concentrated close together.

9. Scattering from a Single Atom

Since the first part of this paper was written two experimental results have been published by W. L. Bragg[3], which have an important bearing on

[1] Loc. cit. p. 322 [this Vol. eq. (4) p. 175].
[2] Loc. cit. p. 331 [this Vol. p. 181].
[3] W. L. Bragg, Proc. Roy. Soc. A vol. 89 (1914) 468 [this Vol. p. 75].

our subject. In the first place he has shown that we must suppose that each atom scatters a wave whose amplitude is proportional to its atomic weight. Thus in fluorspar the two fluorine atoms give waves which can destroy by interference the wave coming from one calcium atom. Since all experiments have shown that the atomic weight is proportional to the number of electrons ν in the atom, we conclude that f is closely proportional to ν. This result would hold if we could suppose that the majority of the electrons were crowded together in a region of the order of 10^{-9} cm., and this they certainly will be for the heavier elements. But if this is so there is a certain amount of difficulty with regard to Bragg's second experimental result. From measurements of crystals of a good many substances, he concludes that on the average the relative strengths of reflexion of the several orders for monochromatic radiation are as the numbers $100, 20, 7, 3, 1$. After allowing for the temperature corrections these numbers are fairly well expressed by the formula $1/n^2$; but since the radiation is not appreciably dispersed they are to be compared with (13), and in this formula the reflexion is proportional to $1/n$. Thus, we must attribute a factor $1/n$ to f^2, the coefficient for the scattering of a single atom. Now we saw in the earlier paper [1] that f^2 will certainly decrease with the order of reflexion, and the expression there found seems capable of accounting for the excess scattering from amorphous substances, as in this case experiments have only been concerned with light atoms where there is no great concentration of electrons; but when we are dealing with heavier atoms we have seen that Bragg's first result points to a considerable crowding of electrons in a small space, and in this case it would hardly be expected that the excess effect should be so great as to give a factor $1/n$. Involving as it does a knowledge of the arrangement of the electrons in the atom, it does not seem possible at present to make any better progress in discussing this question.

My thanks are due to Prof. Sir Ernest Rutherford for the kind interest he has taken in this research.

---

[1] *Loc. cit.* p. 329 [this Vol. p. 179].

EWALD'S DYNAMICAL THEORY

Ewalds dynamische Theorie der Röntgenstrahlinterferenzen gehört nach unserer Ansicht auf alle Zeiten zu dem Meisterwerken der mathematischen Physik.

M. v. LAUE
Ergebn. d. Exact Naturwiss. äü (1931) 133

54. Zur Begründung der Kristalloptik. Teil III: Die Kristalloptik der Röntgenstrahlen, by P. P. EWALD (1917)

—

55. Die dynamische Theorie der Interferenzen, by P. P. EWALD (1927)

—

56. Die Intensitäten der Röntgenreflexe und der Strukturfaktor, by P. P. EWALD (1925)

—

57. Über den Aufbau der Kristalle, by H. MARK (1925)

—

54[1]. Die theoretische Erklärung, die Laue zu den von ihm und seinen Mitarbeitern erhaltenen Interferenzerscheinungen der Röntgenstrahlen gab, ist ihrem Wesen nach rein *kinematisch*. Es werden Kugelwellen summiert, die mit bekannten Amplituden und Phasen von den Gitterpunkten eines Kristallstückes ausgehen. Die Rechnung zeigt, daß das entstehende Feld in gewissen Richtungen außerordentlich starke Intensitätsmaxima aufweist, die in der Mitte von engen, durch die endliche Ausdehnung des Kristallbrockens bedingten Beugungsstreifen liegen. Geht man in der Vereinfachung einen Schritt weiter und fragt nur nach den Richtungen der Interferenzmaxima, so genügt die einfachste *geometrische* Betrachtung des Gangunterschiedes der Kugelwellen, wie sie beim optischen Beugungsgitter im Elementarunterricht angewendet wird. Rein geometrisch ist auch die Braggsche Reflexionsbedingung, die die Richtungen der Reflexionsmaxima aus den durchlaufenen Strecken ableitet.

---

[1] Als Habilitationsschrift der hohen philosophischen Fakultät II. Sektion der Kgl. Bayer. Ludwig-Maximilians-Universität zu München eingereicht. Vgl. Teil I: Theorie der Dispersion, *Ann. d. Phys.* **49** (1916) 1–38; Teil II: Theorie der Reflexion und Brechung, *Ann. d. Phys.* **49** (1916) 117–143. (Als I und II zitiert.)

Wenn auch für sehr viele Zwecke die Lauesche, ja sogar die noch einfachere geometrische Erklärung der Erscheinung genügt, so sind diesen Theorien ihrer Natur nach überall dort Grenzen gezogen, wo es sich um Intensitätsfragen handelt. Beide Überlegungen besagen übereinstimmend, daß beim Maximum der Interferenz im Idealfall ebener Wellen und ungestörten Kristallgefüges *alle* Atome des Kristalls in voller Phasenharmonie zusammenwirken. Alle Strahlen haben daher gleiche maximale Amplitude—abgesehen von Faktoren, die wegen der Polarisation der Schwingungen zuzufügen sind.

Bei der Laueschen Theorie macht sich dann hinterher das herabgesetzte Auflösungsvermögen des endlichen Gitterstückes in den verschiedenen Interferenzen verschieden stark bemerkbar; hierdurch entsteht, wenn Kugelwelle und Spektralbereich an Stelle von ebener und monochromatischer Welle eingeführt werden, eine unterschiedliche Stärke der Interferenzstrahlen (Lorentzscher Faktor).

Die praktisch wichtige Verbesserung der Laueschen Theorie durch Einführung von Kugelwelle und Spektralbereich steht ebensosehr auf rein kinematischem Boden, wie die theoretisch wesentliche Ergänzung der Intensitätserklärung durch die Hinzuziehung der Störung des Kristallaufbaues infolge der Wärmebewegung (Debye). Die Intensitätsformeln, die durch die genannten Erweiterungen entstehen, scheinen zurzeit dem praktischen Bedürfnis zu genügen.

Und doch ist für das theoretische Verständnis der Vorgang, wie die Röntgeninterferenzen entstehen, mit der kinematischen Theorie keineswegs erledigt. Solange man infolge der Schwäche der Interferenzstrahlen glauben durfte, daß nur ein ganz geringer Bruchteil der Energie des Primärstrahles in die Interferenzstrahlen abgespalten würde, konnte man sich vielleicht dabei beruhigen, daß im ganzen Kristall die Atome (Dipole) gleichartig schwingen, so, als wenn jeder einzelne isoliert von der einfallenden Welle angeregt würde. Es wurde aber erkannt, daß die überlegene Stärke des Primärstrahles durch die Zusammenfassung aller Wellenlängen erzeugt wird, ja, daß, auf gleichen Wellenlängenbezirk bezogen, die Intensität der Sekundärstrahlen so groß sein kann, daß vom Primärstrahl nichts übrig bleibt (Braggs selektive Absorption). Unter diesen Umständen ist es unmöglich daran festzuhalten, daß die Dipolschwingungen als bekannt angesehen werden; die Rückwirkung des entstehenden Feldes auf die Schwingungen muß berücksichtigt werden, ihre Wechselwirkung aufeinander. Nur eine *dynamische* Theorie der Ausbreitung der Röntgenstrahlen, die von denselben Gesichtspunkten ausgeht wie die optische Dispersionstheorie, kann die befriedigende Erklärung der Interferenzintensitäten geben.

217

In der optischen Dispersionstheorie hat man bis vor kurzem[1] sich darauf beschränkt, die Ausbreitung einer Lichtwelle *im Innern* eines Mediums zu erforschen, ohne die Zustände am Rande des Mediums, die Abspaltung des reflektierten und gebrochenen Strahles, auf Grund der Elektronentheorie zu berücksichtigen. Für die Fortpflanzung der Röntgenstrahlen sind die Verhältnisse tief im Innern naturgemäß ebenfalls einfacher als am Rande. Dementsprechend wird die erste Aufgabe sein, das Analogon zur optischen Dispersionstheorie im unbegrenzten Medium aufzustellen, indem untersucht wird, welches die Bedingungen dafür sind, daß ein Röntgenstrahl sich im allseits unendlichen Kristall so fortbewegt, daß sein Feld gerade durch die von ihm selbst unterhaltenen Dipolschwingungen entsteht. Hierdurch allein erhält man aber noch keine befriedigenden Ergebnisse. Denn während in der Optik eine Materialkonstante, der Brechungsindex, Zweck dieser Untersuchung ist, spielt sie für Röntgenstrahlen als Größe, die nur um geringste Beträge von der Einheit abweichen kann (soviel steht experimentell fest), eine sehr untergeordnete Rolle. Ihre Bedeutung liegt hier in dem engen Zusammenhang, der zwischen Brechungsindex und Feldamplitude besteht und der es nötig macht, die Phasengeschwindigkeiten der verschiedenen Interferenzstrahlen zu berücksichtigen, um ihre Amplitudenverhältnisse zu gewinnen. Diese, nicht die Phasengeschwindigkeiten, sind das Ziel der Theorie.

Um zu experimentell aussichtsreichen Ergebnissen zu kommen, darf man nicht bei der Betrachtung des Kristallinnern stehen bleiben, sondern muß die Strahlen in der Tiefe des Kristalls zu den von außen einfallenden und den nach außen austretenden Strahlen in Beziehung setzen. Die Betrachtung muß zu diesem Zwecke an einen *begrenzten* Kristall anknüpfen, bei dem der Übergang zwischen Innen- und Außenraum durch eine *Randzone* vermittelt wird. Entsteht zum Schluß überhaupt der Zustand, der für das Kristallinnere gefunden worden war? Man sieht, daß die Beantwortung dieser Frage durchaus notwendig ist, um überhaupt den Anschluß zwischen Außenraum und Kristallinnerm, zwischen selbstgenügsamer Theorie und experimentell verwertbarer zu gewinnen. Ohne Lösung der Randaufgabe, d.h. ohne Aufstellung der Fresnelschen Formeln, sei es im Sinne Maxwells oder der Elektronentheorie, wäre auch die optische Dispersionstheorie ein Fragment und die Intensitäten von gebrochenem und reflektiertem Strahl blieben unerklärt. Das gleiche gilt in erhöhtem Maße für die Theorie der Röntgenstrahlen, weil hier jede Erfahrung über etwaige Randbedingungen im Sinne der Theorie kontinuierlicher Medien fehlt und naturgemäß fehlen muß.

Die vorliegende Theorie nimmt als Bild des Kristalls ein einfachstes

[1] Vgl. jedoch II., sowie C. W. Oseen, *Ann. d. Phys.* **48** (1915) 1.

ideal regelmäßiges rechtwinkliges Gitter von schwingungsfähigen, elastisch gebundenen Ladungen, die in ihrer Wirkung Dipolen gleichkommen.

Der Gesichtspunkt, daß die Wechselwirkung der Strahlen berücksichtigt werden muß, um ihre Intensität zu erklären, ist schon von C. G. Darwin[1] angewandt worden. In seiner Untersuchung über die Braggsche Spektrometeranordnung behandelt er die Reflexion ebener monochromatischer Wellen an der Kristalloberfläche, also einen Sonderfall unseres Problems. Dabei wird von ihm für die Amplitude, die der Primärstrahl nach Durchgang durch die r ersten Netzebenen aufweist, gefunden $T_r = T_0 . x^r$, wobei x die Wurzel einer Gleichung ist, die in unserem Sinne als die quadratische Dispersionsgleichung zu deuten wäre. Statt wie Darwin angenähert $x = -1 + \sqrt{(q^2 - v^2)}$ zu setzen, worin q der 'Reflexionskoeffizient' der Netzebenen, v nach unserer Bezeichnungsweise etwa der Anregungsfehler ist, —beides kleine Größen—lasse man stehen $x = \exp\{-i\sqrt{(v^2 + q^2)} + i\pi\}$; so tritt in dieser Formel die Ähnlichkeit mit unseren Resultaten hervor: der Faktor $\exp(i\pi r)$ in der Amplitude T_r ist der Phasenfaktor der Welle, die sich nach der alten Laueschen oder Braggschen Theorie unter dem Reflexionswinkel ausbreitet, d.h. so, daß zwischen den Strahlen, die an aufeinanderfolgenden Ebenen reflektiert worden sind, der Phasenunterschied 2π liegt. Die Phase der Welle, die sich wirklich im Kristall ausbreitet, angeregt mit dem Fehler v, weist gegen diese Welle die Phasenkorrektur $\exp\{-ir\sqrt{(v^2 - q^2)}\}$ auf. Der Doppelsinn der Wurzel, den Darwin ohne Grund verwirft und einschränkt, gibt zwei Lösungen, die im Falle reeller Wurzel größere bzw. kleinere Phasengeschwindigkeit haben als die Vergleichswelle, während bei imaginärer Wurzel die Amplitude nach dem Inneren hin exponentiell zu- bzw. abnimmt. Dies sind genau die Ausbreitungsweisen, aus denen wir die exakte Lösung zusammensetzen werden. Aus der Realitätsbetrachtung der Wurzel erhält Darwin für die Intensität des reflektierten Strahles drei Gebiete, nämlich einen Streifen vollständiger Reflexion für $|v| < q$ und beiderseits ein Gebiet ungenauerer Erfüllung der Reflexionsbedingung mit schnell abnehmendem Reflexionsvermögen. Das Mittelgebiet vollständiger Reflexion deckt sich mit unseren Ergebnissen; nur in ihm gibt es für dicke Kristallplatten eine von der Dicke des Kristallstückes unabhängige Amplitude des reflektierten Strahles, in ihm wird bei weitem der Hauptteil der Energie reflektiert, die überhaupt in den Sekundärstrahl gelangt. In dem Außengebiete der Reflexion bleibt die Stärke des reflektierten Strahles von der Kristalldicke abhängig, wenn man die Randbedingung am unteren Rande einer Kristallplatte berücksichtigt. Dies muß aber geschehen, weil bei den experimentellen

[1] C. G. Darwin, *Phil. Mag.* **27** (1914) 315 u. 675 [this Vol. pp. 169 and 203.]

Ausmaßen die Felder an der Rückseite einer Kristallplatte trotz der Massenabsorption erheblich bleiben, und deshalb ist die Art, wie Darwin durch Grenzübergang zu verschwindender Absorption sich für die Außengebiete bestimmte Intensitäten des reflektierten Strahles verschafft, nicht einwandfrei. Im Hinblick auf die Ausgestaltung der Theorie für mehrere Interferenzstrahlen scheint mir der von Darwin verkannte Charakter seiner Gleichung für x gerade das Wichtigste zu sein, das auch Darwin bei konsequenter Berücksichtigung der Randbedingungen auf die unten als Pendellösung bezeichnete Ausbreitungsform des Feldes geführt hätte.

Die Lauesche Theorie als Grundglied einer Entwicklung

Die bisherige experimentelle Erfahrung hat gelehrt, daß die Geschwindigkeit der Röntgenstrahlen durch die Dispersionselektronen (Dipole) der Körper nur in sehr geringfügigem Maße beeinflußt werden kann. Daher darf in der Laueschen Theorie, die als erste Näherung einer Dispersionstheorie aufgefaßt werden soll, die Geschwindigkeit der Wellen gleich c (3.10^{10} cm/sec) gesetzt werden; umgekehrt sind die geometrischen Folgerungen aus Laues Formeln ein Zeichen, wie genau die vorausgesetzte Beziehung zutrifft. Setzt man die Frequenz der Röntgenwellen in die optische Dispersionsformel ein, die unter der Annahme abgeleitet wird, daß die Eigenfrequenzen der Elektronen nahe dem optischen Gebiete liegen, so erhält man für den Brechungsindex einer einzelnen Röntgenwelle einen Wert, der um ca. 10^{-4} kleiner ist als 1, und diese Abweichung wird wohl allgemein die Größenordnung geben, um die auch im Falle der Ausbreitung mehrerer Interferenzstrahlen im Kristall der Brechungsindex, d.h. das Verhältnis von Lichtgeschwindigkeit c zu Phasengeschwindigkeit q, sich von 1 unterscheidet. In der optischen Dispersionstheorie wird gezeigt, daß die Veränderung der Phasengeschwindigkeit auf die Wechselwirkung der Elektronen zurückzuführen ist. Aus der Kleinheit der Änderung im Falle der Röntgenstrahlen kann somit auf die Kleinheit der Wechselwirkung geschlossen werden, und wenn in der aufzustellenden Theorie die Quadrate der Abweichungen vernachlässigt werden, so ist das mathematisch zu verstehen als Entwicklung des Problems nach den Größen, die die Wechselwirkung messen, und Beschränkung auf die Wechselwirkung niedrigster Ordnung.

In diesem Sinne ist die Lauesche Theorie das Grundglied der Entwicklung, da in ihr die Wechselwirkung Null ist. Der Lauesche Gedankengang sei kurz zusammengefaßt, indem hierbei gleich einige abkürzende Bezeichnungen eingeführt werden mögen. Ist ω die Frequenz, so ist eine ebene Welle gegeben durch die periodische Funktion

$$\exp\{-i\omega t + i(\alpha x + \beta y + \gamma z)\}.$$

Diese Welle schreitet mit der Geschwindigkeit

$$q = \omega / \sqrt{(\alpha^2 + \beta^2 + \gamma^2)}$$

fort. Fassen wir $(\alpha\,\beta\,\gamma)$ als Komponenten eines Vektors $\mathfrak{k}$ auf, des *Ausbreitungsvektors*, so ist q bestimmt durch die Länge des Vektors; die Richtung der Wellennormalen durch seine Richtung; und die periodische Funktion wird kürzer unter Einführung des Vektors $\mathfrak{r} = (x, y, z)$ geschrieben

$$\exp\{-i\omega t + i(\mathfrak{k}r)\}.$$

Die Länge $|\mathfrak{k}| = k$ soll die *Ausbreitungskonstante* heißen. Zwei Wellen mit gleichem Vektor $\mathfrak{k}$ heißen *gleichlaufend*.

Die Lauesche Theorie geht davon aus, daß Richtung und Geschwindigkeit des einfallenden Strahles, also sein Ausbreitungsvektor $\mathfrak{k}_0$, bekannt ist. Es wird behauptet, daß im Kristall eine Dipolwelle entsteht, gleichlaufend mit der einfallenden Welle. Hierin liegt die erste Vernachlässigung der Wechselwirkung, da in Wahrheit andere Dipolschwingungen entstehen. Nun werden die Kugelwellen, die von den schwingenden Dipolen ausgehen, für unendliche Entfernung vom Kristall summiert und festgestellt, in welchen Richtungen maximale Amplitude auftritt. Bei dieser Feststellung wird zum zweiten Male von den Wechselwirkungen abgesehen, indem vorausgesetzt wird, daß auch die abgespaltenen Interferenzstrahlen im Kristallinnern die Phasengeschwindigkeit c haben.

Endlichkeit des Kristalls bei Laue

Es hängt mit dieser Vernachlässigung, wie wir sehen werden, aufs engste zusammen, daß Laue gezwungen ist, die Betrachtungen an einem Kristallstück von endlicher Ausdehnung vorzunehmen. Dieser Umstand bedeutet keine Vereinfachung der Theorie, da von der Größe des Kristalls abhängende Beugungserscheinungen die wesentlichen Teile der Formeln nicht in der einfachsten Gestalt hervortreten lassen. Jede Richtung maximaler abgebeugter Intensität ist nämlich, wie in der Theorie des (endlichen) optischen Beugungsgitters, von einem Kegel von Richtungen begleitet, in dem die Intensität aufs heftigste schwankt,—Schwankungen, die durch die Größe und Form des Kristallbrockens bedingt sind und im ganzen genommen eine Verwaschenheit der Interferenzrichtung und damit ein endliches Auflösungsvermögen des endlichen Gitters ergeben.

Diese Komplikation ließe sich vermeiden, wenn der Laueschen Theorie

221

ein unendlich ausgedehntes Gitter zugrunde gelegt würde. Dann fallen die Beugungserscheinungen neben den Maximis fort und das Auflösungsvermögen ist unendlich groß in dem Sinne, daß wenn die Bedingungen für maximales Zusammenwirken aller Dipole streng erfüllt sind, die Amplitude unendlich ist; sind sie nur um ein Kleines verfehlt, so ist die Amplitude endlich und daher verschwindend gegenüber dem Maximum. Bei der starr gegebenen Ausbreitungsweise der Dipolwelle läßt sich im unendlichen nach Lauescher Art behandelten Kristall die rein kinematische Folgerung nicht vermeiden, daß zum Entstehen eines Interfererenzstrahls die Ausbreitungsbedingungen mathematisch scharf erfüllt sein müssen.

Unbegrenztheit des Kristalls in der dynamischen Theorie

Anders ist es in der dynamischen Theorie, in der die Bewegung der Dipole durch das selbsterzeugte Feld bestimmt wird. Der Kristall besitzt hier eine gewisse Schmiegsamkeit und Anpassungsfähigkeit für den Fall, daß die Anregung zur Abspaltung von Interferenzstrahlen nicht die beste ist. Daher liefert auch geringere Güte der Anregung noch erhebliche Interferenzstrahlen und das dynamische Auflösungsvermögen ist im Gegensatz zum kinematischen auch im unendlichen Kristallgitter endlich.

Ja, der dynamisch regulierte Kristall übt sogar einen gewissen 'Selbstschutz' gegen zu großes Ansteigen der Intensität aus, indem er die Phasengeschwindigkeit der Dipolwelle vom Wert c abweichen läßt. Sobald die Geschwindigkeit $q \neq c$ ist, sind nämlich auch im unendlichen Kristall die entstehenden Amplituden endlich; die obige extreme Folgerung der Laueschen Theorie hängt an der Annahme $q = c$.

In dem *engen Zusammenhang zwischen Phasengeschwindigkeit und Amplitude* liegt der Kern der dynamischen Theorie und deshalb soll gleich hier die folgende, leicht zu erweiternde Überlegung zum Verständnis dieses Punktes beitragen.

Der Kristall sei durchzogen von einer Dipolwelle vom Ausbreitungsvektor $\mathfrak{k}$. Ihre Phasengeschwindigkeit sei q.

Wir suchen den Teil des Feldes im Punkte P (Fig. 1), der gleichlaufend

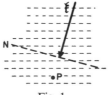

Fig. 1.

hiermit ist. Fassen wir eine Netzebene $N \perp \mathfrak{k}$ ins Auge. In ihr schwingen die Elektronen in gleicher Phase. Die von ihr ausgehenden Kugelwellen haben sich in einiger Entfernung zu einer Wellenfront geglättet, die parallel $\mathfrak{k}$, aber mit der von q verschiedenen Geschwindigkeit c fortschreitet; ihr Ausbreitungsvektor sei $\mathfrak{k}_0$. Das Feld in P ist die Summe der Wirkungen aller von P aus entgegen der Richtung $\mathfrak{k}$ liegenden Netzebenen; es wird unendlich, wenn alle Wirkungen in gleicher Phase eintreffen, was $k = k_0$ voraussetzt (Maximum der Resonanz des entstehenden Feldes auf die Dipolwelle). Je mehr k von k_0 abweicht, um so geringer ist die Zahl der Netzebenen, deren Wirkungen merklich in gleicher Phase in P ankommen, desto vollständiger die gegenseitige Vernichtung. Wird $k = k_0(1 + \varepsilon)$ gesetzt, so ist der Rechnung gemäß die Amplitude des Feldes proportional $1/\varepsilon$. ε, die Abweichung des Brechungsindex vom Wert 1, heißt der *Resonanzfehler*. Die Lauesche Theorie beschäftigt sich mit dem Fall $\varepsilon = 0$ und muß deshalb den Kristall endlich groß nehmen, um unendliche Amplituden zu vermeiden.

55. Verdeutlichen wir uns das aus einem Primärstrahl von bekannter Frequenz ω und Richtung $\mathfrak{s}_1$, aber unbekannter, etwas von c abweichender Geschwindigkeit q_1 durch Summation der Kugelwellen[1] entstehende Interferenzfeld im reziproken Gitter, so besteht es (Abb. 76) aus einer Reihe von starken Interferenzwellen, deren Richtungen $\mathfrak{s}_1$ und Geschwindigkeiten

$$q_i = \omega \lambda_i / 2\pi \quad (\omega \text{ die Kreisfrequenz})$$

durch die Pfeile vom Ausbreitungspunkt A zu den der Ausbreitungskugel *nah* benachbarten Gitterpunkten des reziproken Gitters dargestellt werden. Die Pfeillänge beträgt dabei $1/\lambda_i$, und weicht ab von dem Radius $1/\lambda_0$ der Ausbreitungskugel (λ_0 die zur Frequenz ω gehörende Vakuumswellenlänge). Die Ausbreitungskugel geht nicht mehr durch den Null-

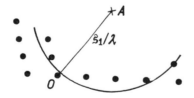

Abb. 76. Konstruktion der Interferenzfelder im Kristall.

[1] Diese Summation wurde zum erstenmal ausgeführt von P. P. Ewald, Münchner Dissert. 1912 (Göttingen 1913), und zwar gültig für beliebige Wellenlängen, so daß der Fall der Röntgenstrahlen, der Fall des sichtbaren Lichtes und—in der Grenze—der Fall elektrostatischer Potentiale eingeschlossen ist ($\lambda = \infty$) (vgl. *Ann. d. Phys.* **64** (1921) 253).

punkt, da auch die Geschwindigkeit des Primärstrahles offengelassen wurde. Der Wert ε ist also der nach außen positiv gezählte Abstand eines Gitterpunktes von der Ausbreitungskugel, gemessen mit deren Radius als Einheit. Die Nähe eines Gitterpunktes an der Ausbreitungskugel gibt direkt ein Maß für die Amplitude des zugehörigen Interferenzstrahls. Rückt des Punkt auf die Kugel, so wird die Amplitude unendlich groß, tritt er durch die Kugel hindurch, so ändert die Amplitude das Vorzeichen (Phasensprung um 180°). Diese für Resonanzvorgänge charakteristischen Erscheinungen führten auf die Bezeichnung 'Resonanzfehler' für ε.

Aus der Abb. 76 ist abzulesen, daß auch jetzt noch der *Reziprozitätssatz* gilt, der kurz so ausgesprochen werden kann: Sowohl für die Lage wie Intensität der Interferenzstrahlen eines Bündels ist es ganz gleichgültig, welcher von ihnen als 'Primärstrahl' bezeichnet wird, d.h. durch welchen der Strahlen man sich die Sekundärwellen der Atome angeregt denkt.

Wir betrachten nun als Grundlage für den Aufbau der dynamischen Theorie die zur einfachen Laueschen Theorie gehörige Konstruktion der Interferenzstrahlen mit Hilfe der in Abb. 76 geschilderten Ausbreitungskugel. Diese gibt an, welche und wieviele Punkte des reziproken Gitters überhaupt in genügender Nähe der Ausbreitungskugel gelegen sind, um —auch unter Berücksichtigung der Wechselwirkung—starke Interferenzen zu erzeugen. Dies seien *n* Punkte. Die Abgrenzung, bis zu welchen Abstand von der Laueschen Ausbreitungskugel solche Punkte zu berücksichtigen sind, ist nicht ängstlich zu nehmen, denn es ergibt sich, daß die weiter entfernten Punkte von geringerem Einfluß auf das Ergebnis sind.

Um nun die Ausbreitung des Feldes im Innern zu schildern, denken wir uns die Richtung $\mathfrak{s}_1$ des einen 'Primär'strahls gegeben; dann kann die Auswahl des dynamisch möglichen röntgenoptischen Feldes nur in der Festlegung des Ausbreitungspunktes *A* in der Richtung $\mathfrak{s}_1$ bestehen. Man erhält sie durch Betrachtung des Kräftespiels bei den Atomschwingungen (die man als 'Dipolschwingungen' auffaßt), genau wie in der optischen Dispersionstheorie. Doch soll hier nur das Ergebnis geschildert werden: Es zeigt sich nämlich, daß die Festlegung des Ausbreitungspunktes *A* nicht eindeutig, sondern 2*n*-deutig ist (*n* die Anzahl der Interferenzstrahlen), so daß auf $\mathfrak{s}_1$, 2*n* dynamisch mögliche Ausbreitungspunkte entstehen. Es werde nun die Richtung $\mathfrak{s}_1$ etwas abgeändert, aber nicht so stark, daß dadurch die Anzahl *n* der Interferenzstrahlen modifiziert wird. Dann schließen sich die zu jeder Richtung gehörenden 2*n* Ausbreitungspunkte zu einer 2*n*-schaligen Fläche, der '*Dispersionfläche*', zusammen. Diese Fläche ist der geometrische Ort für die dynamisch möglichen Ausbreitungspunkte, sofern überhaupt die betrachteten *n* Interferenzstrahlen in merklicher Stärke entstehen.

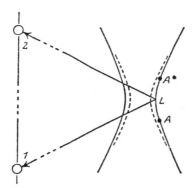

Abb. 77. Vollständige Dispersionsfläche für 2 Strahlen.

Es sei die Dispersionsfläche für den einfachsten Fall zweier Strahlen: Primärstrahl und ein Sekundärstrahl (reflektierter Strahl) wirklich aufgezeichnet, allerdings maßstäblich gegenüber dem reziproken Gitter ungeheuer (etwa 10^5 mal) vergrößert (Abb. 77). Die Fläche muß aus vier Schalen bestehen; es sind hier zwei auf der Einfalls- (Zeichen-) Ebene senkrecht stehende Hyperbelzylinder, welche als Asymptotenebenen die Normalebenen zu den beiden Strahlrichtungen haben. Der Punkt L der Abbildung ('Lauepunkt') bedeutet denjenigen Punkt der Einfallsebene, der von beiden Gitterpunkten des reziproken Gitters den Abstand $1/\lambda_0$ hat; die Pfeile $L1$ und $L2$ geben die Richtungen der beiden Strahlen gemäß der Laueschen Theorie. L liegt bei einfachen Gittern auf der einen Hyperbelschale; bei Gittern mit Basis haben die Schalen—bei gleichem Mittelpunkt—engeren oder weiteren Abstand. Nach der dynamischen Theorie sind Strahlen von etwas abweichenden Richtungen und Wellenlängen (bzw. Geschwindigkeiten q) ebenfalls möglich, z.B. wenn A als Ausbreitungspunkt genommen wird, ein Primärstrahl von geringerer Neigung und Überlichtgeschwindigkeit als Phasengeschwindigkeit und ein Sekundärstrahl, der stärker geneigt ist und $q < c$ hat (umgekehrt für $A*$). Der punktierte Hyperbelzylinder bezieht sich auf Strahlen, deren elektrischer Vektor in der Strahlenebene liegt, der ausgezogene auf Strahlen mit $\mathfrak{E} \perp (\mathfrak{s}_1, \mathfrak{s}_2)$. Daß die Dispersionsfläche hier und in den folgenden Zeichnungen zwischen dem Lauepunkt und den Gitterpunkten 1, 2 hindurchgeht, bedeutet negatives ε, d.h. Brechungsindex $\mu < 1$, wie es dem 'Normalfall' für Röntgenstrahlen entspricht (s. unten). Bei 'anomaler Dispersion' (Röntgenfrequenz höher als die 'Eigenfrequenzen' der beugenden Atome) wäre die Lage umgekehrt.

Die Dispersionsfläche ist der Schlüssel für die Behandlung der Röntgenoptik, so wie das Fresnelsche Ellipsoid der Schlüssel zur Kristalloptik ist. Es ist daher gut, sich die Entstehung dieser Fläche noch weiter

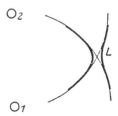

Abb. 78. Entstehung der Dispersionsfläche.

plausibel zu machen. Wäre Strahl 1 allein vorhanden, so würde er nach den Grundsätzen der Dispersionstheorie eine gewisse, von c nur um etwa 10^{-6} abweichende Geschwindigkeit haben. Man kann, solange keine Interferenzstrahlen entstehen, genau wie in der Lichtoptik, von einem Brechungsindex als einer Materialkonstante sprechen und zu seiner Berechnung die übliche Dispersionsformel heranziehen. Wollte man sich die Ausbreitung dieses einen Strahls im Bilde klarmachen, so müßte man als 'Dispersionsfläche' um den Punkt 1 als Ausgangspunkt (Abb. 78) eine Kugel vom Radius $1/\lambda = \mu/\lambda_0$ schlagen, da die Konstante μ (wenigstens mit der gebrauchten Genauigkeit der theoretischen Betrachtung) von der Richtung des Strahls nicht abhängt. Für die Mehrzahl der Elektronen des Stoffes liegt normalerweise die Röntgenfrequenz höher als ihre Eigenfrequenzen. Daher befindet man sich, optisch gesprochen, im Gebiet jenseits der Eigenschwingungen, mit $\mu < 1$. Nur die am festesten gebundenen K-Elektronen haben evtl. Eigenfrequenzen ihrer Bindung, die die Röntgenfrequenz noch übertreffen, so daß ein positiver Beitrag zu $\mu^2 - 1 = = 2\pi N(e^2/m)(\omega^2_0 - \omega^2)^{-1}$ entsteht, der unter Umständen groß werden kann. Wir setzen in den Zeichnungen den 'normalen' Fall $\mu < 1$, $\lambda > \lambda_0$ voraus und bezeichnen die Summe über alle Resonatoren der Basis $\varepsilon_0 = (2\pi/v) \sum (e^2/m)(\omega_0^2 - \omega^2)^{-1}$ als den 'normalen Resonanzfehler'. Mit diesem wäre die Dispersionskugel um Punkt 1 zu zeichnen. Eine zweite Dispersionskugel vom gleichen Radius $1/\lambda$, um den Punkt 2 geschlagen, würde alle Ausbreitungspunkte enthalten, die einen im Punkt 2 endigenden Strahlpfeil liefern können, solange nur dieser eine Strahl im Kristallinnern vorhanden ist. An der Durchsetzungslinie beider Kugeln wären aber beide Strahlen zugleich stark und die Wechselwirkung bedingt, daß der Ausbreitungspunkt von den Kugeln heruntertritt, d.h. die Dispersionsfläche spaltet sich auf (Abb. 78 für die eine Polarisationsrichtung) Auch in komplizierteren Fällen (z.B. gleichzeitige Abspaltung von mehreren Interferenzstrahlen bei symmetrischen Laueaufnahmen) gibt die entsprechende Überlegung einen ersten Überblick über die Dispersionsfläche. Wegen der Kleinheit des Aufspaltungsgebietes dürfen die Kugeln durch ihre Tangentialebenen und die Dispersionsfläche durch den Hyperbel-zylinder ersetzt werden.

54.   *Notwendigkeit des Randproblems*

Mit der Aufstellung der Dispersionsgleichung, ihrer Deutung als Dispersionsfläche und der Bestimmung von Geschwindigkeiten und Amplitudenverhältnissen der Interferenzwellen ist somit dasselbe erreicht wie in der Kristalloptik mit der Ermitielung der Normalenfläche. Genügt dies, um sich Rechenschaft zu geben über die Intensitäten der Interferenzstrahlen, wie sie bei einem Versuche zu erwarten sind, selbst wenn vorausgesetzt wird, daß dessen Bedingungen sich durch Verwirklichung ebener monochromatischer Wellen und eines völlig regelmäßigen Kristalls besonders durchsichtig gestalten ließen? Die Frage muß auf das entschiedenste verneint werden. Die Normalenfläche und die Dispersionsfläche sind kurz zusammengefaßte Aussagen über die Ausbreitungsweise von Wellen *im Innern* des Kristalls. Die Erklärung des Experiments muß von der *von außen einfallenden Welle* $\mathfrak{E}_0$ ausgehen und zeigen, welche Zustände im Innern durch sie bedingt werden. Während der bisherige Teil der Theorie der Röntgeninterferenzen sich mit Zuständen befaßt hat, die in unveränderter Form den Kristall durchziehen, müssen nun gerade veränderliche Zustände betrachtet werden, bei denen wie im Experiment, der Energiestrom von einer Richtung in ein ganzes Bündel von Richtungen aufgespalten wird, bei denen Strahlrichtungen, die nicht in die Gitterabstände hineinpassen, allmählich unterdrückt und andere auf ihre Kosten um so stärker herausgehoben werden. Wird hierbei der Zustand erreicht, der als gültig für das Kristallinnere gefunden worden ist? Treffen schließlich die für ihn errechneten Amplitudenverhältnisse ein, und welche sind es bei der Möglichkeit für den Ausbreitungspunkt, auf einer der $2n$ Schalen der Dispersionsfläche zu liegen? Oder erstreckt sich gar, wie Laue annahm, der Einfluß der einfallenden Welle bis in solche Tiefen, daß alle Dipole praktisch nur durch sie zu ihren Schwingungen angeregt werden, wie es ja am Rande sein muß, wo die Interferenzwellen noch keine große Stärke haben; und ist hierdurch die ganze bisherige Betrachtung über den Haufen geworfen?

Diese Fragen erläutern zur Genüge die Zweifel, die man hegen muß, ob die bisher aufgestellte Theorie imstande ist, auch nur für die Erklärung des einfachsten Experimentes von Wert zu sein. Sie wäre es in der Tat nicht, wenn es nicht durch sie gelänge, die Zustände im Innern mit der einfallenden Welle in Verbindung zu setzen, wenn sie nicht die Grundformen der Wellenausbreitung herstellte, aus denen die Lösung für das Randproblem sich aufbaut.

Das Randproblem in der Optik

Zur Veranschaulichung des Zusammenhanges zwischen den bisherigen Betrachtungen und dem Randproblem kann auf die eigentliche Kristalloptik zurückgegriffen werden. Es falle auf den Kristall, der den unteren Halbraum erfüllt, eine ebene linearpolarisierte Welle $\mathfrak{E}_0$ auf. Es ist in II gezeigt worden, daß der Zustand im Innern sich aus den elementaren Schwingungsformen des unbegrenzten Kristalls aufbauen läßt, deren Ausdruck in der Optik die zweischalige Normalenfläche ist. Werden nämlich dieselben Dipolschwingungen im begrenzten Kristall angesetzt, wie im

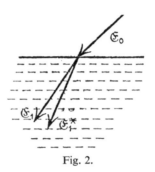

Fig. 2.

unbegrenzten, so gehen vom Rand ebene Wellen aus, die zu den im unbegrenzten Kristall bestehenden Wellen hinzutreten. Diese Wellen (*Randwellen*) haben weder gleiche Richtung noch gleiche Geschwindigkeit wie die *Binnenwellen* des unbegrenzten Kristalls, sondern ihre Geschwindigkeit ist c und ihre Richtung hängt mit Richtung und Geschwindigkeit der Binnenwellen nach dem Brechungsgesetze zusammen. Zu jeder Binnenwelle gehört eine Randwelle von gleicher Polarisation. Gelingt es, im halben Kristall sowohl einfallende Wellen wie Randwellen zum Verschwinden zu bringen, indem nur Binnenwellen benutzt werden, wie sie nach Angabe der Normalenfläche im Kristallinnern vorkommen dürfen, so ist auch für den halben Kristall der dynamisch mögliche Zustand gefunden. Die einfallende optische Welle kann durch zwei verschieden polarisierte Randwellen aufgehoben werden, wenn diese mit ihr gleiche Richtung haben. Es ist also nötig, an den beiden Schalen der Normalenfläche zwei Dipolwellen derart auszusuchen, daß die Randwellen ebenso fortschreiten, wie die einfallende Welle. Diese Dipolwellen und die mit ihnen gleichlaufenden Binnenwellen $\mathfrak{E}_1$ und $\mathfrak{E}_1{}^*$ haben im allgemeinen Richtungen die sowohl voneinander, wie von der Richtung der einfallenden Welle abweichen (Fig. 2). So entsteht anstatt einer einzigen Fortsetzung des einfallenden Strahles wegen der Randbedingungen ein Strahlenpaar (Doppelbrechung), das der Kristall sich aus der ihm gemäß der Normalenfläche zur Verfügung stehenden Mannigfaltigkeit von elementaren Schwingungsformen durch *Anpassung* an die Bedingung der äußeren Anregung heraussucht.

Lösung des Randproblems bei Röntgenstrahlen

Ganz ähnlich liegen die Verhältnisse für Röntgenwellen. Auch hier kommt durch das Auftreten des Randes zu jeder Binnenwelle eine Randwelle von der Geschwindigkeit c und entsprechender anderer Richtung hinzu. Das elementare Interferenzfeld im berandeten Kristall besteht daher aus n Binnenwellen und n Randwellen. Letztere, sowie die einfallende Welle stören das dynamische Gleichgewicht, das herrschen würde, wenn allein Binnenwellen sich gemäß den Anweisungen der Dispersionsfläche ausbreiten würden.

Die $2n$ Möglichkeiten, dynamisch richtige Binnenwellen anzusetzen, können nun dazu benutzt werden, um einfallende und Randwellen zum Verschwinden zu bringen. Hierfür müssen die Randwellen des einen Strahls—er heißt *Primärstrahl*—der Richtung nach sämtlich mit dem einfallenden Strahl zusammenfallen. Dies erfordert geeignete Wahl der Ausbreitungspunkte der $2n$ elementaren Interferenzfelder auf den $2n$ Schalen der Dispersionsfläche. Es zeigt sich, daß gleichzeitig bei den anderen Interferenzrichtungen gerade die Randstrahlen der $2n$ elementaren Felder zusammenfallen. Hierdurch ist es möglich, die $2n$ Amplituden der zu überlagernden Felder so zu bestimmen, daß die $(n-1)$ Randstrahlen der Sekundärstrahlen verschwinden und zudem der Randstrahl des Primärstrahls das einfallende $\mathfrak{E}_0$ aufhebt. Im Kristallinnern bleiben dann allein $2n$ Systeme von Binnenwellen übrig, von denen jedes dynamisch möglich ist. 55. Welches Feld wird im Kristallinnern durch diese Anregung entstehen und wie wird die Intensität der wieder austretenden Interferenzstrahlen sein?

Die Antwort möge wieder nur für den wichtigsten Fall zweier Interferenzstrahlen gegeben werden (Primärstrahl und reflektierter Strahl). Es sei (Abb. 79 u. 80) $P1$ der Pfeil, der die einfallende Welle darstellt, daher P der 'Anregungspunkt'; ferner sei L der 'Lauepunkt', die Hyberbel die Dispersionsfläche für Strahlen, deren elektrischer Vektor senkrecht zur

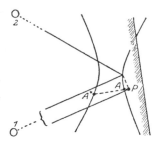

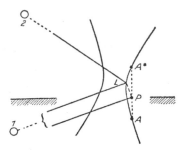

Abb. 79. Einfallender und
reflektierter Strahl, Lauefall.

Abb. 80. Einfallender und
reflektierter Strahl, Braggfall.

Strahlenebene schwingt (auf solche mögen wir uns der Einfachheit halber
beschränken). Die Richtung der Kristalloberfläche sei durch die schraffierte Linie außerhalb der Abbildung angedeutet; der Allgemeinheit wegen
setzen wir nicht voraus, daß die Oberfläche die Spiegelebene, die zu den
beiden Strahlen gehört, sei. Dann ist die Behauptung der Theorie: durch
den Anregungspunkt P entsteht im Kristallinnern das Röntgenfeld, das
durch die Ausbreitungspunkte A und A^* völlig gekennzeichnet ist, wenn
noch hinzugefügt wird, mit welcher Stärke die den Punkten A bzw. A^*
entsprechenden Felder auftreten. A und A^* werden von P aus erhalten,
indem man senkrecht zur Oberfläche fortschreitend die Schnitte mit der
Dispersionsfläche aufsucht*. Wir haben nun zwischen zwei charakteristisch verschiedenen Fällen zu unterscheiden: im 'Lauefall' dringen beide
Strahlen in das Kristallinnere ein. Die Kristalloberfläche liegt etwa parallel
der Richtung 1 2 oder ähnlich. Die durch die Senkrechte zur Oberfläche
gefundenen Ausbreitungspunkte A und A^* liegen auf verschiedenen Hyper-
belzweigen (Abb. 79).—Der andere Fall ist der 'Braggfall', auf den sich
Abb. 80 bezieht. Hier gehören A und A^* zur selben Hyperbelschale, aber
wenn der einfallende Strahl gedreht wird, d.h. der Anregungspunkt P
auf der Normalen zu $1P$ verschoben wird, so gelangt man zu Anregungen,
bei denen überhaupt kein reeller Schnitt mit der Dispersionsfläche entsteht. Diesen letzten Fall werden wir sogleich näher betrachten. Vorher
beschäftigen wir uns mit den Folgerungen aus der Existenz zweier reeller
Schnitte A und A^*, wobei es zunächst einerlei ist, ob diese Schnitte beim
Lauefall oder beim Braggfall auftreten.

Im Kristallinnern entstehen dann sowohl in der Richtung des Primär-
strahls wie in der des Sekundärstrahls genau genommen je zwei Strahlen
von etwas verschiedenen Richtungen und Geschwindigkeiten. Zwei solche

*[Cp. this Vol. p. 262 last sentence.]

230

Wellen lassen sich zu einer einzigen von langsam veränderlicher Amplitude (Schwebungen) zusammenfassen.

Im *Lauefall* setzt am Rand die Primärwelle (welche bis auf eine kleine Brechung als Fortsetzung der einfallenden angesehen werden kann) mit einem Schwebungsmaximum von der Größe der einfallenden Amplitude ein, die Sekundärwelle hat einen Schwebungsknoten, ihre Amplitude ist Null. Verfolgt man das Feld vom Rand aus in größere Tiefen, so wächst die Amplitude der Sekundärwelle auf Kosten der Primärwelle an. Dem Schwebungscharakter entspricht es, daß die Sekundärwelle bei zunehmender Tiefe wieder geringere Amplitude—bis auf Null herab—erhält. Die Energieströmung erfolgt dann wieder ganz in Richtung der Primärwelle. Dies Pendeln des Energiestroms zwischen den Richtungen 1 und 2 führt auf die Bezeichnung *'Pendellösung'*. Es besteht eine weitgehende formale Analogie zwischen der (räumlichen) Ausbreitung der Energie in Primär- und Sekundärstrahl und der zeitlichen Verteilung der Energie in einem Paar gekoppelter Pendel (etwa zwei Pendeln, die an einer gemeinsamen Querschnur aufgehängt sind). Man befindet sich, wenn anders die Interferenz stark auftreten soll, stets in der nächsten Nähe der vollständigen Resonanz. Unter diesen Umständen wird Energie, die dem ersten Pendel erteilt wird, nach einiger Zeit sich fast ganz beim zweiten vorfinden, um dann wieder aufs erste zurückzufließen.

Bei der Pendellösung ist der ganze Kristall parallel zur Oberfläche in Schichten zerlegt, die durch die Tiefe einer vollen Schwebung gegeben sind und an der Oberfläche ansetzen. An der Oberseite jeder Schicht fängt sozusagen der Kristall aufs neue an, insofern, als der Sekundärstrahl dort wieder mit der Amplitude Null anhebt (Abb. 81). Die Weite einer solchen Schicht wird um so größer, je näher Richtungen und Geschwindigkeiten der beiden von A und A^* in Abb. 79 bzw. 80 ausgehenden Wellen des Primärstrahls bzw. Sekundärstrahls zusammenfallen. Hier tritt nun schon ein wesentlicher Unterschied zwischen Laue- und Braggfall auf: im Lauefall (Abb. 79) können A und A^* nicht näher als in die Entfernung der Hyperbelscheitel aneinanderkommen. Daher übersteigt die Schichtweite nicht eine gewisse Größe, die auf etwa $\frac{1}{20}$ mm (bei $\lambda = 1.10^{-8}$, $\varepsilon = 10^{-6}$, Abbeugungswinkel χ klein) abgeschätzt werden kann. Die Schichttiefe variiert im allgemeinen so schnell mit wechselndem Einfallswinkel, daß sie experimentell wegen der Schwierigkeit der Herstellung genügend ebener einfallender Wellen nicht nachweisbar ist. In der unmittelbaren Umgebung des Laueschen Einfallswinkels ist der Nachweis aussichtsreicher.

Denkt man sich den Kristall in einer Tiefe H parallel zur Oberfläche abgebrochen (Kristallplatte), so treten die Strahlen mit der Amplitude aus, die sie in der Tiefe H gerade erreicht haben.

EWALD

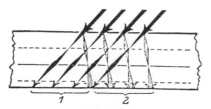 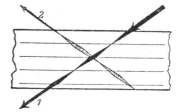

Abb. 81. Pendellösung im Lauefall.*   Abb. 82. Pendellösung im Braggfall.*

Im *Braggfall*, zu dem wir nunmehr übergehen, können die Schnitte A und A^*, da sie auf der gleichen Hyperbelschale liegen, sich beliebig nahekommen. Die Schichtweite wird dabei größer und größer, und in dem Maß, als P sich dem Lauepunkt L nähert, würde sie leichter nachweisbar werden, wenn nicht gleichzeitig die Empfindlichkeit der Schichttiefe gegen kleine Änderungen des Einfallswinkels immer größer würde. Der Wert $\frac{1}{100}$ mm der Schichtweite wird erreicht, wenn der einfallende Strahl schätzungsweise 5 bis 20″ vom Laue-Braggschen Reflexionswinkel entfernt ist. Rückt P bei Variation der Einfallsrichtung, von unten kommend, (Abb. 80) in L hinein, so verschmelzen die Wellenpaare von A und A^* zu einer einzigen und die Schichtung wird unendlich. Das gleiche, nur in umgekehrter Reihenfolge, wiederholt sich, wenn P über das Gebiet hinaustritt, in dem keine reellen Schnittpunkte mit der Dispersionsfläche entstehen.

Es sei noch bemerkt, daß im Braggfall die Amplitude des an der Oberfläche einer Platte von der Dicke H austretenden reflektierten Strahls gleich ist der Amplitude des Strahls 2 in der Tiefe 0, die des durchgelassenen gleich der Amplitude des Strahls 1 in der Tiefe H. Der reflektierte Strahl setzt an der Unterseite der Platte mit der Amplitude 0 ein (Abb. 82); seine Amplitude nimmt nach oben hin erst zu, dann wegen der Schwebungen bei genügender Dicke der Platte wieder ab. Mit welcher Amplitude er austritt, hängt von der Plattendicke H ab. Bei Annäherung der Ausbreitungspunkte A und A^* aneinander findet schließlich auch in einer dicken Platte keine volle Schwebung mehr Platz, und der reflektierte Strahl nimmt monoton nach oben hin zu.

Was geschieht, wenn der Anregungspunkt P in Abb. 80 so liegt, daß keine reellen Schnitte mit der Dispersionsfläche entstehen? Es ist dann

*[Regarding fig. 81 and 82 one has to consider Ewald's remark (*Handbuch* p. 267): 'Es muss darauf aufmerkzam gemacht werden dass die Umspülung des kleinen Kristalls mit Röntgenstrahlen ("Bademethode") wesentlich ist. Es kann hierdurch im ganzen Kristall die Wechselwirkung zwischen Primär- und Sekundärstrahl eintreten, die bei Begrenzung des Einfalls durch Blenden mangelhaft ist'; cf. Ewald, *Acta* **11** (1958) 891 fig. 3. Ed.]

kein Interferenzsystem der bisher betrachteten Art dynamisch möglich. Man sieht aber leicht, daß der Ansatz exponentiell gedämpfter Wellen zu dynamisch möglichen Feldern führt. Für die Befriedigung des Randproblems kommen nur Wellen in Frage, deren Amplitude in Ebenen parallel zur Oberfläche gleich ist, aber mit wachsender Tiefe z exponentiell zu- oder abnimmt. Das sind inhomogene Wellen, wie sie z.B. bei Behandlung der optischen Totalreflexion im dünneren Medium auftreten. Aus diesem Grunde heißen die Lagen der Anregung P, die zu keinem reellen Schnitt mit der Dispersionsfläche führen, das *Gebiet der Totalreflexion* Analytisch stellen sich inhomogene Wellen durch komplexe Ausbreitungsvektoren

$$\mathfrak{K}_i = \mathfrak{k}_i + ik_0\kappa\mathfrak{z}$$

dar: der reelle Teil ist der Ausbreitungsvektor, der die Phasengeschwindigkeit und die Stellung der Ebenen konstanter Phase angibt und der bisher allein benutzt wurde. Der imaginäre Teil, der durch den Einheitsvektor $\mathfrak{z}$ senkrecht zur Oberfläche den Vektorcharakter, durch die unbestimmte Größe κ die Größe erhält, gibt die Ebenen konstanter Amplitude und den Sinn und die Größe des exponentiellen Amplitudenabfalles an. Um uns die beiden inhomogenen Wellen im Kristallinnern an der Dispersionsfläche vorzustellen, ergänzen wir diese (Abb. 83) durch die Verbindungslinie der Hyperbelscheitel. Fällen wir von P aus auf diese das Lot (bei symmetrischer Reflexion), so ergibt der Schnittpunkt A, mit 1 bzw. 2 verbunden, die reellen Teile der Ausbreitungsvektoren. Die beiden, in Richtung jedes Interferenzstrahls auch jetzt noch vorhandenen Wellen, geben keine Schwebungen mehr, da sie gleiche Richtung und Phasengeschwindigkeit haben. Die eine von ihnen wächst aber mit der Tiefe z exponentiell an, die andere nimmt ebenso ab. Damit an der Unterseite der Platte der reflektierte Strahl mit der Amplitude 0 anfängt (kein einfallender

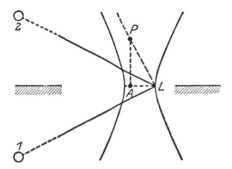

Abb. 83. Konstruktion der Ausbreitungsvektoren im Gebiet der Totalreflexion.

Strahl an der Unterseite!), muß die exponentiell anwachsende Lösung an der Unterseite so stark werden, wie dort die exponentiell gedämpfte Lösung ist. An der Oberseite ist deshalb bei dickeren Kristallen die anwachsende Welle unmerklich schwach und ohne Einfluß auf den reflektierten Strahl. Man kann überhaupt im Gebiet der Totalreflexion zur Grenze unendlich dicker Kristallplatten übergehen, da die Unterseite wegen der Dämpfung von verschwindendem Einfluß ist. Die Lösung stellt sich dann so dar (Abb. 84), daß bei beiden Wellen die Intensität nach dem Innern hin exponentiell abfällt: jede Netzebene reflektiert ein- und denselben Bruchteil der auf sie fallenden Energie, und diese reflektierte Energie erreicht (im Gegensatz zum Lauefall) nicht mehr die tieferen Netzebenen; daher das exponentielle Gesetz. Alle einfallende Energie muß zur Oberfläche wieder austreten.

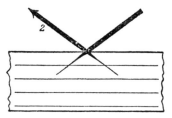

Abb. 84. Extinktion im Gebiet der Totalreflexion.

Abhängigkeit der Intensität von der Struktur

In einem Kristall mit Basis ist die Dispersionsfläche enger oder weiter als in einem entsprechenden einfachen. Ihr Mittelpunkt hingegen liegt vom Lauepunkt in der gleichen Entfernung ε_0 ($\mu = 1 + \varepsilon_0$) wie bisher; daher sind die Abweichungen vom Braggschen Gesetz ebensogroß, als wäre die Basis in einem Punkt konzentriert. Aber der Scheitelabstand der beiden Hyperbeläste hat jetzt die Größe

$$4\varepsilon_0|S| = 4\varepsilon_0|\textstyle\sum_t m_t \exp\{2\pi i(\mathfrak{h}\mathfrak{r}_t)\}|.$$

$|S|$ ist der Betrag der Strukturamplitude. Da somit das Gebiet der Totalreflexion proportional zu $|S|$ ist, sollte das gleiche für die reflektierte Gesamtintensität gelten.

56. Die primitive Theorie der Röntgeninterferenzen geht von der Vorstellung eines übermächtigen einfallenden oder Primär-Strahls aus, unter dessen alleinigem Einfluß die Schwingungen der Atome im Kristall entstehen. Besitzt der Kristall eine ausgedehnte Basis, so wird durch das Zusammenwirken der Basisbestandteile index (t) die Amplitude des Interferenzstrahls $(h_1h_2h_3)$ proportional zu

$$S_h = \sum_t A_t \exp\{2\pi i(\mathfrak{h}\mathfrak{r}_t)\}, \tag{1}$$

wo A_t die relative Amplitude der Atomsorte t, $\mathfrak{r}_t$ ihre Verschiebung gegen den Eckpunkt der Zelle, $\mathfrak{h}$ der Fahrstrahl im reziproken Gitter von dessen Anfangspunkt zu seinem Gitterpunkt $(h_1h_2h_3)$ ist und wir S_h als 'Strukturamplitude' bezeichnen.

Für die Intensität des Interferenzstrahls pflegt man hieraus auf Proportionalität mit

$$|S_h|^2$$

zu schließen (Strukturfaktor).

Würde man in der Optik der sichtbaren Strahlen ebenso vorgehen, so wäre das Mangelhafte dieses Verfahrens höchst auffällig: 1. Man setzt im Kristallinnern eine Welle von gleicher Richtung und Geschwindigkeit voraus, wie außen (einfallender Strahl). 2. Man läßt die einfallende Welle an jedem Atom die gleiche Anregungsarbeit vollbringen, einerlei wieviel Resonatoren im Kubikzentimeter vorhanden sind. Punkt 1 würde für Röntgenstrahlen wegen des sehr geringen Brechungsindex bei der Diskussion des geometrischen Strahlenganges vielleicht zur Not statthaft sein, solange nicht Präzisionsmessungen erklärt werden sollen (Abweichungen vom Braggschen Gesetz). Hingegen kann man wegen 2 niemals hoffen, auf Grund der naiven Theorie irgendwelche brauchbaren Intensitätsaussagen zu erhalten.

Betrachten wir die Art, wie in der molekulartheoretischen Optik der sichtbaren Wellen das Problem der Reflexion und Brechung behandelt werden muß[1]. Den Ausgangspunkt bildet die Dispersionstheorie, d.h. die Kenntnis derjenigen optischen Felder, die sich im unbegrenzten Körper ohne irgendeine Einwirkung von außen fortpflanzen können. Die Ergebnisse dieser Untersuchung lassen sich zusammenfassen in einer Fläche, der Dispersionsfläche, die den Zusammenhang von Richtung, Geschwindigkeit und Polarisation der Wellen angibt (in der Kristalloptik die Fresnelsche Normalenfläche). Wenn man so eine Übersicht über die dynamisch überhaupt möglichen Wellenarten im Innern erhalten hat, kann man daran gehen, das Randproblem in einem berandeten Kristall zu lösen, auf

---

[1] W. C. Oseen, *Ann. d. Phys.* **48** (1915) 1; Bothe, *Ann. d. Phys.* **64** (1921) 693; P. P. Ewald, *Ann. d. Phys.* **49** (1916) 1 u. 117; sowie besonders: P. P. Ewald, *Physica* **4** (1924) 234–251.

den von außen eine Welle einfällt. Es zeigt sich, daß es hierzu nur einer passenden Kombination von Zuständen bedarf, deren jeder bereits als dynamisch möglich erkannt, d.h. durch die Dispersionsfläche darstellbar ist. Die Auswahl dieser Zustände wird durch das Vorhandensein des Randes bestimmt, und zwar insbesondere durch die Forderung, daß der Rand eine völlig abschirmende Wirkung auf das Kristallinnere ausübe, so daß die einfallende Welle keine Störung des an der Dispersionsfläche ausgewählten dynamisch möglichen Zustandes herbeiführt.

Man sieht, wie in der Optik gerade das Gegenteil von dem eintritt, was bei der einfachen Theorie der Röntgeninterferenzen vorausgesetzt wird: denn man geht gerade darauf hinaus, die in das Kristallinnere nicht passende einfallende Welle systematisch zu vernichten und aus dieser Forderung ergeben sich die Amplituden und Polarisationsverhältnisse des gebrochenen und reflektierten Strahls.

Wörtlich das gleiche Verfahren wie für die Optik gilt auch für die Röntgenoptik. Die oft beliebte Darstellung, daß die Röntgenreflexion als Volumreflexion der optischen als Oberflächenreflexion gegenüberstehe und deshalb andere Gesetze befolge, ist bei der völligen Analogie beider Vorgänge, wenn sie nur ordnungsmäßig behandelt werden, nicht sehr glücklich. Ich habe in einer früheren Arbeit[1] gezeigt wie die Röntgenoptik aufzubauen ist. Es ergaben sich zunächst nur kleine Abweichungen auch in geometrischer Hinsicht von den Angaben der Laue-Braggschen Theorie, —Abweichungen, die sich mit der Verfeinerung der Meßtechnik in zunehmendem Maße bestätigen und deshalb das Zutrauen zur Anwendbarkeit der klassischen Rechenmethode auf die Interferenzprobleme trotz aller quantenmäßigen Vorgänge bei der Streuung der Röntgenstrahlen stärken.

Aus diesem Grunde halte ich es nunmehr für angebracht, die ausführliche Theorie auch in den Dienst der Intensitätsberechnung zu stellen und ich möchte im Folgenden auf eine Folgerung hinweisen, die mit den bereits bestätigten Abweichungen vom Braggschen Gesetz sehr eng zusammenhängt. Leider muß ich mich dabei z.T. auf die noch unveröffentlichte Ausdehnung der Theorie auf Gitter mit Basis berufen (die letztzitierte Arbeit behandelt nur einfache Gitter).

Die Abweichungen vom Braggschen Gesetz entstehen durch die Eigentümlichkeiten der in Fig. 1 wiedergegebenen Reflexionskurve. Ordinate ist dabei das Verhältnis der reflektierten zur einfallenden Intensität, Abszisse eine Größe ζ, die für den Fall symmetrischer Reflexion unter dem $\sphericalangle\,\theta$ gegen die Oberfläche (d.h. Oberfläche parallel den spiegelnden Ebenen)

---

[1] *Ann. d. Phys.* **54** (1918) 519–597 [this Vol. p. 216].

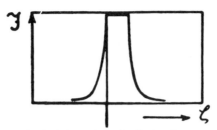

Fig. 1. Theoretische Reflexionskurve.

mit dem Winkel θ so zusammenhängt

$$\zeta = \sin 2\theta \cdot (\theta - \theta_0), \tag{2}$$

wo θ_0 der nach der Braggschen Reflexionsbedingung

$$n\lambda = 2d \sin \theta_0 \tag{3}$$

zu erwartende Reflexionswinkel ist. Der mittlere Teil der Reflexionskurve (Ordinate 1) bedeutet Totalreflexion der gesamten unter diesen Richtungen auffallenden Energie über einen Bereich von $\zeta = 0$ bis $\zeta = 4/\Omega$. Hierbei ist für das einfache aus einer 'Dipolsorte' aufgebaute Gitter

$$\Omega = \frac{v}{2\pi} \frac{m}{e^2} (\omega_0{}^2 - \omega^2) \tag{4}$$

($1/v$ = Anzahl Dipole pro Kubikzentimeter, ω_0 Eigenfrequenz der Dipole). Rechts und links an das Gebiet der Totalreflexion schließt sich ein Intensitätsabfall an, also allmähliches Verschwinden des reflektierten Interferenzstrahls. Das Verhältnis der gesamten zwischen Kurve und Achse eingeschlossenen Fläche zu dem der Totalreflexion allein entsprechenden Gebiete ist etwa 100 : 80. Das bedeutet, daß in einem einfachen Gitter 80 Proz. der reflektierten Intensität durch Totalreflexion entsteht. Dies dürfte eher zu niedrig als zu hoch abgeschätzt sein.

Durch die unsymmetrische Lage der Reflexionskurve gegen den Braggschen Winkel θ_0 entstehen die Abweichungen vom Braggschen Reflexionsgesetz.

Die bisherigen Angaben bezogen sich auf ein einfaches Gitter und sind des öfteren entwickelt und angewandt worden[1].

Bei einem Gitter mit Basis liegen die allgemeinen Verhältnisse sehr ähnlich. Auch dort gibt es ein Gebiet der Totalreflexion, an welches sich beiderseits Gebiete des allmählichen Verschwindens der Intensität an-

---

[1] Siehe z.B. *Physikal. Z.* **21** (1920), Vortrag auf der Naturforscherversammlung in Bad Nauheim.

schließen. Für die Größenverhältnisse dieser Gebiete sind in der allgemeinen Theorie zwei Größen maßgebend, die sich aus den auf die einzelne Dipolsorte t bezüglichen Größen wie folgt aufbauen:

$$\frac{1}{\Omega} = \Sigma_t \frac{1}{\Omega_t}; \qquad \frac{1}{\Omega_h} = \Sigma_t \frac{\exp 2\pi i(\mathfrak{h}\mathfrak{r}_t)}{\Omega_t}. \qquad (5)$$

Die erste Größe hängt nur von der gesamten 'optischen Dichte' des Kristalls ab, d.h. von der Gesamtzahl und Art der Dipole der Basis; Ω_h hingegen ist von den Einzelheiten der Basisanordnung abhängig. Wir führen für Ω_t noch eine andere Darstellung ein: unterliegen die Dipole der Sorte t der Anregung durch eine zeitlich periodische Feldstärke E, so ist die Schwingungsgleichung für einen Dipol (Moment $\mathfrak{p} = e$. Elongation).

$$m(\omega_0^2 - \omega^2)\mathfrak{p} = e^2 E$$

und somit $1/\Omega_t$ proportional zu dem Moment pro Volumeinheit, das durch die Dipolsorte t unter dem Einfluß des Feldes E entsteht. Wenn oben (Gl. 1) die relative Amplitude der einzelnen Atomsorte durch A_t bezeichnet wurde, so ist demnach bis auf einen hier belanglosen Faktor

$$1/\Omega_t = A_t \qquad (6)$$

zu setzen. Hiermit ergibt sich die Beziehung zur Strukturamplitude S_h,

$$1/\Omega_h = \Sigma A_t \exp\{2\pi i(\mathfrak{h}\mathfrak{r}_t)\} = S_h. \qquad (7)$$

Nach dieser Vorbereitung können wir die zwei wesentlichen Punkte besprechen, die für die Reflexionskurve eines Kristalls mit Basis gelten.

1. Die Intensitätskurve zerfällt wieder in ein Gebiet der Totalreflexion mit anschließenden Übergangsbögen. Die Mittellinie der Kurve bleibt unverschoben, unabhängig von den Struktureinzelheiten. Diese Verschiebung ist nämlich allein durch Ω bestimmt. Daher kommt es, daß die Abweichungen vom Braggschen Gesetz auch für Kristalle unbekannter Struktur sich richtig voraussagen lassen.

2. Das Gebiet der Totalreflexion füllt nicht mehr den ganzen Zwischenraum bis zum Braggschen Winkel aus, sondern es ist schmäler. Man hat, wie in der Optik die zwei Polarisationsfälle: Schwingungen senkrecht zur Strahlenebene und Schwingungen in der Strahlenebene zu unterscheiden. In ζ gemessen ist die Breite des Gebiets der Totalreflexion

$$\left. \begin{array}{l} \text{für Schwingungen senkrecht zur Strahlenebene: } 4|S_h| \\ \text{für Schwingungen parallel zur Strahlenebene: } \quad 4|S_h|\cos 2\theta \end{array} \right\} \quad (8)$$

Die Breite des Gebiets der Totalreflexion ist proportional dem Betrag der Strukturamplitude. Innerhalb dieses Gebiets ist die Intensität des reflektierten Strahls gleich der einfallenden Intensität, ganz unabhängig von der Basisanordnung. Der 'Strukturfaktor' hat somit keinen unmittelbaren Einfluß auf die Amplitude der reflektierten Welle, wie in der Laue-Braggschen Theorie vorausgesetzt wird, sein Einfluß auf die Intensität entsteht in ganz anderer Weise.

Betrachten wir die Intensität als gänzlich hervorgebracht durch die Totalreflexion, indem wir zunächst von der in den Übergangsbögen der Reflexionskurve enthaltenen Intensität absehen, für welche die Verhältnisse etwas komplizierter liegen. Dann ist wegen des durch Gleichungen (2) und (7) gegebenen Zusammenhanges für unpolarisierte einfallende Strahlung die Intensität proportional zu

$$4|S_h| \frac{1 + \cos 2\theta}{\sin 2\theta} = 4|S_h| \cot g\, \theta. \tag{9}$$

Im Gegensatz zu der üblichen Auffassung ergibt sich die Intensität, soweit sie von der Totalreflexion herrührt, proportional zum Betrag der Strukturamplitude selbst, nicht zu deren Quadrat. Außerdem ergibt sich diese Intensität umgekehrt proportional zu tg θ.

Zur Stütze dieser Behauptungen lassen sich eine Reihe von Erfahrungen heranziehen.

W. L. Bragg[1] sagt in einer seiner letzten Arbeiten (über die Aragonitstruktur): 'Wir würden erwarten, daß die Intensitäten sich wie das Quadrat des Strukturfaktors verhalten .... Die Zahlen der letzten Kolonne zeigen, daß die Intensität offenbar *proportional zum Strukturfaktor selbst, nicht zum Quadrat* ist. Dies bestätigt eine sehr interessante Meßreihe von W. H. Bragg an Calcit, in der er zum gleichen Ergebnis kommt[2]'.

Auch Intensitätsmessungen von Sir W. H. Bragg an kleinen Diamantkristallen[3] sprechen dafür, daß der Hauptbetrag der reflektierten Intensität durch Totalreflexion entsteht. Die von ihm (nach Abzug einer Korrektur für die allgemeine Streuung) auf ± 5 Proz. genau angegebenen Intensitäten ordnen sich gegen 1/sin θ aufgetragen auf zwei glatte, nach unten schwach konkave Kurven, die den zwei vorkommenden Werten des Strukturfaktors entsprechen. – Reproduktionen der Kurven in 'X-Rays and Crystal Structure (1924)', sowie in 'Kristalle und Röntgenstrahlen' Fig. 137 (hier mit derjenigen Indizierung, die einfachen kubischen Achsen entspricht). – Gegen cotg θ aufgetragen (Fig. 2) strecken sich die Kurven zu Geraden. Ihre Neigung steht im Verhältnis $\sqrt{2}$, dem Verhältnis der

[1] *Proc. Roy. Soc.* London (A) **105** (1924) 16.
[2] *Phil. Trans. Roy. Soc.* London (A) **215** (1915).
[3] *Proc. London Phys. Soc.* **33** (1921) 304–310.

beiden S-Werte des Diamant (nicht S^2). Somit bestätigen diese Messungen sowohl die geforderte Winkelabhängigkeit der Intensität, als auch ihre Abhängigkeit vom Bau der Basis. Allerdings besteht scheinbar eine Abweichung gegen die Formel (9) darin, daß die Geraden der Fig. 2 nicht vom Nullpunkt ausgehen. Erst wenn alle beobachteten Intensitäten um einen konstanten Betrag gehoben werden dürften, wäre Formel (9) erfüllt.

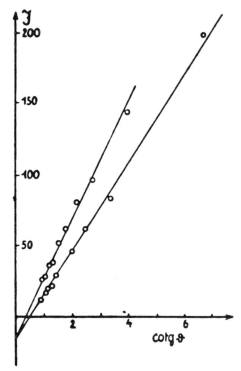

Fig. 2. An Diamant reflektierte Intensitäten.

Diese Hebung ist aber in der Tat berechtigt, da Bragg bei der erwähnten Korrektur für Streustrahlung fälschlicherweise auch die Streuung der K_α-Strahlung selbst und des gleichfarbigen Teils des Bremsspektrums abzieht, obwohl bei der Reflexionsstellung des Kristalls diese Wellenlängen für die ungeordnete Streuung fortfallen (da sie geordnet gespiegelt werden). Man darf somit annehmen, daß die Intensitätszählung von dem Punkt aus zu erfolgen hat, wo sich die beiden Geraden auf der Ordinatenachse schneiden. Es zeigt sich also, daß unsere sehr einfache Überlegung, obwohl sie ausschließlich die Erscheinung der Totalreflexion zur Erklärung der Intensitäten heranzieht, die wesentlichen Züge der Braggschen Beobachtungen vortrefflich wiedergibt. Hierfür mag die geringe Wärmebewegung im Diamant ein günstiger Nebenumstand sein.

Stuttgart, Seminar f. theoret. Physik der Technischen Hochschule.

57. Es ist daher angenehm, daß es gelingt, auch noch auf eine andere Weise die 'Mosaikstruktur' der Krystalle zu prüfen. Wenn man nämlich den in der Fig. 2 und 3 schematisierten Versuch anstellt und den reflektierten Strahl in einer kleinen—etwa 10 cm—und einer größeren Entfernung—etwa 10 m—auf die Platte bringt, so muß im Falle eines idealen Krystalles die Breite dieser Reflexionen sich nur sehr wenig voneinander unterscheiden, da die Divergenz des reflektierten Bündels nur 5" beträgt,

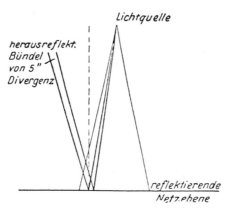

Fig. 2. Von einem idealen Krystall wird aus einem monochromatischen Bündel nur ein Bereich von wenigen Sekunden herausreflektiert.

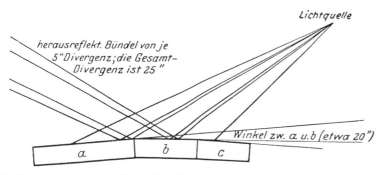

Fig. 3. Reflexion von einem Krystallstück, welches aus mehreren getrennten Bereichen besteht.

241

was in 10 m Entfernung eine lineare Verbreiterung von 0,3 mm ergibt. Im Falle eines Mosaikkrystalles erhält man viel stärkere Verbreiterungen und kann aus dem Öffnungswinkel des reflektierten Strahles auf die maximalen vorkommenden Winkel zwischen den einheitlichen Krystallchen schließen; bei einer Abweichung von 1′ z.B. ist die Reflexion in 10 m Entfernung bereits 3 mm breiter als in 10 cm Entfernung. Aber auch über die Verteilungsfunktion selbst kann man direkt experimentellen Aufschluß erhalten, wenn man die Reflexion ihrer ganzen Breite nach durchphotometriert; aus der relativen Intensität kann man die Zahl der eine bestimmte Orientierung besitzenden Kryställchen erschließen. In Fig. 4 sind die Reflexionen zweier sich verschieden verhaltender Diamanten wiedergegeben; das eine Bild zeigt 2 scharfe Linien, $K\alpha$ und $K\alpha'$ von Rhodium. Es ist in einer Entfernung von 10 m aufgenommen; die Linien sind gegenüber einer Aufnahme in 10 cm Entfernung nur um 0,3 mm verbreitert, was dem theoretischen Divergenzbereich entspricht: der Diamant ist ideal, das andere Bild zeigt einen nicht idealen Krystall. Die Reflexion ist stark verbreitert und besitzt an 2 Stellen deutliche Intensitätsmaxima, welche zeigen, daß zwei Orientierungen der kleinen Kryställchen, aus denen der Diamant besteht, besonders bevorzugt sind. Der gesamte Divergenzbereich beträgt etwa 3 Minuten.

 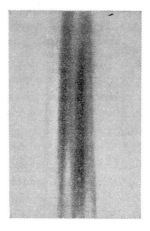

K_α $K_{\alpha'}$

Fig. 4. Das linke Bild zeigt die Reflexion des *Rh K*α-Dubletts an einem Diamanten, welcher ein einziger Krystall ist, während das rechte Bild die Reflexion derselben Strahlung an einem nicht einheitlichen Diamanten darstellt. Äußerlich sehen beide Krystalle gleich klar und einwandfrei aus.

242

Historisch ist bemerkenswert, dass schon, als die Interferenz-erscheinungen an Röntgenstrahlen aufkamen, Gegner der Atomtheorie aussprachen, man könne diese Erscheinungen mit einer dreifach periodischen Dielektrizitätskonstante er-klären und brauche dazu nicht an die Existenz von Atomen zu glauben. Der jetzige Stand der Theorie rechtfertigt durchaus den ersten Teil dieser Behauptung, man führt die Interferenz-erscheinungen tatsächlich am besten auf eine periodisch wechselnde Dielektrizitätskonstante zurück; aber er setzt diese Dielektrizitätskonstante in den engsten Zusammenhang mit der Atomtheorie. Es ist bemerkungswert, daß die Beant-wortung der Frage, wie die dynamische Theorie auf diesen Fall abzuändern ist, mathematisch wesentlich einfacher ist als die dynamische Theorie der älteren Form.

M. v. LAUE,
Erg. d. Techn. Röntgenkunde **3** (1933) p. 9 and p. 8

58. The Reflexion of X-Rays from Crystals, by R. SCHLAPP (1926)

▄▄

59. Die dynamische Theorie der Röntgenstrahlinterferenzen in neuer Form, by M. v. LAUE (1931)

▄▄

58. The purpose of the following paper is to give an account of the principal phenomena of the X-ray optics of perfect crystals on the basis of the electromagnetic theory of light in continuous media. The method depends on the solution of the equations of propagation of electromagnetic disturbance in a medium whose specific inductive capacity is a periodic function of position. The simplest medium of this type, and the one most amenable to mathematical treatment, is the periodically stratified medium, in which the specific inductive capacity is a periodic function of distance from a given plane. Such a medium appears to suffice for the description of the phenomena under consideration, for the present analysis will be found to reproduce most of the features of propagation and reflexion of X-rays in crystals which have emerged in discussions of the problem by other methods.

(···)

We see, then, that the amplitude of reflexion may be expressed in terms of glancing angle $\phi + \varepsilon$. If ε_1 denotes the half-width of the range of perfect reflexion, the values of the amplitude appropriate to the three regions

$$\varepsilon < -\varepsilon_1, \quad -\varepsilon_1 < \varepsilon < \varepsilon_1, \quad \varepsilon > \varepsilon_1$$

are respectively

$$-\{\varepsilon + \sqrt{(\varepsilon^2 - \varepsilon_1^2)}\}/\varepsilon_1, \quad 1, \quad \{\varepsilon - \sqrt{(\varepsilon^2 - \varepsilon_1^2)}\}/\varepsilon_1$$

These are equivalent to the formulae given by Darwin[1].

The above analysis leads to values of the factors representing the influence on the intensity of reflexion of polarization, structure, and temperature, which are the square roots of the values obtained by a simpler theory in which each plane is assumed to scatter independently of the others. This result is in general agreement with Darwin's later results, and with the more recent investigations of Ewald[2].

In view of the short wave-length of X-rays, in comparison with which ordinary matter must be regarded as coarse-grained, it is remarkable that the crystal should be capable of being treated as a continuous optical medium. A suggested explanation is that when the radiation traverses the crystal in a direction near the reflecting angle, the portions of the incident wave-train which contribute to any wavefront of the reflected train are spaced out at intervals $2d \sin \theta = n\lambda$ behind each other, and therefore meet successive planes in the same phase, so that each reflected wave-front is made up of contributions coming from all the planes. This makes it possible to average out the irregularities of the individual planes over their whole number, or, in other words, to replace the discrete electronic structure of each plane by a continuous distribution.

I wish to express my indebtedness to Sir Joseph Larmor, at whose suggestion this investigation was undertaken.

Department of Applied Mathematics University of Edinburgh.

59. Ewalds dynamische Theorie der Röntgenstrahlinterferenzen[3] gehört nach unserer Ansicht auf alle Zeiten zu den Meisterwerken der mathematischen Physik. Sie bewältigte mit glänzenden Methoden ein zunächst schier unlösbares Problem, rechtfertigte eigentlich erst die elementare,

[1] C. G. Darwin, *Phil. Mag.* **27** (1914) 675 [this Vol. p. 203].

[2] P. P. Ewald, *Phys. Ztschr.* **26** (1925) 29 [this Vol. p. 234].

[3] P. P. Ewald, *Ann. Physik* **54** (1917) 519, 557 [this Vol. p. 216]; *Z. Physik* **2** (1920) 332; **30** (1924) 1.

rein auf Phasenzusammensetzung beruhende Theorie, indem sie deren Unzulänglichkeiten quantitativ abzuschätzen lehrte, zeigte ihre innere Verbundenheit mit der optischen Dispersionstheorie und sagte dabei Abweichungen von den Ergebnissen der älteren Theorie voraus, die wenige Jahre später für die vollständige Deutung der Beobachtungen Hjalmar's sowie für eine exakte Messung der Wellenlängen unentbehrlich wurden. Aber wir glauben aussprechen zu dürfen, daß auch unter denen, die ihre Resultate oft benutzen, nicht allzu viele sie wirklich durchgearbeitet haben. Denn jene glänzenden mathematischen Methoden waren nicht nur schwierig zu finden, sie bereiten in manchen Teilen auch dem Leser Schwierigkeiten. Daran hat auch die Neubearbeitung durch Waller[1] nicht viel geändert, welche im übrigen das Verdienst besitzt, zuerst Gitter mit Basis in die Rechnung einbezogen zu haben. Der Zweck der folgenden Seiten ist, der Theorie eine leichter verständliche Form zu geben. Daß wir trotz weitgehenden Verzichtes auf neue Ergebnisse die neue Form veröffentlichen, scheint uns durch die Wichtigkeit der Sache gerechtfertigt; ebenso, daß wir, um dem Leser das Zurückgreifen auf die genannten Arbeiten zu erleichtern, die geometrische Diskussion Ewald's nochmals zum Abdruck bringen, obwohl wir an ihr fast nichts zu ändern brauchen.

Ewald und Waller benutzen die Vorstellung von Dipolen, welche in den Gitterpunkten oder daneben auch in einigen anderen Punkten der Gitterzelle sitzen[2], während der Zwischenraum leer ist. Die neuere Entwicklung der Atomtheorie führt aber zu der Vorstellung, daß die Elektronenladungen die ganze Zelle ziemlich lückenlos erfüllen, und die schönen Messungen von W. L. Bragg, James und Bosanquet[3] oder z.B. von James, Waller und Hartree[4] beweisen, daß diese Vorstellung den Intensitätsmessungen an Röntgenstrahlen in der Tat weit besser entspricht als die ältere. Darum werden auch wir uns dieser Anschauung bedienen. Wir setzen also voraus, daß die negativen Ladungen überall eine gewisse Dichte haben, daß sie sich aber unter dem Einfluß eines elektrischen Feldes verschieben, also Dichteänderungen erfahren. Diese Verschiebungen setzen wir als zur Feldstärke proportional an, wobei der Proportionalitätsfaktor sich wie für freie Elektronen nach der Korpuskulartheorie berechnet, sofern wir von der Bindung der Elektronen an die Atome absehen dürfen, was für gewisse große Schwingungszahlen gewiß gerechtfertigt ist[5]. Wir brau-

---

[1] I. Waller, Uppsala Universitets Arsskrift 1925.
[2] P. P. Ewald, *Physik. Z.* **26** (1925) 29 [this Vol. p. 234].
[3] W. L. Bragg, R. W. James, C. H. Bosanquet, *Philosophic. Mag.* **41** (1921) 309 [this Vol. p. 265].
[4] R. W. James, I. Waller u. D. R. Hartree, *Proc. Roy. Soc.* **118** (1928) 334.
[5] Vgl. z.B. I. Waller, *Physik. Z.* **30** (1929) 518.

chen aber die Frage, wie dieser Faktor zu berechnen ist, gar nicht zu erörtern. Vielmehr ist unser Rechnungsschema elastisch genug, um sich noch
allen Möglichkeiten anzupassen. Wir beabsichtigen, die Maxwellschen
Gleichungen ganz direkt für einen Körper mit derartig verteilten negativen Ladungen zu lösen. Wir vermeiden dabei die schwierigen Summa-
tionen, welche Ewald und seine Nachfolger für die Berechnung der retar-
dierten Gitterpotentiale nötig hatten.

Die Durchführung dieses Planes erleichtert nun der folgende Gedanke.
Die positiven Ladungen, gebunden an die Atomkerne, nehmen wegen
deren großer Masse an der Streuung der elektrischen Wellenstrahlungen
gar nicht teil. Infolgedessen dürfen wir die Fiktion einführen, als wären
sie nicht in den fast punktförmigen Atomkernen konzentriert, sondern
irgendwie anders verteilt, sofern wir nur daran festhalten, daß sie von der
Welle nicht in Bewegung zu setzen sind. Wir wollen die positiven Ladungen
so verteilt denken, daß sie, solange kein störendes Feld vorhanden ist,
die negativen Ladungen überall genau kompensieren. Ein Feld ruft dann
in jedem Raumpunkt eine zur Feldstärke proportionale elektrische Polarisation hervor, deren Stärke, abgesehen von der Feldstärke, durch einen
von Ort zu Ort wechselnden Proportionalitätsfaktor gegeben ist. Ein
solcher fingierter Körper hat also eine räumlich veränderliche Dielektrizitätskonstante. Im wirklichen Körper mit seinen in den Atomkernen zu-
sammengeballten positiven Ladungen ist das elektromagnetische Wellen-
feld genau das gleiche, während beide Körper sich freilich elektrostatisch
unterscheiden; doch das kommt für unsere Zwecke nicht in Betracht[1].

Ein Punkt könnte Bedenken erregen. Die Beweglichkeit der negativen
und die Unbeweglichkeit der positiven, nach unserer Fiktion räumlich
verteilten Ladungen, muß bei Störung durch die Welle zur Folge haben,
daß beide Ladungen sich nicht mehr genau kompensieren, daß also Raum-
ladungen auftreten. Von diesen haben wir bisher nicht gesprochen und
werden dies auch in der Folge nicht tun. Wir haben das aber auch nicht
nötig, weil sich diese Ladungen von selbst aus der Divergenz des die Polarisation pro Volumeneinheit darstellenden Vektors ergeben, wie ja in der
Maxwellschen Theorie hinlänglich bekannt[2]. Wir brauchen sie neben der
Polarisation nicht gesondert in Rechnung zu setzen. Unsere Fiktion bewirkt, daß wir mit der Maxwellschen Theorie für ruhende Körper aus-
kommen, denn—um es zu wiederholen—jede Aussage über die Änderung

---

[1] Man kann auch unbedenklich dem wirklichen Körper dieselbe Dielektrizitätskonstante
zuschreiben, wie dem fingierten; es kommt nur die feste Raumladung hinzu.
[2] Die Quantentheorie behält für elektrische Raumdichte und elektrischen Strom die
Kontinuitätsgleichung bei, so daß jeder Dichteänderung eine Verschiebung von Ladungen
entspricht.

der negativen Ladungen unter dem Einfluß des Feldes läßt sich—hinreichende Kleinheit dieser Störung vorausgesetzt—in eine Aussage über die Dielektrizitätskonstante des fingierten Körpers verwandeln.

Ein ähnliches Problem—die Ermittelung eines elektrischen Wellenfeldes in einem Körper mit periodischer Dielektrizitätskonstante—hat nun schon Lohr[1] behandelt. Aber seine Ausführungen beruhen auf der Jaumannschen Kontinuitätsphysik, deren Begriffe in die Maxwellsche Theorie zu übertragen vielleicht möglich, aber gewiß nicht einfach ist. Zweifellos hat Lohrs Theorie mit dem folgenden viel gemeinsam, handelt es sich doch auch bei ihm um lineare partielle Differentialgleichungen mit dreifach periodischem Koeffizienten. Und Lohr weist ja auch immer wieder auf die Übereinstimmung seiner Rechnung mit Ewalds Theorie hin. Wir fürchten aber, daß nicht viele Physiker und Kristallographen es fertig bringen, die erforderliche Umdeutung in allen Einzelnheite durchzuführen. Deswegen liegt in den Arbeiten Lohrs doch wohl kein Grund, unsere Form der Theorie nicht zu veröffentlichen.

Das elektrische Feld kennzeichnen wir durch die elektrische Verschiebung $\mathfrak{D}$ und die magnetische Feldstärke $\mathfrak{H}$; die fingierte Dielektrizitätskonstante ε ist entsprechend der Gittertheorie eine dreifach periodische Funktion des Ortes. Wir werden aber nicht ε selbst als dreifache Fourier-Reihe darstellen, sondern, da wir uns für die Polarisation $(1 - 1/\varepsilon)\mathfrak{D}$ interessieren, den hier auftretenden Faktor $\psi = 1 - 1/\varepsilon$. Verstehen wir unter $\mathfrak{a}_1, \mathfrak{a}_2, \mathfrak{a}_3$ primitive Translationen des Gitters, unter $\mathfrak{b}_1, \mathfrak{b}_2, \mathfrak{b}_3$ die zugehörigen Grundvektoren des reziproken Gitters, so setzen wir also[2]

$$1 - 1/\varepsilon = \psi = \sum \psi_m \exp\{-j(\mathfrak{b}_m \mathfrak{r})\}$$
$$(\mathfrak{b}_m = \sum_{\alpha=1}^{3} m_\alpha \cdot \mathfrak{b}_\alpha, \quad j = 2\pi \sqrt{(-1)}). \tag{1}$$

Dabei ist $\mathfrak{r}$ der Radiusvektor von einem beliebigen Gitterpunkt zum Aufpunkt. Geht man von diesem zu dem Punkt

$$\mathfrak{r} + \sum_{\alpha=1}^{3} l_\alpha \mathfrak{a}_\alpha \; (l_\alpha \text{ ganzzahlig})$$

über, so ändert sich der Exponent von $\exp\{-j(\mathfrak{b}_m \mathfrak{r})\}$ wegen der Definitionen

$$(\mathfrak{a}_\alpha \mathfrak{b}_\beta) = \begin{cases} 0 \text{ wenn } \alpha \neq \beta, \\ 1 \text{ wenn } \alpha = \beta, \end{cases}$$

durch die man das reziproke Gitter einführt, um die ganze Zahl $\sum_\alpha l_\alpha m_\alpha$, multipliziert mit $j = 2\pi i$; die e-Funktion also bleibt unverändert. Des-

---

[1] E. Lohr, *Sitzungsber. Akad. Wiss.. Wien, Math.-naturwiss. Kl.* **133** (2a) (1924) 517.

[2] In jedem Glied dieser dreifachen Fourier-Reihe soll der Index m die drei Indices m_1, m_2, m_3 repräsentieren. Insbesondere soll 0 als Index bedeuten, daß alle drei Indices gleich Null sind.

wegen ist jedes Glied der dreifachen Summe periodisch mit den drei Perioden $\mathfrak{a}_1$, $\mathfrak{a}_2$, $\mathfrak{a}_3$.

Die Fourier-Koeffizienten berechnen sich wie üblich aus den Integraldarstellungen:

$$\psi_m = \frac{1}{(\mathfrak{a}_1\mathfrak{a}_2\mathfrak{a}_3)} \int \psi \exp\{j(\mathfrak{b}_m\mathfrak{r})\}\, dv. \tag{2}$$

Die Raumintegration ist über die Gitterzelle auszudehnen, deren Inhalt $(\mathfrak{a}_1\mathfrak{a}_2\mathfrak{a}_3)$ im Nenner dieser Formel steht. Ist ε überall reell, was—wie immer bei optischen Problemen—Fehlen jeglicher Absorption bedeutet, so gilt dasselbe für ψ und deswegen sind ψ_m und ψ_{-m} konjugiert komplex. Sobald aber Absorption stattfindet, unterscheiden sich ψ_m und ψ_{-m} auch im absoluten Wert, weil dann ψ komplex ist.

Zur Ewaldschen Darstellungsart kommen wir zurück, wenn wir ε überall gleich 1 annehmen (also $\psi = 0$), mit Ausnahme der Gitterpunkte. Da in diesen

$$\exp\{j(\mathfrak{b}_m\mathfrak{r})\} = 1 \tag{3a}$$

ist, wird dann für alle Indizes m

$$\psi_m = \psi_0. \tag{4}$$

Jede unserer Formeln muß in die entsprechende bei Ewald übergehen, sofern wir diese Gleichsetzung vollziehen.

Im allgemeinen aber ist ψ_m der Strukturfaktor für das Interferenzmaximum m_1, m_2, m_3. Das erkennt man nach (2) leicht durch Grenzübergang von der üblichen, für einzelne Streuzentren geltenden Form dieses Faktors, denn die Grössen ψ der elementaren Theorie messen die Polarisierbarkeit[1]. Zudem wird es noch im folgenden bewiesen. Was die Versuche von W. L. Bragg, James und Bosanquet u.a. ergeben, ist infolgedessen zunächst die Funktion ψ. Nur insofern man diese der Dichte der negativen Ladungen mit einem konstanten Faktor proportional setzen darf, bestimmen diese Messungen die Ladungsverteilung.

In § 1 werden wir vorübergehend nicht die Fournier-Entwicklung für $1 - 1/\varepsilon$, sondern die für $- 1/\varepsilon$ brauchen:

$$- 1/\varepsilon = \sum \psi'_m \exp\{-j(\mathfrak{b}_m\mathfrak{r})\}. \tag{5}$$

Es ist dann

wenn nicht $m_1 = m_2 = m_3 = 0$; aber
$$\left.\begin{array}{l} \psi'_m = \psi_m, \\[4pt] \psi'_0 = \psi_0 - 1. \end{array}\right\} \tag{6}$$

---

[1] Für diskrete Streuzentren ist $\sum_\alpha \psi_\alpha \exp\{j(\mathfrak{b}_m\mathfrak{r}_\alpha)\}$ der Strukturfaktor des Interferenzpunktes m. Den Zusammenhang zwischen gewissen Fourier-Koeffizienten und dem Strukturfaktor hat zuerst wohl W. H. Bragg: *Trans. Roy. Soc. Lond.* **215** (1915) 253 angedeutet [this Vol. p. 111].

§ 1. *Die dynamische Grundgleichung*

Die Maxwellschen Gleichungen für unser fingiertes Medium lauten:

$$\operatorname{rot} \mathfrak{H} = \frac{1}{c}\frac{\partial \mathfrak{D}}{\partial t} \qquad \operatorname{rot}\left(\frac{\mathfrak{D}}{\varepsilon}\right) = -\frac{1}{c}\frac{\partial \mathfrak{H}}{\partial t} \tag{7}$$

Die beiden Divergenzgleichungen

$$\operatorname{div} \mathfrak{D} = 0 \qquad \operatorname{div} \mathfrak{H} = 0$$

ergeben sich für Schwingungen als Folgerungen hieraus, brauchen also nicht explizit berücksichtigt zu werden. Es handelt sich um monochromatische Schwingungen der Schwingungszahl ν. Wir suchen die Lösung in der Form

$$\begin{aligned}
\mathfrak{D} &= \exp(j\nu t)\,\textstyle\sum_m \mathfrak{D}_m \exp\{-j(\mathfrak{K}_m \mathfrak{r})\}\\
\mathfrak{H} &= \exp(j\nu t)\,\textstyle\sum_m \mathfrak{H}_m \exp\{-j(\mathfrak{K}_m \mathfrak{r})\}
\end{aligned} \tag{8}$$

wobei

$$\mathfrak{K}_m = \mathfrak{K}_0 + \mathfrak{b}_m = \mathfrak{K}_0 + \textstyle\sum m_\alpha b_\alpha \tag{9}$$

sein soll.

Man erkennt in jedem Glied dieser dreifachen Summen die Darstellung einer ebenen Welle, welche in der Richtung des Ausbreitungsvektors $\mathfrak{K}_m$ mit der Phasengeschwindigkeit

$$v = \frac{\gamma}{|\mathfrak{K}_m|}$$

fortschreitet, so daß

$$n = \frac{c}{v} = \frac{c}{\nu}\,|\mathfrak{K}_m| \tag{10}$$

der Brechungsindex dieser Welle ist. Alle diese Richtungen und Geschwindigkeiten sind durch Gleichung (9) miteinander verknüpft. Dabei ist aber $\mathfrak{K}_0$ ein nach Richtung und Betrag noch verfügbarer Vektor. Wir werden, indem wir die Berechtigung unseres Ansatzes nachzuweisen suchen, gerade Aussagen über diesen Vektor bekommen.

Man erkennt in diesem Ansatz sofort die Übereinstimmung mit der Ewaldschen Theorie, welche den Hertzschen Vektor des Wellenfeldes ebenfalls als Summe über eine (im Prinzip) unendlich große Zahl ebener Wellen darstellt und die Ausbreitungsvektoren $\mathfrak{K}_m$ mittels der Gleichung (9) verknüpft.

Nach dem Ansatz (8) ist nun

$$\operatorname{rot} \mathfrak{H} = j\,\textstyle\sum [\mathfrak{H}_m \mathfrak{K}_m]\exp\{-j(\mathfrak{K}_m \mathfrak{r})\}, \qquad \frac{1}{c}\frac{\partial \mathfrak{D}}{\partial t} = \frac{j\nu}{c}\,\textstyle\sum \mathfrak{D}_m \exp\{-j(\mathfrak{K}_m \mathfrak{r})\}.$$

Setzt man beide Ausdrücke entsprechend der ersten Maxwellschen Gleichung einander gleich, so erhält man nach Weghebung des gemeinsamen
Faktors $\exp\{-j(\mathfrak{K}_0\mathfrak{r})\}$ die Gleichsetzung zweier Fourier-Reihen. Da diese
identisch im Ortsvektor übereinstimmen sollen, müssen entsprechende
Glieder einander gleich sein; und dies erfordert, daß

$$k\mathfrak{D}_m = [\mathfrak{H}_m \mathfrak{K}_m] \tag{11}$$

ist. Dabei ist $k = \nu/c = 1/\lambda$ das Reziproke der Vakuumwellenlänge λ.
Weiter ist nach dem Ansatz (8) im Hinblick auf (5)

$$\frac{\mathfrak{D}}{\varepsilon} = -\sum_q \sum_p \psi'_p \mathfrak{D}_q \exp\{-j(\mathfrak{K}_q + \mathfrak{b}_p, \mathfrak{r})\}.$$

Nach (9) ist dabei

$$\mathfrak{K}_q + \mathfrak{b}_p = \mathfrak{K}_{p+q}.$$

Da die Summationsgrenzen von $-\infty$ bis $+\infty$ laufen, kann man ohne
weiteres $p + q = m$ als Summationsindex neben q einführen:

$$\frac{\mathfrak{D}}{\varepsilon} = -\sum_m \sum_q \psi'_{m-q} \mathfrak{D}_q \exp\{-j(\mathfrak{K}_m \mathfrak{r})\}.$$

Man schließt dann, wie oben, auf die Darstellungen:

$$\operatorname{rot} \frac{\mathfrak{D}}{\varepsilon} = j \sum_m [\mathfrak{K}_m, \sum_q \psi'_{m-q} \mathfrak{D}_q] \exp\{-j(\mathfrak{K}_m \mathfrak{r})\},$$

$$-\frac{1}{c}\frac{\delta\mathfrak{H}}{\delta t} = -j\frac{\nu}{c}\sum_m \mathfrak{H}_m \exp\{-j(\mathfrak{K}_m \mathfrak{r})\}.$$

Nach der zweiten Maxwellschen Gleichung müssen beide Reihen identisch
in $\mathfrak{r}$ übereinstimmen. Daher sind entsprechende Glieder einander gleich:

$$k\mathfrak{H}_m = -\sum_q \psi'_{m-q}[\mathfrak{K}_m \mathfrak{D}_q]. \tag{12}$$

Elimination der $\mathfrak{H}_m$ aus (11) gemäß dieser Gleichung ergibt:

$$k^2\mathfrak{D}_m = \sum_q \psi'_{m-q}[\mathfrak{K}_m[\mathfrak{K}_m \mathfrak{D}_q]].$$

Die Rechnungsregel

$$[\mathfrak{A}[\mathfrak{B}\mathfrak{C}]] = \mathfrak{B}(\mathfrak{A}\mathfrak{C}) - \mathfrak{C}(\mathfrak{A}\mathfrak{B})$$

zeigt aber, daß

$$-[\mathfrak{K}_m[\mathfrak{K}_m \mathfrak{D}_q]] = (\mathfrak{D}_q \mathfrak{K}^2_m - \mathfrak{K}_m(\mathfrak{K}_m \mathfrak{D}_q)) = \mathfrak{K}^2_m\left(\mathfrak{D}_q - \mathfrak{K}_m \frac{(\mathfrak{K}_m \mathfrak{D}_q)}{\mathfrak{K}^2_m}\right)$$

gleich $\mathfrak{K}^2{}_m$ mal der zu $\mathfrak{K}_m$ senkrechten Komponente von $\mathfrak{D}_q$ ist; wir nennen diese $\mathfrak{D}_{q[m]}$. Folglich:

$$k^2 \mathfrak{D}_m = - \mathfrak{K}^2{}_m \sum_q \psi'{}_{m-q} \mathfrak{D}_{q[m]}.$$

Ersetzt man nun nach (5) die $\psi'{}_m$ durch die ψ_m, so hat man die *dynamische Grundgleichung* vor sich:

$$\frac{\mathfrak{K}^2{}_m - k^2}{\mathfrak{K}^2{}_m} \mathfrak{D}_m = \sum_q \psi_{m-q} \mathfrak{D}_{q[m]}. \tag{I}$$

Sind alle hierin enthaltenen Beziehungen erfüllt, so genügt Ansatz (8) den Maxwellschen Gleichungen[1].

Wir können schon hier den Nachweis führen, daß unsere Darstellung sich mit Ewalds Theorie vollständig deckt, sobald wir, wie in der Einleitung begründet, alle ψ_m gleich ψ_0 setzen. In diesem Falle folgt nämlich aus (I)

$$\mathfrak{D} = e^{j\nu t} \sum \mathfrak{D}_m \exp\{-j(\mathfrak{K}_m \mathfrak{r})\} =$$

$$= \psi_0 e^{j\nu t} \sum_m \frac{\mathfrak{K}^2{}_m}{\mathfrak{K}^2{}_m - k^2} \left(\sum_q \mathfrak{D}_{q[m]} \right) \exp\{-j(\mathfrak{K}_m \mathfrak{r})\}.$$

Für die Gitterpunkte sind nach (3a) alle Exponentialfunktionen

$$\exp\{-j(\mathfrak{K}_m \mathfrak{r})\},$$

unabhängig von den Indizes m, einander gleich. Folglich dürfen wir $\mathfrak{D}_{q[m]}$ statt mit $\exp\{-j(\mathfrak{K}_m \mathfrak{r})\}$ mit $\exp\{-j(\mathfrak{K}_q \mathfrak{r})\}$ multiplizieren, sofern wir die letzte Gleichung auf Gitterpunkte anwenden. Nehmen wir dann zur $\sum_q$

---

[1] Man kann eine ganz ähnliche Rechnung, wie im Text für das Raumgitter, für ganz beliebig verteilte Elektronenladungen anstellen. Man braucht nur statt der Fourier-Reihe (I) das Fourier-Integral hinzuschreiben, das entsteht, wenn die drei Parameter m nicht mehr ganzzahlig sind, sondern sich kontinuierlich ändern. Auch den Ansatz (8) wird man dann in die Integraldarstellung umschreiben, wobei aber Gleichung (9) formal unverändert bleibt. Dann verläuft die Rechnung wie im Text. Ihr Ergebnis unterscheidet sich von (I) nur dadurch, daß auch hier die (dreifache) Summe durch ein (dreifaches) Integral ersetzt ist.

Zum Raumgitter gelangen wir zurück durch die Annahme, daß von den Fourier-Koeffizienten ψ_m, mit ihren zunächst stetig veränderlichen Indices nur die von Null verschieden sind, bei der die drei Indices ganzzahlig werden. Sind aber die Differenzen $m-q$ in der verallgemeinerten Gleichung (I) ganzzahlig, so kommt man, wie man leicht sieht, gerade zu der obigen Darstellung zurück. Dies beweist, worauf mich Herr F. Möglich aufmerksam machte, die *Notwendigkeit* des Ansatze (8) für Raumgitter.

Man erkennt aber an der Integraldarstellung, daß jede Abweichung von der Periodizität des Raumgitters unregelmäßige Streustrahlung hervorruft. Nur im ganz ungestörten Gitter fällt diese fort.

noch den Faktor e^{jvt} hinzu, so finden wir:

$$\mathfrak{D} = \psi_0 \sum_m \frac{\mathfrak{K}^2{}_m}{\mathfrak{K}^2{}_m - k^2} \, \mathfrak{D}_{[m]}.$$

Diese Beziehung aber stimmt formal überein mit der Ewaldschen Grundgleichung[1], 'in deren Lösung das ganze Problem gipfelt', nämlich mit:

$$\mathfrak{b} = \frac{1}{\Omega} \sum \frac{1}{\varepsilon_m} \, \mathfrak{b}_{[m]}.$$

Nur müssen wir, wie er

$$|\mathfrak{K}_m| = k(1 + \varepsilon_m) \tag{13}$$

setzen und die Quadrate der kleinen Größen ε_m vernachlässigen; weiter ist

$$\psi_0 = \frac{2}{\Omega} \tag{14}$$

zu setzen, und unter Integration über den unendlich kleinen Raum um einen Gitterpunkt, in welchem ε nicht 1 ist, Ewalds Vektor $\mathfrak{b}$ durch

$$\mathfrak{b} = \int \left(1 - \frac{1}{\varepsilon}\right) \mathfrak{D} \, dV$$

zu definieren. Dabei wird $\mathfrak{b}$ wie bei Ewald ein Maß für das elektrische Moment in den Gitterpunkten.

Ewalds Grundgleichung sagt physikalisch aus, daß jeder seiner Dipole vom Feld die Anregung erfährt, die er zur Ausführung der das Feld bestimmenden Schwingung braucht. Wir haben diese Aussage durch Einführung einer Dielektrizitätskonstante in Rechnung gesetzt. Denn die mit ihrer Hilfe auszudrückende Proportionalität zwischen Polarisation und Feldstärke enthält ja die ganze Dynamik der Ladungsträger. Da wir von dieser Dielektrizitätskonstante zwangsweise zu unserer Grundgleichung (I) geführt wurden, sind in der Tat beide Grundgleichungen wesensgleich, abgesehen von der etwas größeren Allgemeinheit der unseren.

§ 2. *Annäherungen in der Lösung der Grundgleichung* (I)

Eine strenge Fortführung der Theorie erforderte die Auflösung der unendlich vielen linearen Gleichungen (I) mit unendlich vielen Unbekannten

---

[1] *Loc. cit., Ann. Physik* **54** (1917) 543; Gleichung (14) [cf. this vol. p. 223].

$\mathfrak{D}_m$. Ein solches Problem ist der heutigen Mathematik wohl nur in Ausnahmefällen zugänglich. Deswegen werden wir uns mit genäherten Lösungen beschäftigen.

Die elementare Theorie führt bekanntlich für die Richtung des einfallenden und des abgebeugten Strahles Einheitsvektoren, $\mathfrak{s}_0$ und $\mathfrak{s}_m$, ein, und faßt ihre Aussagen zusammen in die Gleichung

$$k(\mathfrak{s}_m - \mathfrak{s}_0) = \mathfrak{b}_m.$$

Sie läßt sich geometrisch im Raume des reziproken Gitters veranschaulichen. Denn zieht man vom Nullpunkt des Gitters aus den Vektor $OP =$ $= -k\mathfrak{s}_0$ und schlägt man um den 'Ausbreitungspunkt' P die 'Ausbreitungskugel' mit dem Radius k, so muß nach dieser Gleichung der Gitterpunkt m genau auf der Kugel liegen, wenn der Strahl $\mathfrak{s}_m$ durch Interferenz zustande kommen soll (Abb. 1).

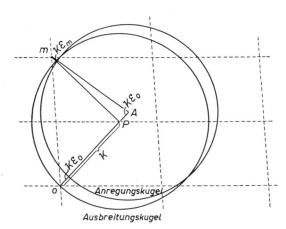

Abb. 1. Ewalds Konstruktion im reziproken Gitter.

Die dynamische Theorie muß nun zweifellos bis zu einem gewissen, sogar sehr weitgehenden Grad mit dieser Aussage übereinstimmen. Sie kann dies, weil nach (9)

$$\mathfrak{K}_m - \mathfrak{K}_0 = \mathfrak{b}_m$$

ist, eine Aussage, die der elementaren Theorie jedenfalls sehr nahe kommt. Aber sie wird auf die Starrheit jener Theorie, die sich in der Aufstellung einer genau zu erfüllenden geometrischen Bedingung ausspricht, verzichten. Sie wird daher nur verlangen, daß die Ausbreitungskugel nahe an den Gitterpunkten vorübergeht, welche den in merklicher Stärke auftretenden Strahlen $\mathfrak{K}_m$ entsprechen. Immerhin führt jene Konstruktion dann zu einer Auswahl unter der zunächst unendlich großen Zahl der $\mathfrak{K}_m$. Die Zahl der danach in Betracht kommenden Strahlen sei N, den Strahl $\mathfrak{K}_0$ inbegriffen.

Wir setzen in (I) alle anderen $\mathfrak{D}_m$ gleich Null; dadurch wird die Zahl der Gleichungen (I) sowie die der Unbekannten $\mathfrak{D}_m$ endlich, und man kann die altbekannten Methoden zur Lösung homogener linearer Gleichungen anwenden. Wir sprechen in diesem Fall von den 'reduzierten Grundgleichungen'.

Im allgemeinen ist jede Vektorgleichung mit drei algebraischen Gleichungen für die Komponenten identisch. Aber hier wissen wir aus (11), daß jeder Vektor $\mathfrak{D}_m$ auf $\mathfrak{K}_m$ senkrecht steht. Es sind also nur die beiden zu $\mathfrak{K}_m$ senkrechten Komponenten von ihm zu ermitteln. Daher ist die Zahl der reduzierten Gleichungen (I) und die der Unbekannten nur gleich $2N$.

Lösbarkeitsbedingung für ein System homogener linearer Gleichungen ist, daß die Determinante ihrer Koeffizienten verschwindet. Im vorliegenden Fall enthält die Determinante alle $|\mathfrak{K}_m|$; und diese lassen sich gemäß (9) auf $|\mathfrak{K}_0 + \mathfrak{b}_m|$ zurückführen. Geben wir also die Richtung von $\mathfrak{K}_0$ vor, so enthält die Determinantengleichung als einzige Unbekannte den Betrag

$$|\mathfrak{K}_0| = k(1 + \varepsilon_0),$$

oder auch den *Anregungsfehler* ε_0 des Strahles $\mathfrak{K}_0$. Alle $|\mathfrak{K}_m|$ hängen von ε_0 linear ab, wie wir am Ende dieses Paragraphen noch zeigen werden. Tragen wir in Abb. 1 von O aus den Vektor $-\mathfrak{K}_0$ ein, wie er sich aus der Determinantengleichung ergibt, so liegt dessen Endpunkt in dem P benachbarten Punkt A, dem 'Anregungspunkt', und zwar gibt es, da die Gleichung für ε_0 vom Grad $2N$ ist, $2N$ solcher Anregungspunkte auf dem genannten Strahl OP. Wir unterscheiden sie durch obere Indizes $A^r(r=1, 2, \ldots 2N)$. Wählen wir einen von ihnen aus, so gibt dessen Lage die Beträge für alle Vektoren $\mathfrak{K}_m$, also die Phasengeschwindigkeiten dieser Strahlen. Der durch (13) eingeführte Anregungsfehler ε_m gibt dann den Abstand $k\varepsilon_m$ des zugehörigen Gitterpunktes m von der 'Anregungskugel' an, die um den Anregungspunkt mit dem Radius k zu schlagen ist. Jedem Punkt A^r entspricht, wenn wir nunmehr die Verhältnisse der je zwei Komponenten der $\mathfrak{D}_m$ aus (I) entnehmen, ein im Raumgitter mögliches Wellenfeld. Im allgemeinen bekommen wir also bei vorgegebener Richtung von $\mathfrak{K}_0$ $2N$ mögliche Wellenfelder. Sie werden sich unterscheiden in den Stärke- und Phasenbeziehungen zwischen den Strahlen sowie in dem Polarisationszustand des einzelnen Strahles.

Dieses Verfahren beseitigt die Sonderstellung des Strahles $\mathfrak{K}_0$, wenig-

stens was seine Intensität anbelangt; er kann sich bei Auflösung der reduzierten Grundgleichungen als schwächer erweisen als andere. Er behält
eine Sonderrolle nur noch hinsichtlich seiner, als genau bekannt vorausgesetzten Richtung. Aber auch diese Bevorzugung wollen wir nunmehr
beseitigen.

Verändern wir nämlich die Richtung $\mathfrak{K}_0$, wenngleich so wenig, daß
die bisher in Betracht gezogenen Gitterpunkte m die allein in Betracht
kommenden bleiben, so beschreibt jeder der Anregungspunkte $A^{\mathfrak{r}}$ eine
Fläche. Die Gesamtheit dieser $2N$ Flächen fassen wir unter dem Begriff
'*Dispersionsfläche*' zusammen; der Name soll sagen, daß man die Bre-
chungsindizes, d.h. die Phasengeschwindigkeiten für alle Wellen $\mathfrak{K}_m$ kennt,
sobald man einen Anregungspunkt A auf ihr gewählt hat, und daß dieser
Brechungsindex dem Abstand des zugehörigen Gitterpunktes von A proportional ist[1]. Die Dispersionsfläche hat im allgemeinen $2N$ Schalen;
doch können von diesen auch mehrere in einzelnen Punkten oder überhaupt zusammenfallen.

*Im Kristall mögliche Wellenfelder sind somit charakterisiert durch die
Angabe der N Gitterpunkte des reziproken Gitters, die den in Betracht zu
ziehenden Wellen $\mathfrak{K}_m$ entsprechen, und durch die 2N Schalen der Dispersionsfläche.*

Diese anschauliche Konstruktion setzt natürlich voraus, daß die Determinantengleichung für ε_0 zu $2N$ reellen Wurzeln führt. Das wird bei absorbierenden Kristallen nicht der Fall sein, da dann die ψ_m beliebige komplexe Werte haben. Daß für nichtabsorbierende Körper trotz der komplexen
Koeffizienten ψ_m meist $2N$ reelle Wurzeln da sind, wird § 4 zeigen. Aber
auch, wenn sich auf diese Art $2N$ reelle Schalen für die Dispersionsfläche
ergeben, können besondere Bedingungen im Einzelfall hindern, einen
reellen Punkt dieser Fläche als Anregungspunkt zu wählen (§ 5), so daß
der Vektor $\mathfrak{K}_0$ einen imaginären Anteil erhält. Setzt man aber

$$\mathfrak{K}_0 = \mathfrak{K}_0^{(1)} + i\mathfrak{K}^{(2)},$$

so lehrt Gleichung (9), daß alle $\mathfrak{K}_m$ denselben imaginären Bestandteil $\mathfrak{K}^{(2)}$
haben. Da dann die in (8) auftretenden Exponentialfunktionen alle den
gemeinsamen Faktor

$$\exp\{2\pi(\mathfrak{K}^{(2)}\mathfrak{r})\}$$

erhalten, klingen alle auftretenden inhomogenen Wellen in der gleichen
Richtung $(-\mathfrak{K}^{(2)})$ und in gleichem Maße ab.

---

[1] Siehe Gleichung (10).

Wir wollen nun noch den Zusammenhang zwischen dem Anregungs-
fehler ε_m des Strahles $\mathfrak{K}_m$ mit dem Anregungsfehler ε_0 angeben, auf den
wir schon hingewiesen haben. Der Gitterpunkt m in Abb. 1 habe von der
um P geschlagenen Ausbreitungskugel den Abstand $k\alpha_m$. Verschieben
wir nun die Kugel bei konstantem Radius um die Strecke PA, so daß
sie zur Anregungskugel wird, so kommt zu diesem Abstand noch die
Projektion von PA auf die Richtung Pm hinzu. Folglich ist der Abstand
des Punktes m von der Anregungskugel

$$k\varepsilon_m = k\alpha_m + k\varepsilon_0 \cos{(\mathfrak{K}_m\mathfrak{K}_0)};$$

oder:

$$\varepsilon_m = \alpha_m + \varepsilon_0 \cos{(\mathfrak{K}_m\mathfrak{K}_0)}. \tag{14a}$$

Diese Gleichung kann in Hinblick auf (13) dazu dienen, die Determinantengleichung auch formal in eine Gleichung vom Grad $2N$ für ε_0 zu verwandeln.

§ 3. *Die einfachsten Beispiele für nichtabsorbierende Kristalle*

1. Ein einziger Strahl ist von Bedeutung. Die reduzierte Grundgleichung lautet dann einfach

$$\mathfrak{D}_0(\mathfrak{K}_0{}^2(1 - \psi_0) - k^2) = 0. \tag{15}$$

Aus ihr folgt:

$$\mathfrak{K}_0{}^2 = \frac{k^2}{1 - \psi_0};$$

oder nach (13) für den Anregungsfehler ε_0:

$$\varepsilon_0 = \frac{1}{2}\,\psi_0;$$

oder nach (10) für den Brechnugsindex n_0:

$$n_0 = \frac{|\mathfrak{K}_0|}{k} = \frac{1}{\sqrt{(1 - \psi_0)}} = 1 + \frac{1}{2}\,\psi_0.$$

Da ψ_0 gleich dem räumlichen Mittelwert $\overline{1 - 1/\varepsilon}$ ist, erhält man als Ver-
allgemeinerung der berühmten Maxwellschen Beziehung zwischen Bre-
chungsindex und Dielektrizitätskonstante:

$$n_0 = \sqrt{(1/\overline{\varepsilon^{-1}})}.$$

256

Die Dispersionsfläche ist hier die Kugel vom Radius $|\mathfrak{K}_0|$. Sie ist doppelt zu zählen, da nach § 2 diese Fläche zweischalig sein solllte. Da man aber in diesem Fall für die beiden Komponenten, die $\mathfrak{D}_0$ in der Ebene senkrecht zu $\mathfrak{K}_0$ hat, dieselbe Grundgleichung (nämlich (15)) erhält, so liegt hier in der Tat der schon als möglich angekündigte Fall des Zusammenfallens zweier Schalen vor.

Da $n_0 - 1 = \frac{1}{2}\psi_0$ von der Größenordnung 10^{-6} ist, sind alle ψ_m, aber auch alle vorkommenden Werte des Anregungsfehlers ε_0 von dieser Größenordnung. Da bei Berücksichtigung mehrerer Strahlen der Strahl $\mathfrak{K}_0$ nach § 2 keine Sonderstellung einnimmt, muß jeder Anregungsfehler ε_m von derselben Ordnung sein, und dies bedeutet nach (14a), daß auch die Größe α_m, welche den Abstand des Gitterpunktes m von der Ausbreitungskugel mißt, nicht wesentlich größer sein darf, sofern der Strahl noch für das Feld in Betracht kommt.

Bei kleinen Kristallstücken wird man unter Umständen von vornherein sagen können, daß ein Strahl bekannter Richtung, nämlich $\mathfrak{K}_0$, an Stärke weit überwiegt, wenngleich noch andere auftreten. Dann wird man ihm die Phasengeschwindigkeit des einzelnen Strahles zuschreiben dürfen, also $|\mathfrak{K}_0| = k(1 + \frac{1}{2}\psi_0)$ setzen und in Abb. 1 den Anregungspunkt A in entsprechendem Abstand von O wählen. Die reduzierten Grundgleichungen (I) lassen dann die weitere Vereinfachung zu, daß man in der rechts stehenden Summe nur das Glied mit $\mathfrak{D}_0$ beibehält. Indem man dann noch nach (13) den Anregungsfehler ε_m einführt, also

$$\frac{\mathfrak{K}^2{}_m - k^2}{\mathfrak{K}^2{}_m} = 2\varepsilon_m$$

setzt, findet man:

$$\mathfrak{D}_m = \frac{\psi_m}{2\varepsilon_m} \mathfrak{D}_{0[m]}. \tag{15a}$$

Nach dieser Gleichung sind die Intensitäten der Strahlen $\mathfrak{K}_m$ umgekehrt proportional zu ihren Anregungsfehlern ε_m. Diese müssen, da ψ_m im allgemeinen von der Grössenordnung 10^{-6} ist, der Größenordnung nach etwa gleich 10^{-4} sein; sind sie größer, so wird $|\mathfrak{D}_m|^2$ unmerklich klein, sind sie kleiner, so versagt die Voraussetzung $\mathfrak{D}_0 > \mathfrak{D}_m$. Halten sie sich aber in dieser Größenordnung, so kann man Abb. 1 zur Abschätzung der Intensitäten der verschiedenen $\mathfrak{K}_m$ benutzen. Man sieht hier wohl am deutlichsten, wie die starre Interferenzbedingung der elementaren Theorie zwar nicht gerade für ungültig erklärt, aber doch in einem physikalischen Sinne gemildert wird.

Hier bewährt sich nun zum erstenmal die in der Einleitung angekündigte Deutung des Fourier-Koeffizienten ψ_m als Strukturfaktor. Er ist in

(15) nämlich der einzige Faktor, in welchem sich die Verteilung des Streuvermögens über die Zelle betätigt. Daß bei fehlender Absorption, wie oben ausgeführt,

$$|\psi_m| = |\psi_{-m}|.$$

ist, enthält den Friedelschen Satz, demzufolge eine Vorzeichenumkehr der drei Indizes m_1, m_2, m_3 eines Strahles dessen Stärke nicht beeinflußt, sofern man auch die Richtung des Strahles $\mathfrak{K}_0$ umkehrt. Das hat dann zur Folge, daß auch bei Kristallen, die selbst kein Symmetriezentrum unter den Symmetrieelementen ihrer Klasse haben, für die Intensität der Röntgenstrahlinterferenzen ein solches Zentrum hinzukommt. (Für die Phasen der abgebeugten Strahlen gilt dies nicht; doch diese entziehen sich ja vorläufig der Beobachtung.) Das steht in voller Übereinstimmung mit älteren Ausführungen des Verfassers sowie Ewalds und Hermanns[1]. Für absorbierende Kristalle entbehrt der Satz, wiewohl er sich empirisch ausnahmslos bestätigt hat, der theoretischen Grundlage.

Daß in (15a) vom Vektor $\mathfrak{D}_0$ nur die zu $\mathfrak{K}_m$ senkrechte Komponente $\mathfrak{D}_{0[m]}$ auftritt, entspricht, wie wir nicht näher auszuführen brauchen, dem Polarisationsfaktor der elementaren Theorie.

2. Zwei Wellen kommen in Betracht, wir nennen sie $\mathfrak{K}_0$ und $\mathfrak{K}_m$. Dieser Fall ist deshalb so einfach, weil man von vornherein zwei ausgezeichnete Polarisationszustände bei ihm unterscheiden kann, nämlich

a) Die elektrische Verschiebung schwingt senkrecht zu beiden Strahlrichtungen.

b) Sie schwingt in dieser Ebene.

In beiden Fällen können wir in den reduzierten Grundgleichungen sofort die Komponenten der Vektoren $\mathfrak{D}_0$, durch ihre absoluten Beträge D_0, D_m ersetzen. Es gilt im Fall a):

$$\frac{\mathfrak{K}^2_0 - k^2}{\mathfrak{K}^2_0} D_0 = \psi_0 D_0 + \psi_{-m} D_m$$

$$\frac{\mathfrak{K}^2_m - k^2}{\mathfrak{K}^2_m} D_m = \psi_0 D_m + \psi_m D_0, \tag{16a}$$

im Fall b), indem wir unter Θ den Winkel zwischen den Strahlen verstehen:

$$\frac{\mathfrak{K}^2_0 - k^2}{\mathfrak{K}^2_0} D_0 = \psi_0 D_0 + \psi_{-m} \cos\Theta \, D_m;$$

$$\frac{\mathfrak{K}^2_m - k^2}{\mathfrak{K}^2_m} D_m = \psi_0 D_0 + \psi_m \cos\Theta D_m. \tag{16b}$$

---

[1] M. v. Laue, *Ann. Physik* **50** (1916) 433; P. P. Ewald u. C. Hermann, *Z. Kristallogr.* **65** (1927) 251.

Die beiden Fälle unterscheiden sich lediglich durch den Faktor $\cos\Theta$, welcher im Fall b) zu ψ_m und ψ_{-m} hinzutritt. Wir erörtern zunächst den Fall a).

Die Determinantengleichung lautet, sofern man nach (13) die Anregungsfehler ε_0 und ε_m einführt

$$\begin{vmatrix} 2\varepsilon_0 - \psi_0 & -\psi_{-m} \\ -\psi_m & 2\varepsilon_m - \psi_0 \end{vmatrix} = 0 \qquad (17)$$

oder mit den Abkürzungen

$$\xi_0 = k\,(\varepsilon_0 - \tfrac{1}{2}\psi_0), \qquad \xi_m = k\,(\varepsilon_m - \tfrac{1}{2}\psi_0)$$

$$\xi_0\xi_m = \tfrac{1}{4}\,k^2\psi_m\psi_{-m}. \qquad (17a)$$

Nun denken wir uns um die Punkte O und m im Raum des reziproken Gitters die Kugeln K_0 und K_m mit dem Radius $k(1 + \tfrac{1}{2}\psi_0)$ geschlagen. ξ_0 gibt den senkrechten Abstand von der ersteren Kugel für den Anregungspunkt, der durch ε_0 und ε_m bestimmt werden soll, die zweite Klammer den Abstand von der zweiten Kugel. Wir wissen, daß wir nur solche Punkte zu betrachten brauchen, welche von O und m nahe gleiche Abstände haben, und daß es genügt, die Verhältnisse in einer durch O und m gehenden beliebigen Ebene zu untersuchen (Abb. 2). Wir brauchen diese Ebene ja nur um die Gerade Om zu drehen, um diese Einschränkung wieder abzustreifen.

Die Kreise, in welchen die Kugeln die Ebene schneiden, mögen sich im Punkt M schneiden. Da es nur auf die nächste Umgebung von M ankommt, messen wir die in (17a) auftretenden Abstände ξ_0, ξ_m statt von den Kreisen aus von deren Tangenten im Punkte M, T_0 und T_m. Diese

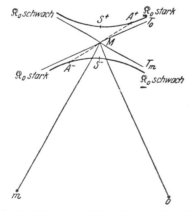

Abb. 2. Dispersionsfläche für zwei Strahlen.

Abstände lassen sich dann sicher linear durch irgendwelche Kartesischen Koordinaten darstellen; somit ist (17a) die Gleichung einer Kurve zweiter Ordnung, und zwar einer Hyperbel, da sie sich der einen Tangente um so mehr nähert, je mehr sie sich von der anderen entfernt. M ist Mittelpunkt der Hyperbel. Für ihre Scheitel S^+ und S^- ist

$$\xi_0 = \xi_m = \pm \tfrac{1}{2} k \sqrt{(\psi_m \psi_{-m})},$$

folglich

$$\varepsilon_0 = \varepsilon_m = \tfrac{1}{2}(\psi_0 \pm \sqrt{(\psi_m \psi_{-m})}).$$

Die reelle Achse der Hyperbel ist

$$S^+ S^- = 2 \frac{|\xi_0|}{\cos(\Theta/2)} = \frac{k}{\cos(\Theta/2)} \sqrt{(\psi_m \psi_{-m})}. \tag{17b}$$

Diese Näherung versagt freilich, wenn Θ dem Wert π zu nahe kommt.
Aus (16a) folgt dann weiter:

$$\frac{D_0}{D_m} = \frac{\psi_{-m}}{2\varepsilon_0 - \psi_0} = \frac{2\varepsilon_m - \psi_0}{\psi_m}$$

oder

$$\frac{D_0}{D_m} = \frac{k\psi_{-m}}{2\xi_0} = \frac{2\xi_m}{k\psi_m} \tag{18}$$

In den Enden A^+ und A^- desselben Hyperbeldurchmessers hat D_m/D_0 entgegengesetzt gleiche Werte. Daher unterscheiden sich die Phasendifferenzen von $\mathfrak{K}_m$ und $\mathfrak{K}_0$, die auf jedem Hyperbelast konstant sind, auf beiden Ästen um π, während das Intensitätsverhältnis in den Enden desselben Durchmessers dasselbe ist. Verschiebt man A^+ aus der in Abb. 2 gezeichneten Lage nach S_+ und darüber hinaus, so wächst ξ_0 und das Intensitätsverhältnis $|D_0|^2/|D_m|^2$ nimmt ab. In S^+ gilt

$$D_0/D_m = \sqrt{(\psi_{-m}/\psi_m)}.$$

Für den nichtabsorbierenden Kristall, den wir hier immer voraussetzen, ist der absolute Wert der Wurzel 1, beiden Strahlen sind gleich stark. Dasselbe gilt auch für S^-, nur haben hier, wie erwähnt, beide Strahlen eine andere Phasendifferenz als in S^+.

Im Fall b), in dem wir, wie erwähnt, überall zu ψ_m und ψ_{-m} den Faktor $\cos \Theta$ hinzuzufügen haben, finden wir wieder eine Hyperbel als Schnitt der Dispersionsfläche mit der Ebene der Strahlen. Nur ist ihre Achse

$$S^+ S^- = k \frac{|\cos \Theta|}{\cos(\Theta/2)} \sqrt{(\psi_m \psi_{-m})}$$

kleiner als im Fall a). Die Strahlen stören sich in ihrer Phasengeschwindigkeit hier weniger als im Fall a), weil nur eine Komponente der elektrischen
Verschiebung des einen in die Richtung der anderen Verschiebung fällt.
Diese Störung verschwindet ganz für $\Theta = \pi/2$. Dann ist nämlich $\xi_0 \xi_m = 0$
die Gleichung der Dispersionsfläche.

Drehung der Zeichenebene um die Gerade Om ergibt somit folgendes
Bild: Die je zwei Äste der beiden Hyperbeln werden zu den vier Schalen
der Dispersionsfläche, welche nach § 2 zu erwarten sind. Die ihnen entsprechenden Wellenfelder unterscheiden sich erstens durch die Schwingungsrichtung (Fall a) und b)), zweitens durch die Phasenbeziehungen
beider Strahlen. Liegt der Anregungspunkt A auf einem der vier Kreise,
welche die je zwei Scheitelpunkte der Hyperbeln (S^+ und S^-) beschreiben,
so sind beide Strahlen gleich intensiv. Entfernt sich A aus einer solchen
Lage, so nimmt der eine Strahl immer mehr an Stärke ab, und im gleichen Maße nähert sich die betrachtete Schale der Dispersionsfläche derjenigen Kugel K_0 oder K_m, welche die Dispersionsfläche für den anderen
Strahl ist. Zwei der genannten Schalen gehen so in K_0, zwei in K_m über.
Jedoch gelten diese Aussagen nur solange, als bei der Drehung nicht noch
andere Strahlen in solche Nähe der Anregungskugel gelangen, daß sie mit
in Rechnung zu setzen sind.

Der Friedelsche Satz

Ununterscheidbarkeit von Kristallen, die durch Inversion auseinander
hervorgehen—gilt für die Dispersionsfläche und alle an sie anschließenden
Überlegungen, weil eine Vertauschung von ψ_m mit ψ_{-m} nichts an der Lage
der Anregungspunkte ändert, solange diese reell sind. Er ist aber auch
hier wegen dieser Bedingung unbeweisbar, sobald man Absorption mit
in Betracht zieht.

§ 5. Die Reflexion von Röntgenstrahlen an der Grenze
nichtabsorbierender Kristalle

Die Grundlage aller einschlägigen Betrachtungen ist der Satz: Längs
zweier zur Begrenzung paralleler Ebenen, von denen die eine ganz im
Inneren, die andere ganz im Äußeren verläuft, müssen die Phasen zweier
Wellen, die sich im Inneren und im Äusseren entsprechen, mit derselben
Geschwindigkeit fortschreiten. Daraus ergibt sich sofort das Brechungs-
gesetz und die Rechtfertigung dafür, daß man nach ihm (oder aus der

Grenze der Totalreflexion, was dasselbe ist) den Brechungsindex $n_0 =$
$= 1 + \frac{1}{2}\psi_0$ mißt, sofern nur ein Strahl im Inneren auftritt.

Weit wichtiger ist der Fall, daß zwei Strahlen auftreten, aber beide
in der Einfallsebene liegen—eine Voraussetzung, die nicht selbstverständlich ist. Wir bezeichnen mit $\mathfrak{K}_0{}^1$ den Ausbreitungsvektor der äußeren
Welle; sein Betrag ist k. Sodann ziehen wir nach dem Vorgang von Ewald
und Waller im Raume des reziproken Gitters den Vektor $OP = -\mathfrak{K}_0{}^\alpha$
[see this Vol. p. 230 figs. 79 and 80. Ed.]. Da P nicht auf der Dispersionsfläche
liegen wird, suchen wir dann die Anregungspunkte A^1 und A^2 so auf der
Dispersionsfläche, daß sie auf der zur Grenzfläche senkrechten Geraden
PP' liegen. Dadurch ist gewährleistet, daß die tangentiellen Komponenten
von $\mathfrak{K}_0$ und $\mathfrak{K}_0{}^\alpha$ übereinstimmen.

CHAPTER V

The *f*-Factor continued; Extinction;

Anomalous Scattering

But the most important of all was the successive isolation and investigation of the atomic scattering factor. Here the experimental advances were magnificently supplemented by the progress through atomic theory. Hartree's calculations of atomic factors, so closely related to W. L. Bragg's work, led through successive steps of improvement to a beautiful confirmation of the atomic factor curves deduced from experimental data by those calculated on the newly developed wave mechanical theory of the atom.

P. P. EWALD,
Current Sci. 1937, p. 13

THE INTENSITY OF REFLECTION BY ROCK-SALT

60. The Intensity of Reflexion of X-Rays by Rock-salt by W. L. BRAGG, Langworthy Professor of Physics, The University of Manchester; R. W. JAMES, Senior Lecturer in Physics, The University of Manchester; and C. H. BOSANQUET, Balliol College Oxford, (1921)

▬

61. The Intensity of Reflexions of X-Rays by Rock-salt, Part II, by W. L. BRAGG, R. W. JAMES, C. H. BOSANQUET (1921)

▬

62. The Distribution of Electrons around the Nucleus in the Sodium and Chlorine Atoms, by W. L. BRAGG, R. W. JAMES, C. H. BOSANQUET (1922)

▬

Introduction

60. 1. Accurate comparisons of the intensity of reflexion of X-rays by crystal-faces were first made by W. H. Bragg[1], who measured by the ionization method the energy of the X-rays reflected by various faces of rock-salt.

Theoretical expressions for the intensity of the reflected beam have been deduced by Darwin[2] and Compton[3].

The experiments described in the present paper have been made with the object of extending the measurements of intensity over a larger range of glancing-angles. Further, a direct comparison has been made between the energy of an incident homogeneous beam, and its reflexion by the crystal. The results so obtained have been compared with those given by the theoretical formula; and it will be shown that there is strong evidence that the formula is accurate. From the observations it is possible to calculate not only the relative values of the factor, which depends on the arrangement of the electrons in the atom, but also its absolute value over a range of angles, so that a direct comparison may be made between the observed value and the value calculated for various models of the atomic structure.

[1] W. H. Bragg, *Phil. Mag.* vol. **27** (May 1914) 881 [this Vol. p. 103].
[2] C. G. Darwin, *Phil. Mag.* vol. **27** (Feb. and April 1914) 315 and 675 [this Vol. pp. 169 and 203].
[3] A. H. Compton, *Phys. Rev.* **9** (Jan. 1917) 1.

Comparison of the Intensity of Reflexion by different Faces

2. The method employed is fundamentally the same as that described by W. H. Bragg. Homogeneous rays are emitted from the focal spot on the target, and are limited to a narrow beam by a slit termed the bulb-slit. The beam falls on the crystal, and the reflected beam is received by an ionization-chamber through a second slit. If the chamber-slit and the bulb-slit are equidistant from the axis of the instrument with which the crystal face coincides, the chamber-slit can be set so that it receives all rays of any particular wave-length reflected by the crystal face, although the reflexion may take place at various points on the face owing to irregularity of the crystal structure. This focussing effect has been described by W. H. Bragg and one of the authors[1].

The intensity of the reflexion cannot be measured by the effect observed when the crystal is set at the position which gives the most intense reflected beam, for the strength of this beam is dependent on the degree of perfection of the crystal face. It is measured by sweeping the crystal with uniform angular velocity through the entire range over which it reflects, and by observing the total ionization produced in the chamber during this process. In this way, every part of the pencil of homogeneous rays will fall at some time on a portion of crystal which reflects it, and will contribute its share to the whole effect. Experiments made with different crystals show that the intensity, measured in this way, is not dependent on the degree of perfection of the crystal, that it is the same for any one face and order, however the crystal may be distorted, and is, in fact, a definite physical quantity on which theoretical calculations may be based.

3. The X-ray spectrometer is of the type devised by W. H. Bragg, which has been described in former papers. The ionization-chamber is filled with methyl bromide, and a potential of 320 volts is applied between the outer walls of the chamber, and the inner electrode which is connected to the electrometer. This potential is sufficient to prevent appreciable recombination of ions with the strongest ionization produced. A Lutz-Edelmann string electrometer is used to observe the charge communicated to the electrode, its sensitivity being adjusted to about 100 divisions to a volt. A null method is employed to measure the charge. The inner rod of a small cylindrical condenser is connected to the electrometer, the outer cylinder being raised to any desired potential by a potential divider and battery. When the crystal is swept through the reflecting angle, a charge is communicated to the electrometer. This charge is neutralized by adjusting

[1] *X-Rays and Crystal Structure*, p. 31.

the potential of the outer cylinder of the condenser until the string in the electrometer returns to its zero. The potential applied to the condenser is then proportional to the total charge which has passed through the ionization-chamber.

4. It is necessary that the incident beam of rays should remain constant in intensity. A Coolidge bulb is used, in which the anticathode consists of a button of rhodium embedded in a tungsten block. A large induction-coil and Sanax break supply a current of 1.5 milliamperes at a potential of about 50,000 volts. It is possible to keep the intensity of the rays constant to within 2 or 3 per cent. and with the Coolidge tube it is also possible to repeat the conditions of the experiment on successive occasions in a satis-factory manner. Such variations in intensity as do occur are probably due to the irregular action of the break.

5. Superimposed on the homogeneous rays, there is a general radiation of all wave-lengths which is also reflected by the crystal. In making a measure-ment of intensity it is necessary to allow for this general radiation. When comparing the intensity for two faces or orders, a preliminary survey is made in each case to enable a measurement to be made of the effect of the general radiation. The chamber is set at a series of angles over a range including the angle at which it receives the homogeneous beam. At each position of the chamber, the crystal is swept through the corresponding reflecting angle and the total ionization measured. A series of readings plotted in this way is shown in fig. 1. The readings are at first approxi-mately constant, being due to the general radiation. As the position at which the chamber is set approaches that at which homogeneous rays are received, the ionization rises rapidly, remains constant again as long as the whole pencil of homogeneous rays enters the chamber, and then

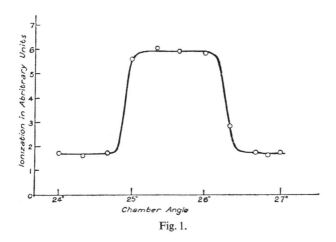

Fig. 1.

falls to a value approximately equal to its former steady value when the homogeneous rays are no longer received.

6. When comparing two crystal faces, this survey is made in each case. One of the faces is then mounted in the spectrometer, the chamber set so that it receives the homogeneous beam, and a series of readings taken by sweeping the crystal backwards and forwards. The crystal faces are interchanged, the chamber reset, and a series of readings taken for the other face. This process is repeated several times, and the means of the intensities for the faces are compared. The preliminary survey indicates what fraction of the total intensity observed must be subtracted, for each face, in order to allow for the general radiation; and when this has been done, the ratio of the corrected readings gives the ratio of the intensity of reflexion by the two faces. A series of readings obtained in this way is given below. It is a comparison of the reflexion by the (311) face of NaCl, mounted so as to face left on the spectrometer, of the same face turned through 180° so that it faces right, and of the third-order reflexion from the face (100) mounted so as to face right. The difference between the values for (311)L and (311)R is due to inaccurate grinding of the crystal surface, the effect of which will be discussed later. It can be shown that, although they differ greatly, their mean represents accurately the strength of reflexion if the face were cut true. In taking the readings, the crystal was turned 5 minutes of arc for every beat of a metronome, beating 100 to the minute.

Comparison of (311) L, (311) R, and (300) R.

Face	Sweep of crystal	Chamber angle	Potentiometer scale	Readings	Mean of readings
(311) L	8°50′–11°20′	20°50′	2	(71, 73, 73, 72)	72.2
(311) R	10°05′–12°35′	21°00′	2	(57, 55, 58, 57, 56, 56)	56.5
(311) L	8°50′–11°20′	20°50′	2	(73, 74, 74, 75)	74.0
(300) R	17°30′–20°00′	38°25′	3	(77, 78, 78, 78)	77.8
(311) L	8°50′–11°20′	20°50′	2	(72, 71, 70, 72, 71, 70)	71.0
(300) R	17°30′–20°00′	38°25′	3	(78, 78, 79, 80, 80)	79.0

A survey of the three reflexions showed that the homogeneous radiation was responsible for 76.9 per cent. of the total effect in the case of the (300)R reflexion, 33.0 per cent. for the (311)R, and 32.2 per cent. for the (311)L reflexion. Since the intensity is very much greater for the (300) face than for the (311) face, different scales on the potentiometer were used. A reading of 72.2 on the second scale represents 72.2 per cent. of a total voltage of 15.72, the corresponding voltage for the third scale being 22.79.

Taking this into account and allowing for the general radiation, one gets a ratio

$$\frac{\text{Mean intensity, face (311)}}{\text{Intensity, face (300) R}} = \frac{3.22}{13.45} = 0.239.$$

In another experiment, (300) R and (300) L were compared, and in this way the relative mean intensities of (311) and (300) measured.

The crystal is not turned continuously during each reading; its setting is altered five minutes of arc at each beat of a metronome by means of a series of spokes on the tangent screw. It would be preferable to turn the crystal with a uniform angular velocity, but it is unlikely that any appreciable error was caused by the method used. In order to make certain that this was the case, the crystal was turned slightly between each reading, in order to ensure that the halting-places did not occur at exactly the same angles.

7. The faces used in this experiment were prepared by grinding, and were of sufficient area to intercept the whole of the incident beam of rays. In general, faces were prepared 3 or 4 centimetres in length and breadth. The perfection of the crystal structure may be judged from the range of angles at which reflexion takes place. In most cases the greater part of the effect was observed to take place within less than a degree of arc as the crystal was turned, the faces being prepared from large blocks of rocksalt which were very little distorted.

The face should be cut so that it is as nearly parallel to the planes of the crystal structure as possible. If this is not the case, there will be a difference in the intensities of reflexion when the crystal is mounted facing right and left on the spectrometer table. This effect is described and explained in the paper by W. H. Bragg referred to above (*Phil. Mag. loc. cit.* p. 888. [this Vol. p. 108]).

The corresponding figures for the face (100) of NaCl are given below:—

	(100)	(200)	(300)
Right-hand side	100	21.3	5.08 [1]
Left-hand side	116.6	21.8	

The error in the orientation of the (100) face was in this case too small to be measured with accuracy; it was less than 30 minutes of arc.

---

[1] The difference between right-hand and left-hand sides was less than the error of determination.

Since the effect of inaccurate grinding of the face is so much less for the second order than for the first order, the intensity of reflexion from (200) NaCl was taken as standard, and all other intensities compared with it. The intensities were in all cases measured on both sides and the mean taken. In most cases the difference between them was small; for the higher orders it did not exceed 5 per cent.

8. It is necessary to use faces which have been ground. The strength of the reflexion is very different, especially for small glancing-angles, when a cleavage surface is compared with one which has been ground. As an example, a comparison is given below of the reflexion from a very perfect cleavage face of a rock-salt crystal (A) with a similar cleavage face on a crystal (D), which was afterwards ground until a layer 1 millimetre thick had been removed.

The intensity of reflexion from crystal (D) was measured with two orientations of the face. In the first, the crystal was set so that the edge, on which the knife was pressed in cleaving the crystal, was horizontal. In the second position, the edge was vertical and therefore at right angles to the horizontal beam of X-rays.

Face	Intensity
A (100) (Cleavage face)	50.8
D (100) before grinding:—	
First position	25.4
Second position	12.9
D (100) after grinding	100

Hence D (100), after grinding, reflected eight times as well as in the second position before grinding.

Comparison of 1st, 2nd, and 3rd orders:—

	(100)	(200)	(300)
Crystal D (after grinding)	100	18.4	4.1
Crystal A (cleavage face)	50.8	18.1	4.7

These comparisons were made for reflexion on the right-hand side only, and must be regarded as approximate. In this case, as in the case of the error due to inaccurate grinding, the effect is much greater for the first-order reflexion. On account of this effect, intensity measurements of the (100) reflexion are doubtful, and this provides an additional reason for using the reflexion (200) as standard.

The difference in intensity for the two positions of the D cleavage face indicates that the reason for the imperfect reflexion may be due to a distortion of a freshly-cleaved surface. A cleaved surface has a rippled appearance, the ripples being parallel to the line on which the knife-edge was pressed in cleaving the crystal. The range of angles, however, over which the crystal reflects is no greater for a cleavage surface than for a ground surface, so that it would not appear that the imperfect reflexion is due to small variations in orientation of the face. Measurements made at various stages in the grinding down of a crystal face indicate that the effect is deep seated, and a depth of a millimetre at least was removed from the face D (100) before it was used in obtaining the results given in this paper.

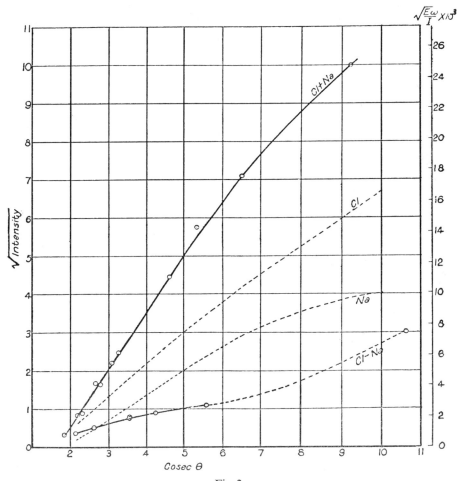

Fig. 2.

10. The comparisons which have been made are plotted in the form of a graph in fig. 2.

11. In fig. 2 the square-root of the relative intensity has been plotted against the cosecant of the glancing-angle. By plotting the intensities in this way, the approximate relation found by W. H. Bragg—that the intensity varies inversely as $\sin^2\theta$—is made evident.

All the points lie on two smooth curves, showing that they form two groups within each of which the intensity is a function of the glancing-angle alone. For instance, the reflexions from the faces (511) and (333) occur at the same angle, and the corresponding intensities 0.74 and 0.72 are identical within the error of observation.

The points which lie on the lower curve are those for which all the indices are odd—the faces (111), (311), (331), (333), (511), (711), (555). These reflexions are from planes which contain alternately sodium and chlorine atoms. The wave-train reflected from the planes containing sodium atoms is 180° out of phase with that reflected by the plane containing chlorine atoms. The other reflexions are either from planes which contain both sodium and chlorine atoms and are identical in their nature, or are reflexions of an even order from planes containing sodium and chlorine atoms alternately. In both cases the sodium and chlorine atoms reflect wave-trains which are in phase with each other.

Since the square-root of the intensity has been plotted, this may be taken as being proportional to the amplitude of the reflected wave-trains. The upper curve, therefore, represents the sum of the amplitudes due to sodium and chlorine atoms, the lower, the difference of these two amplitudes.

Comparison of Incident and Reflected Beams

12. The rays from the bulb consist of heterogeneous radiation of all wavelengths over a certain range, superimposed on the homogeneous radiation whose intensity of reflexion has been measured. In order to compare directly the energy in the incident and reflected homogeneous beams, it is necessary to obtain a homogeneous beam by reflexion from a crystal face, and observe the total amount of radiation reflected by a second crystal, turning with constant angular velocity, on which this homogeneous beam is allowed to fall. In this case, since the rays are homogeneous, no allowance for general radiation need be made.

The amount of energy reflected is proportional to the intensity of the incident beam, and inversely proportional to the angular velocity of rotation. The quantity $E\omega/I$ is therefore a constant characteristic of any one face and order, where

E = Total amount of energy reflected when the crystal is rotated with angular velocity ω radians per second.

I = Total amount of energy passing into ionization-chamber when the incident beam enters it for one second.

This constant $E\omega/I$ will be defined as the 'Reflecting Power' ρ, of the crystal face for the wave-length λ *.

The chamber was placed so as to receive the whole of the incident beam (i.e. that reflected from the monochromator crystal), and the effect measured when the rays entered the chamber for a known time. It was then turned so as to receive the beam reflected from the crystal mounted on the spectrometer table and turned with a known angular velocity.

This was done for the face (100) of NaCl. The reflexions from other faces are so much weaker that it was not convenient to compare them directly with the incident beam. As a check, an absolute measurement was made of the reflecting power for (222), which was found to be in agreement with that calculated by a comparison with (100).

A series of measurements gave for the constant

$$E\omega/I = 0.000612 \text{ for NaCl (100)} \, [1].$$

Since the reflecting powers of the other faces have been determined in terms of that from the face (100), their absolute reflecting powers may now be calculated.

The reflecting power of a face can only be defined satisfactorily in this way. It may be of interest, however, to give approximately the proportion of homogeneous radiation reflected when the crystal face is set at the most favourable angle, although this depends on the state of perfection of the face as explained above. A direct comparison showed that when a narrow

---

* [W. L. Bragg, C. G. Darwin and R. W. James, *Phil. Mag.* **1** (1921) 902:]
'It is in some ways convenient to interpret ρ as follows. Conceive that the radiation was perfectly reflected when it struck the crystal within a given range of angles, and was not reflected at all outside this range. As the crystal rotates with an angular velocity ω, it reflects the incident radiation I for a short time t. The total amount reflected, E, will be equal to It, so that E/I measures the time t, and $E\omega/I$ measures the angular range ωt over which total reflexion takes place. The integrated reflexion ρ is thus the angular breadth of this region (in circular measure). This way of regarding the matter has a very direct application to the case of the perfect crystal.' Ed.]

[1] More recent determinations of this value have shown that the figure 0.000612 is too high. The value varies somewhat with the nature of the crystal face, and a better maen value is .00055.

beam of X-rays falls on the face (100) set so as to reflect it, the intensity of the reflected beam is about one twenty-fifth of the incident beam.

Theoretical Formula for the Intensity of Reflexion

13. Formulae for the intensity of reflexion have been deduced by Darwin and Compton *loc. cit.*). The formula given by Compton is directly applicable, for he calculates the total amount of energy reflected when the crystal is turned at a uniform rate through the reflecting-angle. That given by Darwin may be extended to this case, and is in agreement with Compton's formula.

Let rays from a source S fall at a glancing-angle θ on a plane containing n atoms per unit area, and be reflected. (...)

If the incident rays may be considered as a parallel beam, we get the relation

$$\frac{\textit{Amplitude of reflected beam}}{\textit{Amplitude of incident beam}} = \frac{D'}{D} = \frac{n\lambda}{\sin\theta} \cdot F \cdot \frac{e^2}{mc^2}. \qquad (2)^1$$

Considering now a thin slip of crystal consisting of p planes at a distance d apart, the reflexion will be most intense when

$$m\lambda = 2d\sin\theta.$$

At a glancing-angle $(\theta + \varepsilon)$ the amplitude of the reflected beam will be

$$D'p\,\frac{\sin(p.\pi.\varepsilon.2d\cos\theta/\lambda)}{p.\pi.\varepsilon.2d\cos\theta/\lambda}.$$

If we put

$$\phi = p.\pi.\varepsilon.2d\cos\theta/\lambda,$$

the energy of the reflected beam is proportional to

$$(D')^2 p^2 (\sin^2\phi)/\phi^2.$$

If, now, the crystal is rotated with constant angular velocity ω, the total amount of radiation reflected is proportional to

$$(D')^2 p^2 \int_{-\infty}^{+\infty} \frac{\sin^2\phi}{\phi^2}\,dt = (D')^2 p^2 \int_{-\infty}^{+\infty} \frac{\sin^2\phi}{\phi^2}\,\frac{d\varepsilon}{\omega}$$

$$= (D')^2 p^2 \int_{-\infty}^{+\infty} \frac{\sin^2\phi}{\phi^2}\,\frac{\lambda}{2p\pi d\cos\theta}\,\frac{d\phi}{\omega}.$$

---

[1] [See Darwin, this Vol. p. 172 eq. (1). Ed.]

Since

$$\int_{-\infty}^{+\infty} \frac{\sin^2 \phi}{\phi^2} \, d\phi = \pi,$$

this becomes

$$\frac{(D')^2 p . \lambda}{2d \cos \theta . \omega} = D^2 . \frac{n^2 \lambda^2}{\sin^2 \theta} . F^2 \frac{e^4}{m^2 c^4} . \frac{p\lambda}{2\omega d \cos \theta} .$$

If N = number of atoms per unit volume,
   t = thickness of crystal slip,
we have $n = Nd$, $t = pd$.

The energy in both the reflected and incident beams is proportional to the square of the amplitude of the electric vector. If the energy of the incident beam falling on the crystal per second is I, and it is all intercepted by the slip of crystal, the total energy reflected will be given by

$$\frac{E}{I} = \frac{n^2 \lambda^2}{\sin^2 \theta} . F^2 \frac{e^4}{m^2 c^4} . \frac{p\lambda}{2\omega d \cos \theta} ,$$

or

$$\frac{E\omega}{I} = \frac{N^2 \lambda^3 t}{2 \sin^2 \theta \cos \theta} . F^2 \frac{e^4}{m^2 c^4} . \tag{3}$$

In this calculation it has been assumed that the absorption of the radiation is inappreciable.

As a corollary, we can calculate the reflecting power of a homogeneous fragment of crystal of volume V. The volume of the slip irradiated by a narrow pencil of rays is equal to $St/\sin \theta$, where S is the area of cross-section of the pencil. From the above formula

$$\frac{E\omega}{I} = \frac{N^2 \lambda^3}{2 \sin \theta \cos \theta} . F^2 \frac{e^4}{m^2 c^4} . \frac{t}{\sin \theta} .$$

Now, $I = SI_0$ when I_0 is equal to the intensity of the beam irradiating the crystal, defined as the amount of energy falling on one square centimetre per second, whence

$$\frac{E\omega}{I_0} = \frac{N^2 \lambda^3}{\sin 2\theta} . F^2 \frac{e^4}{m^2 c^4} . V. \tag{4}$$

This result shows that the 'Reflecting power' of a homogeneous fragment of the crystal is proportional to its volume, if the fragment be so small that absorption in it is inappreciable.

275

We will now assume that the crystal consists of a number of such homogeneous crystalline particles, set approximately parallel to each other, but not exactly so. When the rays are reflected from the face of a crystal, the reflexion by particles below the surface is diminished by absorption. It will be assumed that the linear coefficient of absorption μ is a constant. (This assumption will be discussed more fully below.)

Rays reflected by a particle at a depth z beneath the crystal surface suffer absorption by passing through a distance $2z/\sin\theta$ of the crystal. They are therefore reduced in intensity in the ratio $1 : \exp(-2\mu z/\sin\theta)$.

By equation (3) the reflecting power of a thickness t of the crystal is given by the formula

$$\frac{E\omega}{I} = \frac{N^2\lambda^3}{2\sin^2\theta\cos\theta} . F^2 \frac{e^4}{m^2c^4} . t.$$

The total reflecting power of the crystal face is therefore equal to

$$\frac{N^2\lambda^3}{2\sin^2\theta\cos\theta} . F^2 \frac{e^4}{m^2c^4} \int_0^\infty \exp(-2\mu z/\sin\theta)dz$$

$$= \frac{N^2\lambda^3}{2\sin^2\theta\cos\theta} . F^2 \frac{e^4}{m^2c^4} . \frac{\sin\theta}{2\mu} = \frac{N^2\lambda^3}{2\mu\sin 2\theta} . F^2 \frac{e^4}{m^2c^4}. \quad (5)$$

This expression must now be multiplied by a 'polarization factor' $(1 + \cos^2 2\theta)/2$ and a 'Debije factor' $\exp(-B\sin^2\theta)$. The complete expression for the reflecting power R is therefore

$$\frac{E\omega}{I} = R = \frac{N^2\lambda^3}{2\mu\sin 2\theta} . F^2 \frac{e^4}{m^2c^4} . \frac{1+\cos^2 2\theta}{2} \exp(-B\sin^2\theta) \quad (6)$$

The Debije Factor for Rock-salt

14. Debije [1] gives the formula for the factor which expresses the diminution of the intensity of reflexion with rise of temperature in the form $\exp(-B\sin^2\theta)$, where the constant B is a function of the temperature, the wave-length λ, the atomic weight, and the characteristic temperature Θ of the crystal.

W. H. Bragg [2] made a series of measurements of the effect of tempera-

[1] P. Debije, Ann. d. Phys. (4) 43 (1914) 49 [this Vol. p. 162].
[2] W. H. Bragg, Phil. Mag. loc. cit. p. 891 [this Vol. p. 160].

ture in reducing the intensity of reflexion by rock-salt. Intensities were compared at $288°K$ and $643°K$. The results were, within the errors of experiment, consistent with the ratios given by Debye's formula. The latter gives different values for B according to the assumption or otherwise of the existence of the 'Nullpunktsenergie.' Compton (*loc. cit.* p. 47) gives, as the two values for B in NaCl, 4.6 and 3.6 respectively.

The mean value for B at $288°C$., calculated from W. H. Bragg's results, is equal to 4.12, and this will be assumed in the calculations which follow. To assume that the effect of temperature on both curves of fig. 2 is the same, is equivalent to supposing that the average amplitude of vibration of sodium and chlorine atoms is the same. This is very probably not the case, and the authors intend to measure the effect of cooling down the crystal in order to obtain an empirical law over a wider range expressing the temperature effect. However, the factor $\exp(-B\sin^2\theta)$ does not affect very greatly any but the smallest intensities measured, and will therefore not make much difference to the conclusions to be drawn from the curves.

The Linear Coefficient of Absorption 'μ'

15. The coefficient of absorption by rock-salt of the homogeneous radiation was measured in the usual way by interposing plates of rock-salt of various thickness in the path of the direct beam and measuring the diminution in energy of the beam. Experiments were made with plates from 0.05 cm to 0.15 cm thick. The linear coefficient of absorption μ was found to be 10.7.

In the theoretical formula it has been assumed that μ is constant. Now, W. H. Bragg has shown that in the case of the diamond, when the crystal is set so as to reflect the radiation, the absorption-coefficient is abnormally large. It was therefore interesting to try whether such an effect is observable in the case of rock-salt. A slip of crystal 0.92 mm in thickness with faces parallel to (100) was set on the spectrometer table at right angles to the incident homogeneous beam and the absorption measured. It was then turned through an angle of about $66°$ until the (100) planes at right angles to the crystal face reflected the radiation, the reflexion being observed in the usual way. On redetermining the absorption-coefficient it was found to have increased by about 15 per cent. This effect is discussed in Darwin's paper referred to above, and will reduce the intensity of the reflected beam. Its effect will be smaller for higher orders of reflexion, since the increase in absorption is due to multiple reflexion within the crystal interfering with the primary beam, and reflexion is so much weaker in the higher orders.

The effect will not be taken into account in the calculations, since it is not obvious what allowance should be made for it. It is to be remembered, however, that the reflexions from (100) and (110) must be diminished by the increase in the absorption-coefficient.

It may possibly be the case that the effect of grinding a cleavage face, which increases so greatly the intensity of reflexion, is due to the fact that grinding breaks the crystal up into a number of small homogeneous crystals oriented in slightly different directions, so that absorption at the reflecting angle plays a less important part in diminishing the intensity of reflexion.

The Comparison of the Theoretical and Observed Results

16. The formula for the reflecting-power of a face states that

$$\frac{E\omega}{I} = \frac{N^2\lambda^3}{2\mu \sin 2\theta} \cdot F^2 \frac{e^4}{m^2 c^4} \cdot \frac{1 + \cos^2 2\theta}{2} \cdot \exp(-B \sin^2 \theta).$$

Since all the quantities have been measured except F, we can calculate the absolute value of F for a range of values of θ.

If the effect of the electrons in the chlorine atoms be represented by F_{Cl}, and of those in the sodium atom by F_{Na}, then for reflecting-powers corresponding to points on the upper curve of fig. 2 we have

$$F = F_{Cl} + F_{Na};$$

for those corresponding to points in the lower curve

$$F = F_{Cl} - F_{Na}.$$

From the formula

$$F = \left(\frac{E\omega}{I}\right)^{\frac{1}{2}} \frac{mc^2}{e^2} \cdot \frac{2\mu^{\frac{1}{2}}}{N\lambda^{\frac{3}{2}}} \left(\frac{\sin 2\theta}{1 + \cos^2 2\theta}\right)^{\frac{1}{2}} \cdot \exp(+B \sin^2 \theta/2).$$

where N is the number of molecules of NaCl in unit volume of the crystal.

278

Taking

$$e/m = 5.30 \times 10^{17}, \qquad \mu = 10.7,$$

$$e = 4.77 \times 10^{-10}, \qquad N = \frac{1}{2}\left(\frac{1}{2.81 \times 10^{-8}}\right)^3,$$

$$c = 3 \times 10^{10}, \qquad \lambda = 0.615 \times 10^{-8},$$

$$B = 4.12,$$

this reduces to

$$F = 2143\{E\omega \sin 2\theta / I(1 + \cos^2 2\theta)\}^{\frac{1}{2}} \exp(+2.06 \sin^2 \theta).$$

The dotted curves in fig. 2 represent one-half the sum of the ordinates, and one-half the difference between the ordinates, of the upper and lower curves. From these dotted curves the absolute value of F_{Cl} for chlorine, and F_{Na} for sodium, can be calculated directly. They are tabulated below, and the values are plotted against $\sin\theta$ in figs. 4 and 5.

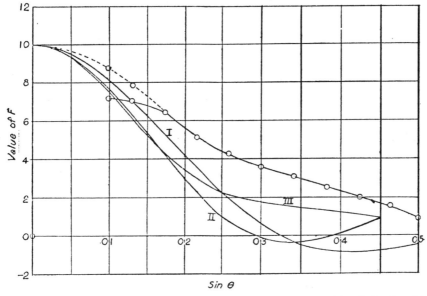

Fig. 4. Values of F for Sodium, calculated for three different models of the ion. The small circles indicate the observed values.

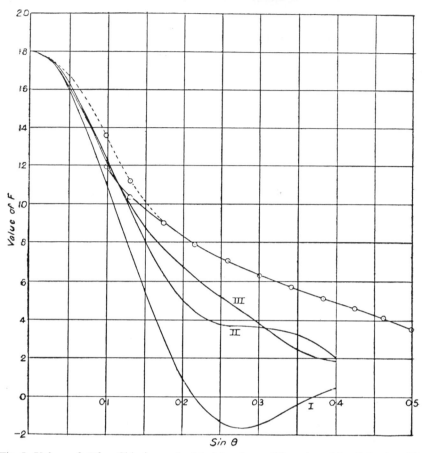

Fig. 5. Values of F for Chlorine, calculated for three different models of the ion. The small circles indicate the observed values.

The values of F for Chlorine and Sodium are:—

Glancing-angle θ	sin θ	F_{Cl}	F_{Na}
(5°44′)	(0.100)	(11.67)	(6.90)
7°30′	0.1305	10.11	6.88
10°0′	0.1736	8.78	6.26
12°30′	0.2164	7.72	4.98
15°0′	0.2588	6.88	4.18
17°30′	0.3007	6.14	3.47
20°0′	0.3420	5.56	2.95
22°30′	0.3827	5.00	2.41
25°0′	0.4226	4.50	1.91
27°30′	0.4617	4.01	1.49
30°0′	0.5000	3.43	0.83

The angle between the scattered and incident beams is twice the glancing-angle θ.

280

It will be seen at once that the values of F are of the right order of magnitude. F should tend to a value 18 for chlorine, and 10 for sodium, as $\sin\theta$ approaches zero, assuming the atoms in the crystal to be ionized. The greatest value of F_{Cl} is 11.67, and of F_{Na} is 6.90, when $\sin\theta = 0.10$.

17. It now remains to take various models of the atom and see how the form of the function F calculated for these models agrees with that actually observed.

It is not intended here to lay much stress on the agreement between the calculated and observed forms of F for all values of θ. The object of the comparison is to demonstrate that any probable arrangement of electrons gives a close agreement between theory and experiment at small glancing-angles, and therefore to prove that the formula for the intensity of reflexion is very probably the true one.

The first atom model is one in which the electrons are supposed to be distributed uniformly throughout a sphere whose radius is 1.02×10^{-8} cm in the case of chlorine, 0.67×10^{-8} cm in the case of sodium.

In the second model the electrons are supposed to be arranged in a series of spherical shells. It is also assumed that, in considering the average effect of the atom, we may take the effect of the electrons in each shell to be equivalent to a uniform distribution of diffracting particles over the whole surface of the shell. The radii of these shells and the number of electrons in each are as follows:—

Chlorine	No. of electrons	Radius	Sodium	No. of electrons	Radius
1st shell	2	0.12	1st shell	2	0.40
2nd shell	8	0.41	2nd shell	8	0.67
3rd shell	8	1.02			

The diameters of the outer shells are those calculated by one of the authors [1] from crystal data.

In the third model the electrons are supposed to be arranged on shells of the same diameters as in the second model, but to be in oscillation about their mean positions along a line joining them to the centre of the atom with a total amplitude equal to their distance from the centre. This extreme case has been chosen to illustrate the effect of such an oscillation of the electrons on the form of the curve.

The values of F for chlorine and sodium calculated for these three types of atom model are plotted against $\sin\theta$ in figs. 4 and 5, the curves corre-

[1] W. L. Bragg, *Phil. Mag.* **40** (August 1920) 169.

sponding to the first, second, and third models being numbered I, II, and III. The measured values of F are shown for comparison as a series of small circles.

Of the three models chosen, the third type is the only one which gives diffraction curves of the same general shape as those actually observed. Both of the other models yield curves which have maxima and minima. (...)

The authors wish to acknowledge very gratefully the kind assistance given them by Dr. W. D. Coolidge, of the General Electric Company, Schenectady, to whom they are indebted for the gift of the Coolidge tube with which the investigations were carried out.

61. 2. In the case of a large crystal, the linear absorptioncoefficient, μ, of the rays in the crystal has to be taken into account in calculating the intensity of reflexion. Two special cases present themselves.

In the first place, a narrow beam of rays may be reflected from the face of a crystal cut parallel to the reflecting planes. In this case, if the intensity I of the incident beam is defined as the *total amount of radiation* falling on the crystal per second, calculation shows that

$$E\omega/I = Q/2\mu, \tag{3}$$

where

$$Q = \frac{N^2\lambda^3}{\sin 2\theta} . F^2 \; \frac{e^4}{m^2c^4} \; \frac{1 + \cos^2 2\theta}{2} . \exp(-B \sin^2 \theta)$$

This is the case dealt with in our previous paper.

The second case is illustrated by fig. 1. A beam of homogeneous X-rays is obtained by reflexion by the first crystal C. This beam is reflected by a second crystal plate S, which is cut so that the reflecting planes are at right angles to its surface, and is turned with angular velocity ω.

In this case, all the rays have to traverse a depth $t_0 \sec \theta$ in the crystal, where t_0 is the thickness of the plate. Calculation shows that

$$E\omega/I = Qt \exp(-\mu t), \tag{4}$$

where $t = t_0 \sec \theta$, and Q and I have the same meaning as in equation (3). This expression has a maximum value $Q/\mu e$, when

$$t = 1/\mu. \tag{5}$$

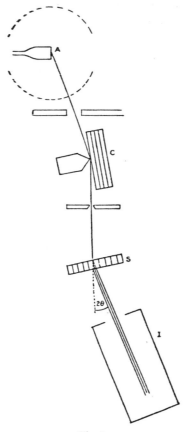

Fig. 1.

The Determination of Q

3. The object of the measurements described here and in the previous paper has been the determination of the absolute value of the quantity F over a range of glancing angles. F can be calculated if Q is determined experimentally, since the other quantities in the expression for Q are known.

In the former paper, Q was found by determining the reflecting power $E\omega/I$ for a crystal face, for which the formula $E\omega/I = Q/2\mu$ holds good. The linear absorption-coefficient μ was measured directly, by passing the homogeneous beam through plates of rock-salt of various thicknesses. It was pointed out, however, that in the case of reflexions at small glancing-angles, the value of μ determined in this way is certainly too low. When X-rays pass through a crystal in such a direction that the crystal reflects

283

the rays, the absorption of the transmitted beam is greater than that for other directions. This effect was first noticed in the case of the diamond by W. H. Bragg [1], and the effect also exists in the case of rock-salt. Fig. 2 shows some determinations made with the apparatus arranged as in fig. 1, but with the ionization-chamber placed so as to receive the transmitted beam. The ordinates represent the strength of the transmitted beam, plotted for a number of crystal settings. It will be seen that the transmitted beam is reduced by 20 per cent. when the crystal is set at the angle at which it reflects the X-rays most strongly.

The value of μ is therefore greater than its normal value (10.7), for beams passing through the crystal in any direction in which they are reflected strongly, and the values of Q, calculated using the value 10.7 for μ, will be too small. This was pointed out in the former paper, but no allowance could be made for this effect, as the increase in μ had not been measured. This increase has now been determined by a direct method, and in this paper the necessary corrections have been made to the values of Q, and so of F.

4. The increase in μ cannot be determined from a curve such as that of fig. 2. The beam falling on the crystal is not absolutely parallel; there-

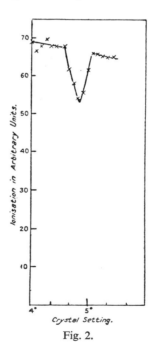

Fig. 2.

[1] W. H. Bragg, *Phil. Mag.* vol. **27** (May 1914) 881.

fore it is not possible to set the crystal so that all the rays of the beam pass through at that angle for which absorption is a maximum. The apparent increase in μ indicated by the curve sets a lower limit to the effect, which may be considerably greater.

When reflexion takes place inside a crystal plate, as in fig. 1, the strength of the reflected beam is given by equation (4),

$$E\omega/I = Qt \exp(-\mu t),$$

where $t = t_0 \sec \theta$.

In this equation, μ is the effective absorption-coefficient appropriate to rays passing through the crystal at the reflecting-angle, since all rays entering the ionization-chamber have passed through at this angle.

If a number of plates of different thickness are taken, the intensity of reflexion measured in each case, and its value plotted against t_0, the points should lie on a curve such as that in fig. 3. The circles in this figure are the experimental determinations of the intensity of reflexion (100) for a number of plates varying in thickness from 0.2 to 2.5 mm, and a curve of the form $y = at \exp(-\mu t)$ has been drawn so as to conform as closely as possible to the absolute experimental values.

The constants of this curve give the values of Q and μ. 'μ' can be measured by noting the value of t at which the curve has its maximum, since at this point $t_0 \sec \theta = 1/\mu$. The maximum occurs at $t_0 = 0.610$ mm; whence $\mu = 16.30$. The value measured directly is $\mu = 10.7$, so that the increase in μ at the reflecting angle is 52 per cent.

The value of Q is given by the equation

$$(E\omega/I)_{\text{max}} = Q/e\mu. \tag{6}$$

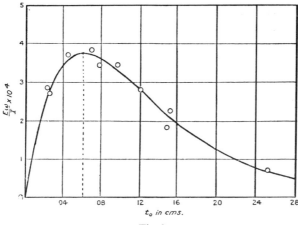

Fig. 3.

The mean of our experimental determinations gave

$$(E\omega/I)_{\text{max}} = 3.65 \times 10^{-4}.$$

Substituting $e = 2.718$, $\mu = 16.30$, we obtain

$$Q_{(100)} = 16.16 \times 10^{-3}.$$

From the value of $Q_{(100)}$ the absolute value of $(F_{Cl} + F_{Na})$ can be calculated, from equation (1).

This yields

$$F_{Cl} + F_{Na} = 20.10$$

at the glancing-angle 6°17′, corresponding to reflexion from (100). In other words, when the rays are diffracted through an angle of 12°34′, the total effect of the 28 electrons in a pair of sodium and chlorine atoms is reduced, by interference, to an effect 20.10 times that due to a single electron.

Effect of Imperfection in the Crystal

5. We may distinguish two degrees of irregularity in a crystal structure. On the one hand, the crystal may be so irregular that the absorption in each homogeneous fragment is entirely due to the conversion of the X-ray energy into cathode-ray energy. The absorption-coefficient will then be the same for rays passing through the crystal in any direction. This absorption-coefficient, which we will call μ_0, can be found by direct measurement, and in the case of these very irregular crystals, it is the correct coefficient to substitute in all the formulae for reflexion. On the other hand, the homogeneous fragments, while still irregularly arranged, may each be sufficiently large for the extinction of the transmitted beam at the reflecting angle to be appreciable, in comparison with the reduction in intensity due to normal absorption. In this case, X-rays, passing through the composite crystal at such an angle that some of the fragments are reflecting, will be absorbed more strongly than rays passing through at other angles. There will be an increase in the effective absorption-coefficient. If the effective coefficient of absorption is now μ, we can state that

$$\mu = \mu_0 + \varepsilon.$$

The coefficient ε will be called the 'coefficient of extinction' of the X-rays in the crystal.

The Measurement of the Extinction-Coefficient

6. Our experimental results show that the regularity in structure of rock-salt is such that ε is appreciable for strong reflexions, but is very small for the reflexions of high order. We have measured the normal coefficient of absorption μ_0 for rays passing through the crystal at any angle, and found it to be equal to 10.7. We have then determined the effective coefficient of absorption μ at the reflecting angle by the method described in paragraph 4. This has been done for the reflexions (100), (110), (200), and (300).

The effective coefficient μ can be calculated readily by plotting the results as in fig. 5.

Since

$$E\omega/I = Qt_0 \sec\theta \exp(-\mu t_0 \sec\theta),$$

$${}^e\!\log(E\omega/It_0 \sec\theta) + \text{const} = -\mu t_0 \sec\theta.$$

In fig. 5, ${}^e\!\log(E\omega/It_0)$ is plotted against t_0. The slope of the curve then gives μ directly, allowing for the factor $\sec\theta$. The results are tabulated below.

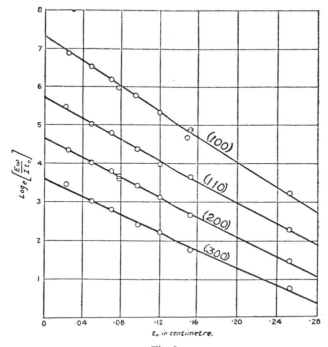

Fig. 5.

Reflexion	Effective coefficient μ	Extinction coefficient $\varepsilon = \mu - \mu_0$	Intensity of reflexion in arbitrary units
100	16.30	5.60	100
110	13.60	2.90	50.5
200	12.66	1.96	19.90
300	10.72	0.02	4.87

Normal coefficient of absorption, 10.70.

In fig. 6, μ is plotted against the intensity of reflexion. It will be seen that the points, with the exception of (200), lie on a straight line which cuts

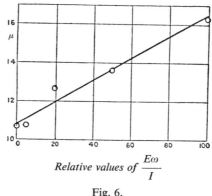

Relative values of $\dfrac{E\omega}{I}$

Fig. 6.

the y axis at 10.80, a value very close to the normal coefficient of absorption 10.70. We may therefore assume, without introducing any large error, that we can calculate for any reflexion from the formula

$$\mu = \mu_0 + kI \tag{6}$$

the value of k being determined from the slope of the curve.

The Relation between Regularity of Structure and Intensity of Reflexion

7. An interesting point was observed in measuring the intensities of reflexion through the crystal plates. In the case of certain plates, the intensity was found to be abnormally high. This abnormality is much more marked in the case of the (100) reflexions than for those which are less intense.

This effect was traced to a greater irregularity in structure of the crystal plates. In every case in which the value came to be abnormally high, it was found that the crystal gave reflexion over a wide range of angles. It was also found that this irregularity could be produced artificially by grinding the crystal plate on coarse emery-paper, plates prepared in this way giving a reflexion over a long range, and abnormally high values for the intensity.

Fig. 7 will illustrate this effect. A single crystal plate was cut across in two equal portions, and from these two plates of the same thickness (0.78 mm) were prepared. The first plate was rubbed down on ground

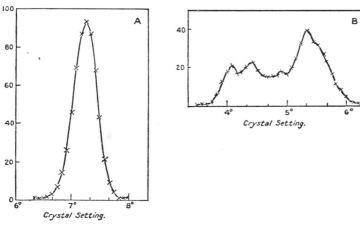

Fig. 7.

A. Intensity of reflexion 0.93.
B.   „   „   „   1.20.

glass with water so as to avoid all mechanical strain. The second was ground down on coarse emery-paper. The curves of fig. 7 show the amount of radiation reflected by the plates over a range of a few degrees. The first gives a narrow maximum, showing that the structure is regular; the second, an irregular curve over a much larger angle. The intensities of reflexion in terms of that of the standard plate were 0.93 and 1.20 respectively for the (100) reflexion, showing how much greater the intensity is for the irregular than for the regular crystal.

Corrected Values for F_{Cl} and F_{Na}

8. From the curve in fig. 3, we can calculate the absolute value of $Q_{(100)}$ and therefore the value of $F_{Cl} + F_{Na}$ for rays diffracted through an angle of $12°34'$ (twice the glancing angle for reflexion from this face). This, as stated above, comes to be 20.10. Since allowance has been made for the extinction-coefficient, this is now an accurate determination. In the previous paper the value of $F_{Cl} + F_{Na}$ was obtained by measurements on the intens-

ity of reflexion from a face, taking μ to be 10.7. These measurements give $F_{Cl} + F_{Na} = 16.68$. The difference between the two values shows the effect of allowing for the extinction-coefficient.

We now have sufficient data to calculate the correct values for F_{Cl} and F_{Na} over the whole range of angles which has been examined. When the glancing-angle is large, the reflexion is so weak that the extinction-coefficient may be neglected. The values for $F_{Cl} - F_{Na}$, given in the previous paper, therefore hold good, allowance being made for the differences due to the re-determination of the absolute intensity of reflexion mentioned above. On the other hand, the measurements described in paragraph 4 make possible the absolute determination of $F_{Cl} + F_{Na}$ for the angle of most intense reflexion, by a method which is independent of any uncertainty as to the value of μ. We can therefore estimate to what extent the (100) reflexion is diminished by the extinction-coefficient in the case of the measurements with a crystal face, and using the formula $\mu = \mu_0 + kI$ we can raise the values of the (110),(222), (200), and other strong reflexions, so as to bring them into line with the new data. The values for F_{Cl} and F_{Na} so obtained are tabulated below, and plotted in fig. 8.

Values of F_{Cl} and F_{Na}

$\sin \theta$	$F_{Cl}+F_{Na}$	$F_{Cl}+F_{Na}$ (Corr. for ε)	$F_{Cl}-F_{Na}$	F_{Cl}	F_{Na}	2θ
.1000	17.12	21.05	4.40	12.72	8.32	11°24′
.1305	15.66	18.21	2.98	10.59	7.61	15°
.1736	13.86	14.89	2.32	8.60	6.23	20°
.2164	11.71	12.35	2.53	7.44	4.91	25°
.2588	10.19	10.51	2.49	6.50	4.01	30°
.3007	8.86	9.11	2.46	5.78	3.37	35°
.3420	7.84	7.90	2.40	5.15	2.75	40°
.3827	6.83	6.83	2.39	4.61	2.22	45°
.4226	5.91	5.91	2.39	4.15	1.76	50°
.4617	5.07	5.07	2.33	3.70	1.37	55°
.5000	3.92	3.92	2.40	3.16	0.76	60°

In fig. 8, both the former values, and those corrected for the extinction-coefficient, are shown. The maximum values for F at $\theta = 0$ would be expected to be 10 for sodium, 18 for chlorine, assuming both atoms to be ionized. The general trend of the corrected curves is towards maxima in the neighbourhood of these values, whereas the uncorrected curves drop too quickly as they approach the y axis, this being particularly noticeable in the curve for sodium. The fact that the corrected curves tend towards

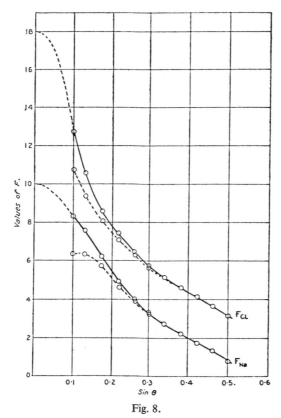

Fig. 8.

The amplitude of the waves diffracted through an angle 2θ by the Chlorine and Sodium atoms are expressed in terms of that scattered by a single electron. The wave-length λ of the rays is equal to 0.616×10^{-8} cm.

these maxima confirms the accuracy, both of the experimental determinations and of the assumptions which have been made in the calculations.

62. We will suppose that there is in every atom an electron which is at a distance a from the centre, and that all directions of the radius joining the electron to the atomic centre are equally likely to occur in the crystal. In finding the effect of these electrons for all atoms (M in number) of the group, we may take it as equivalent to that of M electrons distributed equally over a sphere of radius a. It can easily be shown that, if x is the distance of an electron from the plane, all values of x between $+a$ and $-a$ are equally likely for both cases. Such a shell scatters a wave which is less than that scattered by M electrons in the plane in the ratio $(\sin \phi)/\phi$,

291

where

$$\phi = (4\pi a \sin \theta)/\lambda *.$$

The average contribution of the electron in each atom to the F factor is therefore $(\sin \phi)/\phi$, and not unity as it would be if the electron were at the centre of the atom.

Suppose now that any atom contains a electrons at a distance r_1 from the nucleus, b at a distance r_2, c at a distance $r_3 \ldots n$ at a distance r_n, then the value of F for the average atom would be given by

$$F = a(\sin \phi_1)/\phi_1 + b (\sin \phi_2)/\phi_2 + c (\sin \phi_3)/\phi_3 + \ldots n(\sin \phi_n)/\phi_n \quad (4)$$

Thus, given the distribution of the electrons on a series of shells or rings, we can calculate the value of F for any value of θ. The problem we have to solve here, however, is the converse of this. We have measured the value of F for a series of values of θ, and wish to determine from the results the distribution of the electrons. We have seen above that there is no unique solution of this problem, but we can get some idea of the type of distribution which will fit the experimental curves. (...)

We have solved the simultaneous equations for the distribution in shells with several sets of radii, and drawn a smooth curve through the points so obtained in such a way as to represent the density of distribution of the electrons as a continuous function of the distance from the atomic centre. The density P is so defined that Pdr is the number of electrons

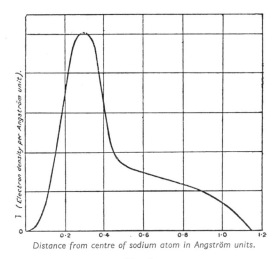

Distance from centre of sodium atom in Angström units.

Fig. 3.

* [This Vol. p. 187. Ed.]

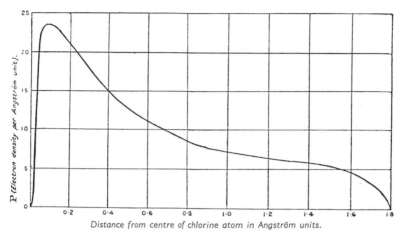

Distance from centre of chlorine atom in Angström units.

Fig. 4.

whose distance from the centre lies between r and $r + dr$. The curves which we obtain for sodium and for chlorine are shown in figs. 3 and 4. The total number of electrons in the atom is represented by the area included between the curves and the axis.

6. We have also made an approximate calculation of the F curve to be expected from an atom of the type proposed by Bohr.[1] In the ionized sodium atom containing 10 electrons, two are supposed to describe circular one-quantum orbits about the nucleus, while, of the remaining eight, four describe two-quantum circular orbits and four two-quantum elliptical orbits. We have calculated the size of these orbits from the quantum relationship and the charges; this can only be done very approximately, owing to the impossibility of allowing for the interaction of the electrons. We take the following numbers:—

Radius of 1 quantum ring	0.05 Å.
„ 2 „	0.34 „
Semi-major axis of ellipses [2]	0.42 „

To get a rough idea of the diffracting power of such an atom, we suppose, first, that the orientation of the orbits is random so that the average atom has a spherical symmetry, and also that the periods of the electrons in their orbits are so large compared with the period of the X-rays that we need not consider the effect of their movements.

[1] *Nature*, **112** (1921) 104.

[2] The elliptical two-quantum orbit of a single electron about the sodium nucleus would have a semi-major axis equal to the radius of the two-quantum circle. We have used the larger value 0.42 to make some allowance for the fact that part of the orbit lies outside the inner electrons, so that the effective nuclear charge is reduced.

The calculation of the effect of the circular orbits offers no difficulties. To allow for the effect of the ellipses, the following method was used. The elliptical orbit was divided into four segments, through each of which the electron would travel in equal times. It was then assumed that, on the average, one of the four electrons describing ellipses would be in the middle of one of these segments. This gives four different values of the radius vector, corresponding in the average atom to four spherical shells of these radii.

We thus calculate the value of F for an atom having

$$
\begin{array}{llll}
2 \text{ electrons on a shell of radius } 0.05 \text{ A.U.} \\
4 \quad ,, \qquad ,, \qquad ,, \quad 0.34 \quad ,, \\
1 \quad ,, \qquad ,, \qquad ,, \quad 0.27 \quad ,, \\
1 \quad ,, \qquad ,, \qquad ,, \quad 0.55 \quad ,, \\
1 \quad ,, \qquad ,, \qquad ,, \quad 0.70 \quad ,, \\
1 \quad ,, \qquad ,, \qquad ,, \quad 0.78 \quad ,, \\
\end{array}
$$

This gives the following figure for F_{Na}:

Sin θ	0.1	0.2	0.3	0.4	0.5
F-calculated	8.73	5.04	3.76	2.53	1.80
F-observed	8.32	5.40	3.37	2.02	0.76

The agreement, of course, is not perfect, but one must remember that no attempt has been made to adjust the size of the orbits to fit the curve. The method of calculation too is very rough, although it must give results of the right order. The point to be noticed is that the curve is quite of the right type, and there is no doubt that an average distribution of electrons of the nature given by such an atom model could be made to fit the observed value of F quite satisfactorily.

7. The points which appear to us to be most doubtful in the above analysis of our results are the following:—

(a) We have assumed that each electron scatters independently, and that the amount or scattered radiation is that calculated for a free electron in space according to the classical electromagnetic theory. It is known that for very short waves this cannot be so, since the absorption of γ rays by matter is much smaller than scattering would account for, if it took place according to this law. On the other hand, the evidence points towards the truth of the classical formula, in the region of wave-lengths we have used (0.615 Å).

(*b*) At the reflecting angle the X-rays suffer an increased absorption. We cannot be sure, therefore, that we have obtained a true measure of Q for the strong reflexions. The F curve may be too low at small angles. It is just here that its form is of the highest importance in making deductions as to atomic structure. Until this important question of the size of the homogeneous elements has been settled, we must regard our results as provisional.

(*c*) The allowance for the thermal agitation of the atom (the Debije factor) is only approximate; it depends on a few measurements made by W. H. Bragg in 1914. In order to see how much error is caused by our lack of knowledge of the Debye factor, we have calculated the electron distribution without making any allowance for it. The result may appear at first rather surprising; the electron distribution so calculated is almost indistinguishable from that which we found before, when allowance for the Debye factor had been made. This is so, although the factor is very appreciable for the higher orders of spectra, reducing them at ordinary temperatures to less than half the theoretical value at absolute zero.

A little consideration shows the reason for this. The form of the F curve at large angles is almost entirely decided by the arrangement of the electrons near the centre of the atom. A slight expansion of the grouping in this region causes a large falling off in the intensity of reflexion. The effect of the thermal agitation is to make the electron distribution appear more widely diffused; however, the average displacement of the atom from the reflecting plane owing to its thermal movements is only two or three hundredths of an Ångström unit at ordinary temperatures, and so we get very little alteration in our estimate of the electron distribution. The uncertainty as to the Debye factor, therefore, does not introduce any appreciable error in our analysis of electron distribution.

8. It is interesting to see whether any evidence can be obtained as to whether a valency electron has been transferred from one atom to the other or not. This may be put in another way: can we tell from the form of the F curves [Fig.8p.291] whether their maxima are at 10 and 18 or at 11 and 17 respectively? It appears impossible to do this; and when we come to consider the problem more closely, it seems that crystal analysis must be pushed to a far greater degree of refinement before it can settle the point. If all the electrons were grouped close to the atomic centres, and if the transference of an electron meant that one electron passed from the Na group to the Cl group, then a solution along the lines of that attempted by Debije and Scherrer for LiF might be possible. The electron distributions we find extend, on the other hand, right through the volume of the crystal. The distance between Na and Cl centres is 2.81 Å, and we

find electron distributions 1 Å from the centre in sodium and 1.8 Å from the centre in chlorine. If the valency electron is transferred from the outer region of one atom to that of the other, it will still be in the region between the two atoms for the greater part of the time, since each atom touches six neighbours, and the difference in the diffraction effects will be exceedingly small. It is for this reason that we think Debije and Scherrer's result for LiF, which were not absolute measurements such as the above, were not adequate to decide whether the transference of a valency electron has taken place.

We have assumed that the atoms are ionized in calculating our distribution curves. If, on the other hand, we had assigned 11 electrons to sodium and 17 to chlorine, we should have obtained curves of much the same shape but with an additional electron in the outermost shells of sodium and one less in those of chlorine.

9. If our results are even approximately correct, they prove an important point. There cannot be, either in sodium or chlorine, an outer 'shell' containing a group of eight electrons, or eight electrons describing orbits lying on an outer sphere. Such an arrangement would give a diffraction curve which could not be reconciled with the experimental results. Eight electrons revolving in circular orbits of the same radius would give the same diffraction curve as eight electrons on a spherical shell, and are equally inadmissible. On the other hand, it does seem possible that a combination of circular and elliptical orbits will give F curves agreeing with the observations.

CALCULATION OF THE ATOMIC SCATTERING FACTOR

63. The Atomic Structure Factor in the Intensity of Reflexion of X-Rays by Crystals, by D. R. HARTREE (1925)

■

64. A note on the paper 'The Atomic Structure Factor in the Intensity of Reflexion of X-Rays, by D. R. HARTREE, by W. L. BRAGG (1925)

■

65. Zur Theorie des Comptoneffects II, by G. WENTZEL (1927)

■

66. The Wave Mechanics of an Atom with a Non-Coulomb Central Field, Part II, by D. R. HARTREE (1928)

■

67. Some Numerical Calculations of Atomic Scattering Factors, by R. W. JAMES and G. W. BRINDLEY (1931)

■

68. The Intensity of X-Ray Reflexion by Diamond, by W. H. BRAGG (1921)

■

69. R. W. G. WYCKOFF (1930)

■

63. In the analysis of the more complicated crystal structures by means of X-rays, it is important to know the F-curves of the atoms concerned, i.e. the relations between the scattering power F of an atom, defined as the ratio of the amplitude of the wavelet scattered by the atom to that scattered by an electron, and the glancing angle. Assuming that the individual electrons of the atoms in a crystal scatter classically, the F-curve for any given atom can be calculated from the dimensions of and progress of time in the core orbits; for some atoms the atomic field can be found approximately by numerical analysis of the optical and X-ray spectra, and the core orbits can then be calculated; it is possible to generalize the results and put them in such a form that an approximate *F*-curve for any atom (or rather ion) can be calculated very simply. Numerical results for some ions are given.

64. In all methods of crystal analysis by means of X-rays, the final test of the structure which is assigned to the crystal as a result of the X-ray measurements consists in a comparison of the observed intensities of X-ray reflexion by different planes of the crystal structure with intensities which have been calculated for the proposed atomic arrangement. The structure which leads to the best agreement between calculated and observed values is chosen as the closest approximation to the truth. Anyone who is familiar with X-ray analysis will realize the unsatisfactory nature of the assumptions usually made in calculating the intensity of reflexion to be expected from a given atomic arrangement, and the uncertainty of the results due to an ignorance of the laws governing the intensity. Experimental observations can be made with a high order of accuracy, but their interpretation is extremely difficult. One factor which is highly important takes account of the amount of X-radiation scattered by the atoms through different angles. The assumption is generally made that the relative scattering powers of the atoms are simply proportional to their atomic numbers, but this approximation to the truth is only made in the lack of a more complete knowledge. The paper on the Atomic Structure Factor by Mr. Hartree is extremely interesting, because it gives estimates of the relative scattering power of atoms based on calculation of orbit-dimensions. Although these estimates may need modification, and other factors which will be referred to below must be taken into consideration in using Mr. Hartree's results, they represent a great advance on the simple assumption of proportionality between scattering power and atomic number. They are extremely interesting in showing, for instance, how fast the effect of negative ions of low atomic weight falls off with increase in glancing angle, when they are compared with atoms of higher atomic weight.

    In testing the figures for the scattering coefficient given in Hartree's paper, there are indications that the actual coefficients fall away rather more rapidly with increasing glancing angle than those which he gives. This may be partly or wholly due to the heat-motions of the atoms, for which no allowance has been made.

65*. Betrachten wir zunächst *die normal Streuung*, d.h. unter Erhaltung der Wellenlänge.

Die Streuung am einzelnen Elektron

Die Intensität J_{norm} der *normalen* Streulinie ist

$$J = J_0 \cdot \varepsilon_{nn}^2 = J_0 \cdot \{\int dS e^{i\kappa(\mathfrak{n}-\mathfrak{n}^*, \mathfrak{r})} u_n^2\}^2 \tag{3}$$

wo J_0 die klassische Streuintensität bedeutet, $u_n =$ Eigenfunktionen, $\kappa = 2\pi \nu/c$, $\mathfrak{n}, \mathfrak{n}^* =$ Richtung des Primär- bzw. Sekundärstrahls, Den Faktor ε_{nn}^2 kann man physikalisch als einen Interferenzfaktor deuten; da nämlich u_n^2 formal als Dichte der elektrischen Ladungsverteilung des Elektrons interpretiert werden kann (Schrödinger), und da $\kappa(\mathfrak{n}-\mathfrak{n}^*, \mathfrak{r})$ die relativen Phasendifferenzen der in den verschiedenen Volumelementen dS gestreuten Strahlen darstellt, kann ε_{nn} als resultierende Amplitude der an einem räumlich ausgedehnten Elektron gebeugten Strahlung aufgefaßt werden. Wie man auch anschaulich ohne weiteres einsieht, wird $\varepsilon_{nn} \cong 1$, d.h. $J_{nn} \cong J_0$ sein, solange die Wellenlänge des Lichtes groß ist gegen die Dimensionen des 'Elektrons', d.h. des Atoms; im entgegengesetzten Grenzfalle aber wird sich die Streustrahlung infolge der *kontinuierlichen* 'Ladungsverteilung' vollkommen durch Interferenz vernichten.

Die inneratomaren Interferenzen

Besitzt das streuende Atom mehrere Elektronen, so wirkt bekanntlich als streuendes Moment die geometrische Resultierende der von den verschiedenen Elektronen ausgeführten erzwungenen Schwingungen.

Für die normale Streulinie erhält man demnach:

$$J_{norm} = J_0 \cdot (\textstyle\sum_n \varepsilon_{nn})^2 = J_0 \cdot \{\int dS \cdot e^{i\kappa(\mathfrak{n}-\mathfrak{n}^*, \mathfrak{r})} \cdot \textstyle\sum_n u_n^2\}^2. \tag{3a}$$

Auch hier kann J/J_0 als Interferenzfaktor gedeutet werden, wobei $\sum_n u_n^2$ als elektrische Ladungsverteilung zu nehmen ist, in Übereinstimmung mit der Schrödingerschen Deutung dieser Größe[1]. $(\sum_n \varepsilon_{nn})^2$ vertritt also den sogenannten *Atomformfaktor* der klassischen Streuungstheorie. Bei der Streuung nach vorn ($\mathfrak{n}^* \cong \mathfrak{n}$) wird

$$\textstyle\sum_n \varepsilon_{nn} = \sum_n \int dS u_n^2 = \sum_n 1$$

---

* [Compared with the original text its sequence has been somewhat changed as we wish to emphasize the normal scattering, which causes the Laue interferences. Ed.].

[1] Vgl. E. Schrödinger, *Ann. d. Phys.* **81** (1926) 109, § 7, S. 134. Ed.].

einfach gleich der Gesamtzahl Z der Elektronen, die Intensität also gleich $J_0 . Z^2$. Bei harten Strahlen, deren Wellenlänge klein gegen den Atomradius ist ($\kappa |\mathfrak{r}| \gg 1$), wird jedoch—zum Unterschied von der klassischen Theorie—die gesamte *normale* Streustrahlung durch Interferenz vernichtet, eben wieder wegen des kontinuierlichen Charakters der Ladungsverteilung $\sum_n u_n^2$ *.

Bei den reinen Kristallinterferenzen, haben W. L. Bragg, James und Bosanquet[1] den Einfluß der inneratomaren Interferenzen durch Elimination der übrigen Einflüsse (Wärmebewegung, Absorption u.a.) isoliert. Hier kommt natürlich allein die kohärente Intensität J_{norm} in Betracht; Braggs Formfaktor F^2 ist nichts anderes als unser J_{norm}/J_0 (3a):

$$F = (\sum_n \varepsilon_{nn}) = 2\varepsilon_{11} + 8\varepsilon_{22} + \ldots = \sqrt{(J_{norm}/J_0)}. \tag{21}$$

Durch die genannten Untersuchungen wurde F für $\mathrm{Rh}K\alpha$-Strahlung ($\lambda = 0,612$ Å), gestreut an Na^+- und Cl^--Ionen (Steinzalskristall), für Streuwinkel zwischen 11 und 60° empirisch ermittelt. Für den Fall des Na^+-Ions haben wir F (21) für verschiedene effektive Kernladungszahlen Z ausgerechnet; Tabelle 3 enthält die F-Werte für $Z = 5,5$, wo die Übereinstimmung mit den Braggschen Werten die beste ist.

Tabelle 3

θ	0°	11°24′	20°	30°	40°	50°	60°
F_{ber}	10,00	8,50	6,25	3,91	2,45	1,70	1,33
F_{beob}	(10,00)	8,32	6,23	4,01	2,75	1,76	0,76

Betrachten wir jetzt *die Comptonsche Streustrahlung.*

Die Streuung am einzelnen Elektron

Im ersten Teil dieser Arbeit[2] wurde die nach größeren Wellenlängen verschobene (Comptonsche) Streustrahlung als das kontinuierliche Spektrum gedeutet, das (nach den Untersuchungen von Smekal, Kramers und Heisenberg zur Dispersionstheorie) emittiert wird, wenn das streuende Elektron

---

* [Also in the classical theory of *crystal* diffraction the atomic scattering factor is the effect of a *continuous* electron distribution, see this Vol. p. 186. Ed.]

[1] W. L. Bragg, R. W. James und C. H. Bosanquet, *Phil. Mag.* **41** 309 und **42** (1921) 1 [this Vol. pp. 265 and 282].

[2] G. Wentzel, *Zs. f. Phys.* **43** (1927) 1.

während des Streuprozesses auf ein Niveau des kontiniuerlichen Eigenwertbereiches hinaufgehoben wird, d.h. wenn es als freies 'Rückstoßelektron' weggeht.

Die Intensitätsverhältnisse ließen sich besonders leicht übersehen im Grenzfalle weicher Röntgenstrahlen. In diesem Falle, auf den wir uns auch hier beschränken wollen, ließ sich das streuende elektrische Moment, welches dem Übergang des Elektrons vom n-ten zum m-ten Zustand entspricht, angenähert folgendermaßen schreiben:

$$\mathfrak{d}_{nm} = \mathfrak{d}_0 \cdot \varepsilon_{nm} \cdot e^{2\pi i\{\nu - (E_m - E_n)/h\}t}, \tag{1}$$

wo $\mathfrak{d}_0$ die Amplitude der erzwungenen Schwingung ist, die ein Elektron nach der klassischen Theorie im Lichtfelde ausführt, und wo

$$\varepsilon_{nm} = \int dS \cdot e^{i(\kappa\mathfrak{n} - \kappa^*\mathfrak{n}^*, \mathfrak{r})} u_n u_m \tag{2}$$

$$\kappa^* = 2\pi\{\nu - (E_m - E_n)/h\}/c,$$

Numerieren wir auch die infinitesimalen Bereiche ΔE des kontinuierlichen Termspektrums mit laufenden Indizes m, so ergibt sich die Gesamtintensität der Streustrahlung durch Summation über alle Eigenwerte m (diskrete und kontinuierliche) zu

$$\sum_m J_{nm} = J_0 \cdot \sum_m |\varepsilon_{nm}|^2 = J_0 \cdot 1, \tag{4}$$

d.h. gleich der klassischen Intensität, wie man leicht aus (2) mit Hilfe der vollständigkeitsrelation für die Eigenfunktionen u_m ableitet. Verschobene und unverschobene Strahlung geben demnach zusammen die klassische Intensität.

Die inneratomaren Interferenzen

Auch hier sorgt der Comptoneffekt wiederum dafür, daß bei harten Strahlen die Aussagen der klassischen Theorie qualitativ erhalten bleiben. Die verschobene Strahlung ist nämlich als kontinuierliches Spektrum inkohärent; die Wahrscheinlichkeit, daß zwei elementare Sekundärstrahlen genau gleicher Wellenlänge zur Interferenz gelangen, ist unendlich gering; von Schwankungen abgesehen addieren sich also die Amplitudenquadrate. Da nun für jedes einzelne Elektron die verschobene Intensität gleich J_0 minus der normalen Intensität $J_0 \cdot \varepsilon_{nn}{}^2$ ist, folgt für das Gesamtatom

$$J_{versch.} = J_0 \cdot \sum_n (1 - \varepsilon_{nn}{}^2) = J_0 \cdot (Z - \sum_n \varepsilon_{nn}{}^2). \tag{4a}$$

Im Grenzfall *kurzer* Wellen, wo $\varepsilon_{nn} \cong 0$ (außer für kleinste Streuwinkel),

301

wird folglich:

$$J_{versch.} \cong J_0.Z, \qquad J_{norm.} \cong 0. \tag{5}$$

Dagegen im Grenzfall *langer* Wellen, wo $\kappa \cong 0$, $\varepsilon_{nn} \cong 1$:

$$J_{versch.} \cong 0, \qquad J_{norm.} \cong J_0.Z^2. \tag{6}$$

Im Übergangsgebiet ist zu beachten, daß ε_{nn} mit wachsendem Streu-winkel θ abnimmt; es wird demnach bei großen θ eher (5), bei kleinen eher (6) gelten. Da für $\theta = 0$ ($\mathfrak{n}^* = \mathfrak{n}$) immer $\varepsilon_{nn} = 1$ ist (s. oben), ist immer in einem gewissen Kegel um die Primärrichtung der Grenzfall (6) realisiert; die Öffnung dieses Kegels entspricht natürlich in ihrer Größen-ordnung und ihrer Abhängigkeit von Wellenlänge und Atom-dimensionen völlig den Formeln der Debyeschen Theorie der inneratomaren Interferen-zen. Man sieht also, daß bezüglich der *Summe* von verschobener und un-verschobener Intensität die Aussagen der klassischen Theorie qualitativ bestehen bleiben. Zugleich aber erkennt man, daß *inneratomare Inter-ferenzen und Comptoneffekt in der neuen Quantentheorie nicht mehr getrennt behandelt werden dürfen, sondern ein einheitliches Problem darstellen.* Tat-sächlich ist ja auch Compton gerade anläßlich seiner Untersuchungen über Interferenzen an räumlich ausgedehnten Elektronen zu seiner grundlegenden Entdeckung gelangt.

Leipzig, Theoretisch-physikalisches Institut

66. The methods of solution of the wave equation for a central field are applied to various atoms. For the core electrons, the details of the inter-action of the electrons in a single n_k group are neglected, but an approxi-mate correction is made for the fact that the distributed charge of an electron does not contribute to the field acting on itself.

For a given atom the object of the work is to find a field such that the solutions of the wave equation for the core electrons in this field (corrected as just mentioned for each core electron) give a distribution of charge which reproduces the field. This is called the self-consistent field and the process of finding it is one of successive approximation.

67. (1) A general account is given of the nature of the atomic scattering factor f and of methods of calculating it theoretically.

(2) Two methods of calculating numerically the scattering factor f_0 for the atom at rest, with sufficient accuracy for use in crystal analysis, are discussed: (*a*) A method of interpolation, based on the values of f_0 calculated

for those atoms for which the charge distributions have been determined by Hartree's method of self-consistent fields. This method appears to give reliable values up to atomic number 25. The limitations of the method are discussed. Tables are given for calculating f_0 for the different electron groups. (b) The method based on the Thomas-Fermi method of approximating to the atomic charge distributions.

68. Another point of interest is the existence of a small (222) reflection. This has been looked for previously but without success. The structure of the diamond cannot be explainied on the hypothesis that the field of force round the carbon atom is the same in all directions: or in other words, that the force between two atoms can be expressed simply by a function of the distance between their centres. If this were so the spheres, which would then represent the carbon atoms appropriately, would adopt the close-packed arrangement. As a matter of fact, each atom is surrounded by four neighbours only.

It is necessary, therefore, to suppose that the attachment of one atom to the next is due to some directed property, and the carbon atom has four such special directions: as indeed the tetra-valency of the atom might suggest. In that case the properties of the atom in diamond are based upon a tetrahedral not a spherical form. The tetrahedra point away from any (111) plane in the case of half the atoms in the diamond and towards it in the case of the other half. Consecutive (111) sheets are not exactly of the same nature; and it might reasonably be expected that they would not entirely destroy each other's effects in the second order reflection from the tetrahedral plane. It is this effect which is now found to be quite distinct, though small *.

69. The 'anomalous' (222) reflection of the diamond indicates that some of its electrons may, under suitable conditions, give rise to appreciable reflections which are probably not to be associated with atomic centers. In such an organic compound as urea it might be expected that similarly bound electrons of the nitrogen and oxygen, as well as of the carbon, atoms would be potential sources of 'anomalous' effects and would result in atomic scattering powers lower than those determined from ionic salts. No 'anomalous' reflections were found, but it may well be that part of the reduced scattering powers of the atoms in urea are to be ascribed to the 'homopolar' bonds with which the atoms of its molecules are held together.

* [C.p. M. Renninger, *Z. Krist.* **97** (1937) 107 Ed.].

THE INTENSITY OF X-RAY REFLECTIONS AND THE IMPERFECTIONS OF CRYSTALS

70. The Interpretation of Intensity Measurements in X-Ray Analysis of Crystal Structure, by W. L. Bragg (1925)

∎

71. The Intensity of Reflexion of X-Rays by Crystals, by W. L. BRAGG, C. G. DARWIN and R. W. JAMES (1926)

∎

72. The Intensity of X-Ray Spectra and the Imperfections of Crystals, by R. W. JAMES (1935)

∎

73. J. WEST (1930)

∎

74a. Studien über die Röntgenreflexion an Steinsalz und den Realbau von Steinsalz, by M. RENNINGER (1934)

∎

74b. M. RENNINGER (1934)

∎

70. The factors which govern the intensity of X-ray reflexion may for convenience be divided into two types. In the first of these must be classed all those factors which cause a general falling away of intensity as the angle of incidence increases. In addition to this the intensity is governed by the structure factor S, the ratio of the actual amplitude to that which would exist if all the electrons of all the atoms were arranged exactly on successive planes (we are now allowing for electronic as well as for atomic configuration).

The Debije effect, or weakening of the spectra due to the heat-motion of the atoms, may perhaps be most conveniently considered as being included in the structure factor S, since its effect on the amplitude may be calculated by the laws of interference which govern the structure factor.

The two points about which most uncertainty exists are: (*a*) the correct method of calculating the structure factor S for any given atomic arrangement, (*b*) the relation of the intensity to the structure factor S. In certain cases it is possible to determine atomic positions accurately without making any precise assumptions about scattering power, and with the most approximate experimental determinations of intensity. This is the case for simple structures containing two or three parameters, which can often be evaluated one at a time by considering certain groups of planes, and it is also the case for structures of the elements where the atoms are all alike so that at any given angle they scatter equally. In more complex crystals it is absolutely necessary to make some assumptions in order to fix the atomic positions.

The following point must be emphasized in this connexion. Even though the dependence of intensity on structure factor is so very obscure, an accurate method of calculating the structure factor furnishes by itself a sufficient guide to the analysis of a structure. If the observed intensities show a parallelism to the calculated structure factors when both are arranged in order of increasing glancing angle, the assigned structure must be right. In comparing each plane with the next at a higher angle, a rise in structure factor should correspond to increased intensity, and a fall in structure factor to a decreased intensity. The absence of certain reflexions, which must be accounted for by a very small factor, is in particular a most important indication of atomic position. The structure factor depends both on the positions of the atoms and on their scattering powers. Since it is so necessary to know this factor, Mr. Hartree's figures should prove most useful.

In the earlier work on X-ray analysis it was assumed that the intensity of reflexion varied as the square of the structure factor, other factors being equal. This assumption is still made in the analysis of the powder-photographs and of the Laue photographs, and it is probably justifiable in these cases. However, it has long been known as an empirical law that strong reflexions from faces of highly perfect crystals measured by the X-ray spectrometer were more nearly proportional to the structure factor itself.

Some experimental work on rock-salt[1] made an estimate of the extinction coefficient ε possible, and it was found that

$$I \infty S^2/(\mu + \varepsilon)$$

for this crystal, where the extinction factor ε is proportional to the intensity of reflexion I. In the case of rock-salt, which is a highly distorted crystal, ε was only about one-half the absorption coefficient μ for the strongest reflexion. In a more perfect crystal ε might be much larger than μ. In this case the law

'$I \infty S^2/(\mu + \varepsilon)$, may be written '$I \infty S^2/(\mu + \alpha I)$'

[1] Bragg, James and Bosanquet, *Phil. Mag.* **42** (July 1921) [this Vol. p. 282].

where α is a constant. When I is large this becomes a law '$I^2 \infty S^2$' or '$I \infty S$'. When I is small it assumes the normal form '$I \infty S^2$'.

Ewald shows that, when perfect reflexion of X-rays takes place over a short range, this range is proportional to the structure factor S, so that a higly perfect crystal should give rise to a law

$$I \infty S.$$

The number of perfectly-arranged planes which are necessary to give complete reflexion increases as I diminishes, so that a crystal which obeys Ewald's law for low orders might obey the law '$I \infty S^2$' for the weaker reflexions of high order. This is again in agreement with experience.

These examples show how much caution must be exercised in comparing calculated and observed intensities of reflexion. One is on far surer ground in correlating structure factor and intensity by tabulating both in order of increasing glancing angle and seeing whether they rise and fall together. The necessary data for such a comparison are provided by any means of observing the intensity of reflexion by all planes of the crystal under equal conditions. With the spectrometer this is done, for instance, by comparing them all with some common standard.

71.   1. *Introduction*

The authors were privileged recently to attend a conference, organized by Prof. P. P. Ewald, of the Technische Hochschule of Stuttgart, at which the question of intensity of X-ray reflexion was the chief subject of discussion. The members of the conference were P. P. Ewald, M. v. Laue, L. Brillouin, R. W. G. Wyckoff, H. Mark, I. Waller, A. D. Fokker, P. Debije, K. Herzfeld, H. Ott, and ourselves, and it was held at Holzhausen, on the Ammersee, in Bavaria, in September 1925. We wish to take this opportunity of recording our gratitude to Prof. Ewald for having arranged the conference. It afforded a unique opportunity of exchanging views, and was the greatest inspiration for future work.

Note.—The following are the chief papers of our own in chronological order to which we shall refer by abbreviated titles.

Darwin, *Phil. Mag.* vol. **27** (1914) 315. D I [this Vol. p. 169].
Darwin, *Phil. Mag.* vol. **27** (1914) 675. D II [this Vol. p. 203].
Bragg, James, & Bosanquet, *Phil. Mag.* vol. **41** (1921) 309. BJB I [this Vol. p. 265].
Bragg, James, & Bosanquet, *Phil. Mag.* vol. **42** (1921) 1. BJB II [this Vol. p. 282].
Bragg, James, & Bosanquet, *Phil. Mag.* vol. **44** (1922) 433. BJB III [this Vol. p. 291].
Darwin, *Phil. Mag.* Vol. **43** (1922) 800. D III.

2. *Two Formulae for Intensity of Reflexion*

The question of the intensity of X-ray reflexion is full of difficulties. Any mathematical expression calculated to give the relationship between incident and reflected energy of radiation for a definite experimental disposition contains a number of factors which need to be evaluated. The three factors which are of especial importance depend on

(a) The amplitude of the wave scattered by each individual atom of the crystal, for definite directions of incident and scattered beam.
(b) The effect of the heat motion of the atoms, giving rise to the temperature factor which reduces the intensity of reflexion as the temperature of the crystal is raised. The existence of this factor was originally pointed out by Debye, and its effect was first observed by Sir W. H. Bragg.
(c) The interaction of the waves scattered by the atoms of the crystal which are in a more or less orderly arrangement.

In order to make any advance, the last of these factors must be satisfactorily evaluated. If this can be done, there is hope of a direct determination of the second factor by experimental measurements at different temperatures, and so of a determination of the first factor by measuring the intensity of reflexion from a number of types of crystal.

The reward of accurate results is great, since they will yield more direct information as to the positions of the electrons in the atom than is obtainable by any other methods. This must be regarded as the main objective, but a knowledge of the scattering powers of the atoms is also essential to the application of X-rays to discover the structure of complex crystals. After fifteen years of crystal analysis we are not in possession of a means of utilizing to the full the very accurate intensity measurements which can easily be made, and have to be content with qualitative tests. All who have worked in this field will appreciate the unsatisfactory nature of the arguments on which analyses are based.

The difficulty in the mathematical calculation of the last factor arises from the nature of the crystals with which we have to work. On the one hand, an orderly arrangement of atoms is present, since all the X-ray diffraction effects arise from such an arrangement. The accurate comparative measurements of X-ray wave-lengths, extending to five significant figures, show that the atoms in a crystal are arrayed in a very perfect manner. On the other hand, it is clear from experimental results that this perfection has its limits. The orderly arrangement does not extend over the whole volume of the crystal from which the reflected radiation originates, and calculations based on the supposition of an absolutely perfect crystal lead to results which are at variance with experiment. There is no question here of a small correction to be applied on account of the imperfection of the crystal. The observed intensity of reflexion may be from ten to fifty times as great as that given by calculations. This shows the necessity of taking into account the actual nature of the crystal, and the caution with which calculations must be applied.

It will simplify the discussion to consider two extreme cases of crystalline arrangement. Some kind of regular arrangement must, of course, be postulated in order that diffraction effects may be observed. On the one hand, a crystal may be regarded as a *mosaic* composed of small crystalline fragments which are approximately parallel to each other, but whose orientations are distributed through an angular range of many minutes of arc on either side of a mean direction. All atoms within each fragment are regarded as being in perfect arrangement. The number of atoms in each fragment is so small that their effect on each other when diffracting radiation may be neglected. This is the extreme case of an imperfect crystal, and may be termed the *ideally imperfect crystal*, or *mosaic crystal*. A very simple mathematical expression gives the intensity of the diffracted radiation. Experimental results seem to show that many crystals do in fact approach this ideal type of imperfection. Calculation shows that the homogeneous fragments must be not more than a few thousand atomic planes in depth in order that the mathematical expression may be valid.

On the other hand, we may suppose the crystal to be absolutely perfect. The physical significance of this statement can also be analysed. It means that the small homogeneous fragments of crystal are arranged so regularly that their orientations do not vary by more than a fraction of a second of arc. An entirely different mathematical formula, but one which is again of a very simple type, applies to the diffraction of X-rays by such a crystal. The intensity of reflexion calculated by the second formula is only a fraction of that calculated by the first formula. Experiment has not yet indicated that this ideal perfection is realized in actual crystals. It appears to be the case that all crystals are neither ideally perfect nor ideally imperfect, but have a structure which lies between the two extremes, and in most cases much closer to the ideally imperfect.

As far as we are aware, the expressions for these two cases were first given by one of us in 1914 in the papers D (I) and D (II). In order to give the expression a precise form which may be used for quantitative work the experimental arrangements must be defined. At the date of those papers it was usual to work without slits so that the whole spherical wave fell on the face of a fixed crystal. Some part of this would be at the proper angle, and the sheet of radiation would be effectually limited only by the length of the slit of the ionization chamber. This method has proved not so convenient in practice as another due to Sir W. H. Bragg. Here the incident beam is defined by slits, so as to be approximately parallel, and the crystal is rotated with constant angular velocity through the settings for which reflexion occurs. It is obvious that there is a very close relationship between the methods, since in each the crystal is equally exposed to radiation at all angles near the angle of reflexion—in the first because of the divergency of the incident beam, and in the second because of the uniform rotation of the crystal. In consequence of this it is very simple to translate the formulae of D (I) and D (II) into the corresponding expressions for the other method, and the latter have the advantage of not containing such quantities as the length of the slit and the distance from source to observing-chamber. In quoting these formulae we shall express them in the second form without further explanation.

(...)

4. *Primary and Secondary Extinction*

It appears to us that the most promising method of discovering the physical nature of the crystal, and of deciding what formulae to use, consists in careful measurements of the integrated reflexion. We may except to find these measurements to lie between two extremes—a lower limit given by the formula for the perfect crystal, and an upper limit by the formula for the ideally imperfect crystal. In order to estimate the degree of perfection we must have some idea of the behaviour of intermediate types, and this has been worked out in D (III). In this paper the ideally imperfect crystal is regarded as the standard, and the integrated reflexion is supposed to be lowered below this standard by two phenomena which are called primary and secondary extinction, which we may now explain. The formula for the perfect crystal shows that total reflexion takes place over a range of several seconds of arc in the case of the more powerful reflexions given by simple planes. In such a crystal all the reflexion must take place in a layer very close to the surface, for the inner parts of the crystal receive no radiation at the correct angle for reflexion, since this radiation has been diverted by the upper layers. If, however, the crystal departs from ideal perfection, and the lower layers are inclined at an angle of more than a few seconds to the upper layer, they will be able to reflect radiation which has traversed the upper layers. Any departure from perfection increases the integrated reflexion to a value greater than that given by formula (3)

$$\rho = \frac{8}{3\pi} N \frac{e^2}{mc^2} F(2\theta, \lambda)\lambda^2 \frac{1}{\sin 2\theta} \tag{3}$$

We have called this shielding of lower layers by parallel upper layers of the *same homogeneous fragment* of crystal 'primary extinction'. It is at its maximum in the perfect crystal, and in fact it is not necessary to use the conception when dealing with the perfect crystal since formula (3) can be applied at once. It is convenient to use it when dealing with crystals which are imperfect, but in which the homogeneous blocks are so large that their lower layers are appreciably screened by the upper layers.

The upper limit to the integrated reflexion is given by formula (1)

$$\rho = \frac{Q}{2\mu} = \left(N \frac{e^2}{mc^2} F \right)^2 \frac{\lambda^3}{2\mu \sin 2\theta} \tag{1}$$

for the ideally imperfect crystal. In this case the homogeneous blocks are so small that every part of them receives its due of radiation. As long as the blocks are sufficiently small for this to be the case, their size and relative orientation do not affect the value of the integrated reflexion. This is only characteristic of the crystal, of the indices of the plane, and of the wavelength, when allowance is made for the effect described in the next paragraph.

A factor comes in which diminishes the integrated reflexion from that given by formula (1) even when the homogeneous blocks are very small. When the primary beam of X-rays traverses the crystal in a direction which permits of reflexion by some of the blocks, its energy is lessened by being partly reflected as well as by being absorbed in the usual way through conversion into β rays. The existence of this apparent increase in absorption at the reflecting angle was first demonstrated experimentally by W. H. Bragg [1]. We have called this increase secondary extinction. In the case of a given crystal, its value will depend on the law according to which the fragments of homogeneous crystal are orientated, and on the direction in which the rays pass through the crystal. We have shown (BJB II) that in the case of the (200) reflexion from rock-salt the secondary extinction may attain a value half as great as the ordinary absorption coefficient, and very probably in other crystals it attains a much higher value.

Both primary and secondary extinction thus depend on the shielding of lower layers by parallel upper layers which divert X-ray energy which would otherwise be reflected. They may be distinguished as follows. In the case of primary extinction the upper and lower layers form part of

[1] W. H. Bragg, *Phil. Mag.* vol. **27** (1914) 881.

the same homogeneous fragment of crystal, so that a phase-relationship exists between waves reflected by them. In the case of secondary extinction the layers are separated by other fragments with a different orientation, so that no such phase-relationship exists. In the first case the calculation deals with amplitude, in the second with intensity. Both types of extinction tend to diminish the integrated reflexion to a value less than that given by formula (1), which therefore gives an upper limit to the intensity of reflexion.

We may therefore hope to estimate the effect of extinction, and get some information about the mosaic structure of the crystal, by comparing calculated and observed intensities of reflexion at small angles where the uncertainty about the other factors is least.

7. *The Estimation of the Degree of Imperfection*

Examples show distinct evidence that some crystals are nearly if not ideally imperfect, while in others there is a partial approach to perfection. It thus becomes important to gauge the degree of perfection, and the numerical results suggest that it is natural to regard the ideally imperfect as the standard and to gauge the departure from this.

We have pointed out above that there are two types of extinction simultaneously operative and that no process can eliminate one, the primary. The reason for this is that the primary extinction depends on the individual fragments, of which each reflects the rays over a few seconds of arc. If it were possible to obtain readings with the crystal at successive settings at intervals only a fraction of a second apart (the rays must be parallel with this degree of accuracy also), we might fit the results to a formula, find the number of layers in the fragments, and extrapolate to the case of small thickness. But the difficulty of doing this is very great, and we have to be content with the integrated reflexion of the fragments. The result of this is that we do not determine Q, but a lesser quantity Q'. It is shown in D (III), p. 816, that

$$Q' = Q(\tanh mq)/mq \qquad (4)$$

where q is the amplitude of the wave reflected from a single plane, and m is the number of planes.

The matter is quite otherwise for the secondary extinction. This depends on the impoverishment of the radiation striking the deeper fragments on account of the reflexion from the outer ones. In this case it is possible to measure not merely the integrated reflexion, but the actual amount E_u

at each setting u of the crystal (compare the curve in BJB II, fig. 7). It was suggested in D III that from this curve it should be possible to deduce a function of the setting angle u, called $G(u)$ (pp. 811 and 921), from which Q' could be determined by integration over all values of u. The quantity $G(u)du/Q'$ is the fraction of the crystal by volume in which the fragments are orientated with settings between u and $u + du$. Again, knowing the form of $G(u)$, it should be possible to calculate the extinction coefficient ε, this being the addition to be made to the ordinary absorption coefficient in (1) so as to be able to derive Q from the integrated reflexion.

This quantity was directly measured in BJB II by taking the integrated reflexions *through* a set of crystals of varying thickness.

When a crystal plate of thickness t_0 is rotated, and the rays are reflected at planes which are at right angles to the plate, the integrated reflexion is given by

$$\rho = Qt \exp(-\mu t),$$

where $t = t_0 \sec \theta$, and $\mu = \mu_0 + \varepsilon$. By plotting ρ against t both Q and μ can be measured.

The ordinary coefficient of absorption μ_0 (10·7 for Rh K_α) is measured by passing the rays through the plate at an angle where reflexion does not occur, and so ε can be obtained. A value of 5.6 for ε when the (200) reflexion is taking place, and of 2.9 for (220), was observed, these values being average one for the specimens of rock-salt employed.

A calculation in D III made with the object of comparing these values of ε with values based on the $G(u)$ curve gave distinctly unsatisfactory results—the calculated value of ε was about 1 as compared with the observed of about 5, though the data were perhaps not good enough to condemn the process out of hand. The matter has since been investigated with great skill and accuracy by Wasastjerna[1], who obtained much the same results, and there was thus a rather serious discrepancy to be faced. It would appear that this discrepancy is due to a fact overlooked in D III. The assumption was made that the crystal was uniform in character throughout, so that all points of its face posesss the same $G(u)$. But if the gross structure of the crystal is warped, it is possible that the part illuminated through the top of the slit will reflect best in a different position from that illuminated through the bottom. All parts of the crystal may contribute to measurements of the stationary reflexion E_u, and so the reflexion curve may be spread out quite wide; but yet the crystal fragments in each part

[1] By an ingenious slit-system, Wasastjerna explored the amount of radiation reflected at different depths of a crystal face. His value for ε is close to that given in BJB II.

of the face may be strongly concentrated in one direction, with consequent large extinction. In fact $G(u)$ must be regarded as a function of y, the co-ordinate along the axis of rotation, and E_u as a rather complicated average effect from which the corresponding average for $G(u)$ cannot be derived. The function $G(u)$ which comes into our formula depends on the divergence in orientation from a mean direction of the fragments encountered along the path of a reflected beam, which will be only a fraction of a millimetre in length within the crystal. It depends on the local imperfection, not the gross imperfection, of the crystal.

We may observe that this difficulty does not arise in the experimental method of BJB II, for there only averaged quantities occur throughout; but it is necessary to assume that the warping was about the same in extent for all plates used.

The other problem is to measure the mean of the depth of the coherent fragments. If Q is known from other sources, we can deduce this by measuring Q' and so solving (4) for mq, for q is determined by Q. But if the problem is to determine Q, this method is not available. All we can do is to take various crystals of the same substance (of which some should preferably show external signs of being fragmented), and evaluate Q' for each of them. The greatest value may be presumed to be not far from Q.

To summarise:—We have three different types of imperfection—those responsible for primary and for secondary extinction, and the general warping of the crystal. Unless we know F from other sources, the first can only be evaluated by investigating so many crystals that in some the correction is absent. When known it tells us how thick the perfect fragments of each crystal specimen are. The second can be found by direct experi-ment, and tells us the angular width over which the fragments are spread in each part of the crystal. The third is of the type usually to be seen di-rectly by the surface reflexion of ordinary light. It could be studied by taking reflexion curves with varying lengths of the slits defining the beam of X-rays.

72.   *Summary of theoretical results*

We may at this stage conveniently summarise the theoretical results discussed above. At one extreme we have the perfect crystal, which reflects X-rays according to formula (8),

$$\frac{E\omega}{I} = \frac{8}{3\pi} \frac{N\lambda^2}{\sin 2\theta} |F| \frac{e^2}{mc^2} \frac{1 + |\cos 2\theta|}{2} \tag{8}^1$$

reflection from *ideal crystal* large enough for the whole of the incident beam to fall on the face.

E = the total energy reflected
ω = the angular velocity of the rotating crystal
I = the energy falling per second in the whole incident beam.

the intensity being proportional to the structure amplitude $|F|$ of the crystal unit. At the other extreme we have the mosaic crystal, built up of a number of optically independent regions, each of which is so small that the simple reflection formula (4),

$$\frac{E\omega}{I_0} = QV; Q = \frac{N^2\lambda^3}{\sin 2\theta} \left(|F|\frac{e^2}{mc^2}\right)^2 \frac{1 + \cos^2 2\theta}{2} \tag{4}^2$$

reflection from *crystal fragment* bathed in the incident beam.

I_0 = the intensity of the incident beam (the energy incident per sqcm on a plane perpendicular to the direction of the beam)
V = the volume of the crystal fragment.

may be applied to it. We have seen that such crystal fragments must not be more than a few thousand planes in thickness. The reflection formula for such a *mosaic crystal* is given by (9),

$$\frac{E\omega}{I} = \frac{Q}{2\mu} \tag{9}^3$$

with Q given in (4) and
μ = the absorption coefficient.

For strong spectra equation (9) must be corrected for *secondary extinction*, which is due to the screening of crystal blocks during the reflection, owing to the chance parallelism of other independent blocks. The correction for secondary extinction amounts to increasing the effective absorption coefficient. Between the two extremes we must have a continuous series of crystal types. We may think of the mosaic gradually passing into the perfect crystal by the increase in size of the perfect regions, until one of them occupies the whole crystal. In an intermediate type, the independent blocks will still be differently orientated, but will be too large for (4) to be applicable. The intensities from the individual blocks will not be proportional to their volumes, because the lower portions of the

[1] [This Vol. p. 210 eq. (11).]
[2] [This Vol. p. 275 eq. (4).]
[3] [This Vol. p. 276 eq. (5).]

given block will be screened by the upper portions of the same block. This effect is called *primary extinction*. It could be allowed for by (6)

$$\frac{E\omega}{I_0} = QV\,(\tanh mq)/mq \qquad (6)^1$$

m = number of perfectly arranged planes, each reflecting a fraction q of the incident amplitude.

if the sizes of the perfect blocks could be estimated. There seems to be no way of making this estimate, and crystals which show any considerable degree of primary extinction are difficult or impossible to deal with quantitatively.

Comparison with Experiment

Since the formulae for the integrated reflection are so very different for the mosaic and the perfect crystal, it ought to be possible to tell whether a crystal approximates more to one type or to the other by measuring the absolute intensity of reflexion of a spectrum, and comparing it with those to be expected from the two formulae. The application of this method shows very definitely that the majority of real crystals have a texture which is something between the two extreme types, but that most of them approximate rather more closely to the mosaic type than to the ideally perfect type. Complete quantitative tests have been made for only a few crystals. They involve first of all absolute measurements of the integrated reflections for a series of spectra, and of the dependence of the intensity on the temperature. The next step is to calculate the integrated reflection from the two theoretical formulae. This involves a knowledge of the atomic scattering factors, or f factors of the atoms of which the crystal unit is built up. The f factors calculated by the method of Hartree refer to atoms at rest, and it is necessary to correct for the temperature vibrations and for the zero-point vibrations of the crystal lattice using the measured temperature factor. The measured and calculated integrated reflections can then be compared. This process has been carried out fully for rock salt[2], for potassium chloride[3] and for metallic aluminium[4], all of which appear to be very nearly ideal mosaics, and to show a comparatively small amount

[1] [This Vol. p. 311 eq. (4).]

[2] R. W. James, I. Waller and D. R. Hartree, *Proc. Roy. Soc. London* (A) **118** (1928) 334.

[3] R. W. James and G. W. Brindley, *Proc. Roy. Soc. London* (A) **121** (1928) 155.

[4] R. W. James, G. W. Brindley and R. G. Wood, *Proc. Roy. Soc. London* (A) **125** (1929) 401.

Table I.

Integrated reflections from Al. (Mo Ka radiation). Temp. 17° C.

Absolute Integrated reflections $\times 10^6$

Spectrum	θ	Calculated		Observed
		Perfect Crystal	Mosaic	
111	8°43'	19.6	818.3	580
200	10°6'	16.2	618.6	436
222	17°40'	6.30	157.9	144.1
400	20°32'	4.47	91.3	86.4
333	27° 6'	2.19	28.3	26.2
600	31°45'	1.31	12.0	12.2
444	37°23'	0.76	5.14	4.95
800	44°33'	0.40	2.09	2.10
555	49°23'	0.37	1.39	1.43

of secondary extinction. We give here, in Table I, the results for aluminium from the measurements of James, Brindley and Wood.

It is clear from these results that the observed integrated reflection from aluminium is altogether too high for the perfect crystal formula. The observed value for (111), for example, is about 30 times that calculated for the perfect crystal. On the other hand, it is seen that the agreement between the observed values and those calculated from the mosaic formula is surprisingly good. The intensities of the strong spectra are all weaker than the calculated values, but this is readily explained by assuming that the single crystal of Al used in the experiments was a mosaic crystal, showing a certain amount of secondary extinction, which, as we have seen, affects the stronger spectra. It would appear that primary extinction was almost entirely absent. It is particularly to be noted that the agreement here is an absolute one: no points have been arbitrarily set equal.

The agreement in the cases of sylvine and rock salt was nearly as good, and we must conclude that these crystals are mosaics. The mosaic nature of rock salt had been inferred by Darwin from the early measurements of Moseley and Darwin of the intensity of reflection of white radiation, which they found altogether too strong for a perfect crystal.

(b) Diamond. Some experiments by Sir William Bragg[1] on diamond showed that the integrated reflections were proportional to $|F|$ and not

[1] W. H. Bragg, *Proc. Physic. Soc.* **33** (1921) 304.

316

to $|F|^2$. It was found also that if small diamonds were bathed in the radiation, the reflected intensity was not proportional to the volume of the crystal. This is not due to ordinary absorption, which was negligible with the radiation used, but to the primary extinction. Over the reflecting range the reflection is practically complete after the radiation has penetrated to a depth considerably less than the thickness of the crystal. Only a fraction of the crystal volume thus contributes anything to the reflection, which is mainly a surface effect. These results indicated that diamond approximates closely to the perfect crystal type. Careful measurements by Ehrenberg, Ewald and Mark[1] of the breadth and intensities of the reflections from diamond confirm this view, and a discussion of the results by Brindley[2] shows that the intensities agree well with the perfect crystal formula of Darwin. Diamond appears to approach more closely than any other crystal yet investigated to the ideally perfect type.

(c) Calcite. As an example of a crystal of an intermediate type we may take calcite. The following table shows some figures based on some measurements by Sir William Bragg[3]. It appears that calcite although not an

Table II

Dependence of integrated reflection for calcite on glancing angle. Rhodium radiation. $\lambda = 0.615\text{Å}$.

| | Absolute Integrated Reflection $\times 10^6$ | | |
| | Calculated | | |
$\sin \theta$	Perfect Crystal	Mosaic	Observed
0.1	30.9	1220	240
0.1	9.4	280	70
0.3	3.8	63	27
0.4	2.1	24	8.6
0.5	1.7	12.5	2.4

ideally perfect crystal is far from being irregular enough to be classed as a mosaic. It is of course well known that calcite crystals freshly cleaved may have very perfect surfaces.

The sweep-curves are extremely narrow, and there is probably considerable primary as well as secondary extinction.

[1] W. Ehrenberg, P. P. Ewald and H. Mark, *Z. Kristallogr.* **66** (1928) 547.
[2] G. W. Brindley, *Proc. Roy. Soc. London* (A) **140** (1933) 301.
[3] W. H. Bragg, *Phil. Trans. Roy. Soc. London* (A) **215** (1915).

317

The sweep-curve and the state of perfection of the crystal

In conclusion we shall discuss briefly the question as to how far the state of perfection of the crystal may be inferred from the sweep-curve. It would appear that, although the sweep-curve may be taken as a general indication, in the sense that if a crystal reflects over a wide range it is not likely to be a perfect crystal, and that, in general, crystals which are nearly mosaics show wide sweep-curves, caution is required in interpreting such evidence. From the extreme case of the crystal of sapphire illustrated in fig. 1, we see that a wide sweep-curve may only be evidence of a large-scale imperfection of the crystal. The separate regions of the sapphire crystal are evidently fairly perfect, and it would certainly show a large extinction. The irregularities which diminish primary extinction, and the lack of perfect orientation which diminishes secondary extinction are as we have seen, small-scale phenomena, and although a crystal which shows the large-scale irregularites which produce a wide sweep-curve will probably possess the small-scale ones which cause it to reflect as a mosaic, the correlation between the two effects is not exact. Some crystals show a relatively small amount of extinction although their sweep-curves are quite narrow.

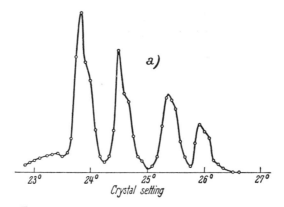

Fig. 1a. $3\overline{3}0$ spectrum from a composite corundum crystal with RhKα.

Considerations of this kind make it difficult to estimate secondary extinction from the sweep-curves, and meet some of the difficulties raised by Darwin in his discussion of experimental results in his paper on imperfect crystals.

Manchester

73. The result of secondary extinction is effectively to increase the true absorption coefficient μ_0 to μ according to the relation

$$\mu = \mu_0 + gQ \qquad (4)$$

where g is supposed constant for the crystal. We require to evaluate g.

Of the two methods normally employed for this purpose, one is experimental and seeks to find g by determining the effective absorption coefficient μ in (4) for one or more reflexions measured through a crystal slip. The other is based on trial and error. The first method is laborious and, with some crystals, difficult since it depends on a series of observations made on a slip which is gradually ground to a thin flake. The second method depends to some extent on a partial solution of the structure with respect to some direction, and upon a knowledge of the atomic F curves.

In the present experiments a further method of evaluating g has been tried, which, when it can be applied, has much to recommend it; for it is rapid and convenient, and supplies in addition a set of absolute intensities of reflexion from general planes (hkl) not usually measured on the spectrometer. It consists in taking a powder photograph of a portion of the crystal used in the spectrometer experiments, and estimating by photometric measurement, the relative intensities of the various lines[1]. Now, provided the powder be sufficiently fine both primary and secondary extinction will be absent, and the relative intensities of reflexion deduced from the lines on the photograph will represent the relative values which would have been obtained with the spectrometer if both types of extinction had been absent. By comparing therefore a series of planes examined by both powder and ionisation methods one can find the value of g. At the same time one can use the corrected spectrometer results to calibrate in absolute measure the whole of the powder results.

74a. An verschiedenen Steinsalzexemplaren wird mittels Doppelspektrometer die Reflexionsbreite von (200) und das integrale Reflexionsvermögen für drei auftretenden Ordnungen der Spaltfläche mit Cu-Strahlung gemessen. An einem nach der Kyropoulos-Methode künstlich gezogenen Exemplar wird eine für Steinsalz bis jetzt unbekannte geringe Halbweite von 7,1″ gefunden. Das integrale Reflexionsvermögen dieses Kristalls ergab sich für alle drei Ordnungen in guter Übereinstimmung mit dem von der dynamischen Theorie für den Idealkristall geforderten. Noch wesentlich besser wird die Übereinstimmung durch Absorptionsberücksichtigung nach Prins. Die idealen Bereiche (Kristallite) sind von der Größenordnung 1 mm und darunter. Sie sind um Minuten gegenseitig verschwenkt. Jedoch ist das Reflexionsvermögen für jede Stelle des Kristalls dasselbe und damit auch für den ganzen Kristall.

[1] With a sufficiently sensitive instrument this experiment is preferably carried out on the ionisation spectrometer.

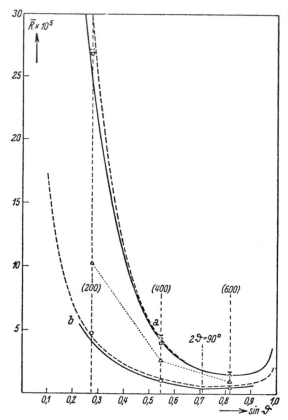

Fig. 7. Winkelabhängigkeit des integralen Reflexionsvermögens von Steinsalz für die geraden Reflexe der Cu-K_α-Linie (1,54Å) und symmetrische Bragg-Reflexion.

a) Für den Mosaikkristall, nach der kinematischen Theorie
    – – – ohne
    ——— mit   Berücksichtigung von sekundärer Extinktion.

b) Für den Idealkristall
    – – – nach der gewöhnlichen dynamischen Theorie (Darwin-Ewald).
    ——— mit Absorptions-Berücksichtigung nach Prins.

Meßwerte:
    ○ für künstlichen Kristall, unberührte Spaltfläche,
    △ „ natürlichen   „   „   „
    □× „   „   „   geschliffen und poliert.

                (□ Wagner-Kulenkampff, × Verfasser)

320

Die gute Übereinstimmung der Meßwerte an dem künstlichen Kristall mit den von der dynamischen Theorie geforderten Werten, s. Fig. 7, zeigt, daß die einzelnen Kristallite des Kristalls dem 'Idealkristall' recht nahe kommen, wenn auch die gefundene Reflexionsbreite den von der Theorie verlangten Wert etwas übersteigt. Dies kann jedoch, wie schon oben vermutet wurde, an einer Superposition der gefundenen Kurve aus mehreren nahe beieinanderliegenden Einzelmaximis liegen.

Der Kristall als Ganzes ist zwar nicht das, was man sich gewöhnlich unter einem 'Ideal'-Kristall vorstellt, ein in seiner ganzen Ausdehnung regelmäßig gebauter Kristall. Vielmehr besteht er aus 'Kristalliten' von ungefähr 10^{-2}—10^{-1} cm und darüber Lineardimensionen, von denen jeder für sich so vollkommen ist, daß sich bei Röntgenreflexionen in ihm ein 'dynamisch abgeschlossener' Zustand, ein Gleichgewichtszustand der Wechselwirkung ausbilden kann.

Die Einzelkristallite sind um Minuten gegeneinander geneigt, so daß bezüglich spektrometrischer Brauchbarkeit der Kristall durchaus nicht ideal ist, außer bei Verwendung eines sehr klein ausgeblendeten Bereichs reflektierender Oberfläche, oder für weiche Strahlung im Drehkristall-Spektrographen, wo Verbreiterung der Linien durch Mosaikstruktur nur infolge der Kleinheit der Bauelemente, nicht infolge ihrer Verschwenkung oder der Eindringungstiefe verursacht sein kann.

Das Vorhandensein einer optisch feststellbaren Verwerfung der Spaltfläche, einer Aufteilung in kleine, aber makroskopische Einzelbereiche, die wir 'Kristallite' nannten, sagt, wie die hier berichteten Versuche zeigen, über das Vorhandensein einer wirklichen Mosaikstruktur gar nichts aus.

Dreierlei Störungen im regelmäßigen Aufbau eines Kristalls sind nun nach allem anzunehmen:

1. *Makroskopische Verwerfung.* Optisch feststellbare Aufteilung in 'Kristallite' von mehr als 10^{-3}—10^{-2} cm Größe. Das Vorhandensein oder Nichtvorhandensein dieser Unterteilung kann nur den Gesamtwinkelbereich, nicht aber die Intensität der Reflexionen mitbeeinflussen (wenigstens für weiche Strahlen, s.u.).

2. *Wirkliche Mosaikstruktur,* Verwerfungen gleicher oder verschiedener Art, mit viel feinerer Aufteilung in Blöcke von 10^{-7}—10^{-4} cm Größe[1], deren Vorhandensein oder Nichtvorhandensein hauptsächlich die Röntgen-Intensitätsgesetze bestimmt. Grenzfall ist der 'ideale' Mosaikkristall, bei dem die Blöcke entweder sehr stark verschwenkt und $< 10^{-5}$ cm oder auch nur extrem klein, $< 10^{-6}$ cm sind.

[1] Ab 10^{-3}–10^{-4} cm beginnt die primäre Extinktion abzunehmen und die durch das kinematische Auflösungsvermögen bedingte Reflexionsbreite des Einzelkriställchens die Größenordnung von Sekunden anzunehmen.

3. Die *Smekalschen*[1] *Lockerstellen*. Diese würden eine Aufteilung in ideale Bereiche von der Größe 10^4—10^6 Bausteinen, also etwa 10^{-6} cm Lineardimensionen bedeuten, für alle Kristalle, ideal und nicht ideal reflektierende. Da eine wirkliche Mosaikstruktur, mit Bereichen solch geringer Größe, sämtliche Röntgenlinien auf die Größenordnung von Bogengraden verbreitern würde, kann es sich hierbei nur um Unterbrechungen der kohärent zusammenhängenden Gitterbereiche durch Poren handeln. Die Poren dürfen Neigung und Abstand der Netzebenen nicht stören. Wie Smekal[2] selbst betont, sollen die Lockerstellen in keinem Zusammenhang mit der röntgenmäßig festgestellten Mosaikstruktur stehen.

Selbstverständlich können 1 und 2 ineinander übergehen. Aber wie unsere Versuche zeigen, kann 1 unabhängig von 2 auftreten. Und wahrscheinlich auch 2 unabhängig von 1, denn es gibt wohl auch optisch einwandfreie Spaltflächen von Mosaikkristallen[3].

Herrn Prof. Dr. P. P. Ewald danke ich herzlichst für viele wertvolle Anregungen und stetes förderndes Interesse.

Stuttgart, Institut für theoret. Physik der Techn. Hochschule

74b. Tabelle VII. Vergleich verschiedener Werte für $F_{Na+Cl}^{290°}$.

Ordnung	$\sin\lambda/\lambda$	Absolut oder Relativ / Einkristall oder Pulver / λ	Bragg James Bosanquet	Havighurst	James Firth	Brentano	Bearden		Verfasser	Theoretisch Hartree Korrigiert für Nähe der Cl-K-Kante*
		Absolut oder Relativ	A	R	A	R	A	A		
		Einkristall oder Pulver	E	P	E	P	E	E		
		λ	0,62	0,71	0,71	1,54	0,71	0,71	1,54 $\lambda\ll\lambda_k$	$\lambda/\lambda_k=0,35$ $\lambda=1,54$ Å
(200)	0,178		19,55	20,8	20,65	22,6	20,0	20,0	20,85 / 19,75	20,06
(400)	0,355		11,10	11,60	11,60	11,60	11,95	12,55	12,67 / 12,02	12,27₅
(600)	0,533		6,56	6,69	6,89	6,46	6,68	7,43	7,84 / 7,35	7,56
$F(200)/F(600)$			2,98	3,12	2,99	3,50	2,98	2,69	2,65 / 2,68	2,65

* [This Vol. paper 77.]

[1] A. Smekal, *Handbuch der Physik*. 2. Aufl. Bd. XXIV, 2.

[2] A. Smekal, l. c., s. Z. 10 C.

[3] P. Kirkpatrick und P. A. Ross, *Phys. Rev.* **43** (1933) 596.

75. Ein einfacher Versuch zur Auffindung eines selektiven Effektes bei der Zerstreuung von Röntgenstrahlen, by H. MARK und L. SZILARD (1925)

━

76. Über die Dispersion und Streuung von Röntgenstrahlen, by H. KALL-MANN und H. MARK (1927)

━

77. Zur Dispersionstheorie der Röntgenstrahlen, by H. HÖNL (1933)

━

78. Über die Dispersion und Absorption von Röntgenstrahlen, by J. A. PRINS (1928)

━

75. Es wird eine Methode angegeben, die eine sprunghafte Änderung im Beugungsvermögen für Röntgenstrahlen mit großer Empfindlichkeit nachzuweisen gestattet. Sie beruht darauf, daß von der Oktaederebene des Rb Br in erster Ordnung zwar keine Röntgenstrahlung reflektiert wird, welche das Brom- und Rubidiumion in gleicher Weise zerstreuen, die Reflexion aber auftritt, sobald die Strahlung vom Bromion selektiv anders gebeugt wird als vom Rubidiumion. Eine solche selektive Beugung wurde z.B. für Strontium-$K\alpha$-Strahlung gefunden, welche härter ist als die Absorptionskante des Broms, aber weicher als die des Rb, so daß sie wohl vom Br, nicht aber vom Rb selektiv absorbiert wird.

Bestrahlt man irgend eine Substanz mit Röntgenlicht, so gehen von ihr sekundäre Röntgenstrahlen aus, welche man im Rahmen der klassischen Theorie als Kugelwellen ansehen kann und welche sich dadurch charakterisieren lassen, daß man angibt, wie sich ihre Amplitude zur Amplitude des Primärstrahles verhält und welchen Phasenunterschied die sekundären Kugelwellen gegen die Primärwellen besitzen. Stellt man die Frage, wie sich Phasendifferenz und Amplitudenverhältnis verändern, wenn man die Frequenz des auffallenden Primärstrahles variiert, so ist es wohl sicher, daß man im allgemeinen beide als langsam veränderliche Funktionen der Wellenlängen ansehen darf. Es könnte aber sein, daß bei bestimmten Wellenlängen, welche für die zerstreuende Substanz charakteristisch sind, fast sprunghafte Änderungen auftreten. Wenn man das Bild, welches sich die klassische Theorie vom Zerstreuungsvorgang macht, als richtig ansieht, so muß man z.B. erwarten, daß bei kontinuierlicher Verkleinerung der Primärwellenlänge eine derartige sprunghafte Änderung dann eintritt, wenn man aus dem langwelligen Bereich diesseits der Absorptionskante, innerhalb dessen die Strahlung von der Substanz nur sehr wenig absorbiert wird, durch Überschreiten der Absorptionskante in denjenigen Frequenzbereich eintritt, in welchem die Strahlung sehr stark absorbiert wird. Dies ist um so mehr zu erwarten, als der von der klassischen Theorie geforderte Zusammenhang zwischen Amplitude und Phase der sekundären Kugelwellen einerseits, und dem Absorptionskoeffizienten andererseits für das optische Gebiet sich in dem bekannten anomalen Gange des Brechungsindex in der Nähe der Absorptionslinie widerspiegelt.

Um eine derartige, etwa vorhandene sprunghafte Änderung im Gebiet der Röntgenfrequenzen wirklich nachzuweisen, kann man die Reflexionen von Röntgenstrahlen an einem Rubidiumbromidkristall untersuchen; Rubidium und Brom stehen im periodischen System nahe beisammen, sie sind nur durch ein Edelgas voneinander getrennt. Da bei der Bildung des Salzes das Rubidiumion ein Elektron abgegeben und das Bromion eines aufgenommen hat, ist außerdem die Elektronenzahl der beiden Ionen die gleiche. Es ist daher nach der bisherigen Erfahrung[1]—von selektiven Effekten abgesehen—zu erwarten, daß Röntgenstrahlen von beiden Ionen in gleicher Weise zerstreut werden. Belichtet man z.B. die (111)-Ebene (Oktaederebene) von Rubidiumbromid unter dem Glanzwinkel in erster Ordnung mit Kupfer K-Strahlen, so ist zu erwarten, daß keine Reflexion eintritt; denn die (111)-Ebenen sind abwechselnd gleich dicht mit Brom und Rubidiumionen belegt, und wenn diese Ebenen die Röntgenstrahlen in gleicher Weise zerstreuen, so heben sich ihre Wirkungen gegenseitig gerade auf. Tatsächlich fanden wir diese Reflexion bei Verwendung von Kupfer-, Eisen-, Kobalt- oder Zinkstrahlung vollkommen ausgelöscht. *Belichtet man aber mit einer Wellenlänge, welche von Bromionen anders zerstreut wird, als von Rubidiumionen, so muß die Reflexion auftreten.* Dies liefert eine empfindliche Methode, um einen Sprung in Phase oder Amplitude der sekundären Kugelwellen nachzuweisen.

Wir haben nun an mehreren wohlausgebildeten Rubidiumbromidkristallen von etwa 6 mm Kantenlänge die Oktaederebene angeschliffen und dann Strontium-$K\alpha$-Strahlung daran in verschiedenen Ordnungen reflektiert. Diese Strahlung ist ein wenig härter als die Absorptionskante des Broms, aber weicher als die betreffende Kante des Rubidiums; ihre Wellenlänge liegt in dem schmalen Bereich zwischen den beiden Kanten und

---

[1] W. H. Bragg und W. L. Bragg, *Proc. Roy. Soc.* **88** (1913) 428; **89** (1914) 248 [this Vol. pp. 56 and 59] und W. P. Davey, *Phys. Rev.* **21** (1923) 143.

die Strahlung wird daher vom Brom selektiv absorbiert, nicht aber vom Rubidium. Wenn sie daher vom Brom auch anders zerstreut wird als vom Rubidium, so müßten nunmehr die sonst ausgelöschten Reflexionen der ungeraden Ordnungen von (111) hier auftreten. Sie treten in der Tat mit recht merklicher Intensität auf, dagegen verhält sich der Kristall der Emissionslinie des Broms gegenüber wie gegen Kupferstrahlung. Die Emissionslinie des Broms wird also vom Bromion nicht merklich selektiv zerstreut, wie man dies nach einer Arbeit von R. Clark und W. Duane[1] hätte erwarten können.

Zur Herstellung der verwendeten Rubidiumbromidkristalle haben wir reinstes Rb Br aus fast gesättigter wässeriger Lösung durch langsames Abdunsten auskristallisiert; nach mehreren Wochen bildeten sich hierbei neben unbrauchbaren Kristalldrusen auch ganz wasserklare Würfel bis zu 6 mm Kantenlänge. Die Analyse mehrerer solcher Kristalle ergab einen Bromgehalt von 48,10, 48,35, 48,45 Proz., während sich 48,33 Proz. berechnet. Da es uns nicht gelang, die Oktaederebene als Wachstumsfläche zu erhalten, haben wir sie durch Anschleifen für die spektroskopischen Aufnahmen freigelegt. Da der Kristall sehr hygroskopisch ist, muß man dabei schnell verfahren und ihn sofort mit einem wasserschützenden Lack überziehen, weil er sonst in kurzer Zeit unbrauchbar wird.

Die Fig. 1a zeigt eine Spektralaufnahme von Strontiumstrahlung an der (111)-Ebene in einer Seemannschen Kamera. Man erkennt die erste und zweite Ordnung der Reflexion, welche der Lage nach genau mit der theoretisch geforderten übereinstimmen. Das Intensitätsverhältnis ist jedoch

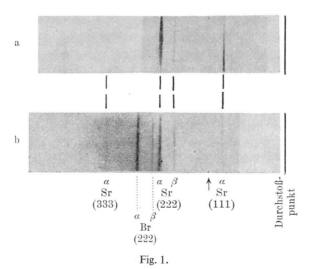

Fig. 1.

[1] R. Clark und W. Duane, *Journ. Optical Soc.* **8** (1922) 90.

zugunsten der ersten Ordnung verschoben, da bei dieser Aufnahme—welche im wesentlichen die Auffindung der ersten Ordnung bezweckte—die Wackelvorrichtung so eingestellt war, daß der Kristall in der Reflexionsstellung erster Ordnung etwa fünf- bis achtmal solange verweilte, als unter dem Glanzwinkel der zweiten Ordnung.

Die Fig. 1b zeigt eine Spektralaufnahme eines anderen Rb Br-Kristalls in derselben Kamera. Diesmal wurde eine Antikathode aus $SrBr_2$ verwendet; die Drehung des Kristalls erfolgte gleichmäßig. Man kann auf diesem Diagramm zunächst die erste Ordnung der Strontiumlinie erkennen (Sr α 111); etwa 2 mm links von ihr müßte die erste Ordnung der Bromemissionslinie liegen (durch einen Pfeil angedeutet); sie ist jedoch nicht[1] vorhanden, obwohl, wie man an den Reflexionen der zweiten Ordnungen erkennen kann, die Intensitäten der Brom- und Strontiumstrahlung im Primärstrahl von derselben Größe waren.

Kaiser Wilhelm-Institut für Faserstoffchemie und Institut für theoretische Physik der Universität

76. Bei der Berechnung der Intensitäten der an Kristallen interferenzmäßig gestreuten Röntgenstrahlen geht man im allgemeinen von der Laueschen bzw. Ewald-Darwinschen Theorie der Kristallinterferenzen aus und ergänzt die Intensitätsangaben dieser Theorien durch mehrere Faktoren. Erfahrungsgemäß gelingt es aber nicht mit Hilfe dieser Ergänzungen in Übereinstimmung mit dem Experiment zu kommen, so daß man genötigt ist, noch andere Einflüsse ins Auge zu fassen. Als solche kommen zunächst in Betracht der Anteil an 'comptonmäßig' gestreuter Strahlung und die Möglichkeit eines Zusammenwirkens der einzelnen Elektronen eines Atoms, die zur Folge hätte, daß die 'Form' und Größe des Atoms sich bei den Intensitäten bemerkbar macht. Diesen beiden Einflüssen wendet sich heute das Hauptinteresse zu. Allen Rechnungen hierüber liegt eine Annahme über die Abhängigkeit des elektrischen Momentes $\mathfrak{p}$ der Atomelektronen von der einfallenden Welle $\mathfrak{E}_0$ zugrunde, und zwar setzt man für diese Abhängigkeit gemäß der klassischen Theorie gewöhnlich folgenden Ausdruck an:

$$\mathfrak{p} = \frac{e^2}{4\pi^2 m} \sum_i \frac{z}{v_{0i}{}^2 - v^2} \mathfrak{E}_0. \qquad (1)$$

Hierin bedeutet z die Zahl der Atomelektronen (Ordnungszahl); v die Frequenz der einfallenden Welle von der Feldstärke $\mathfrak{E}_0$ und v_{0i} die Eigen-

[1] Wenigstens nicht mit einer merklichen Intensität.

frequenz des i-ten Elektrons; in dieser Gleichung ist über alle z Elektronen des Atoms zu summieren.

Bei der Anwendung dieser Gleichung auf die Streuung von Röntgen-strahlen geht man im allgemeinen so vor, daß man für ν_{0i} die Frequenz der Absorptionskanten einsetzt. Dieses ist aber sicherlich nicht zutreffend, denn man weiß aus der Kenntnis des Röntgenabsorptionsspektrums, daß nicht nur *eine* Eigenfrequenz an der Stelle der Absorptionskante liegt, sondern daß sich eine kontinuierliche Folge von Eigenfrequenzen an die Absorptionskante anschließt. Man hat bei Gleichung (1) noch für jede Elektronensorte über ein kontinuierliches Eigenfrequenzbereich zu inte-grieren, und dabei zu berücksichtigen, daß die verschiedenen Eigenfre-quenzen auch verschiedene Stärke im Sinne der Ladenburg-Kramersschen Dispersionstheorie besitzen.[1]

Führt man eine solche Überlegung durch, so erhält man Gleichungen, die in der Tat nicht nur in der Nähe der Kanten, sondern auch in einem beträchtlichen Frequenzgebiet davor und dahinter eine erhebliche Ab-weichung von Formel (1) aufweisen, die bewirkt, daß in der Nähe der Kante nicht zu schwerer Elemente sich dieses anormale Streuvermögen der K-Elektronen trotz der Wirkung der viel zahlreicheren übrigen Elek-tronen noch deutlich bemerkbar machen kann und daher experimentell faßbar wird.

Während beim Vorliegen *einer* Absorptionslinie die Dispersion δ, * wenn man von der langwelligen Seite kommt, zunächst stark nach der negativen Seite ansteigt, in der Mitte der Absorptionslinie Null ist und dann stark positiv wird und positiv bleibt, ist das Verhalten in einem kon-tinuierlichen Absorptionsgebiet ganz anders. Es steigt hier $\delta = 1 - n$ bei Annäherung von der langwelligen Seite an die Kante ebenfalls zunächst stark negativ an, wie man dies aus der ausgezogenen Kurve der Fig. 1 sehen kann, erreicht ganz in der Nähe der Kante das Minimum, um erst ziemlich weit hinter der Kante Null zu werden und dann ins Positive zu gehen. (Beim Vergleich mit Fig. 1 beachte man, daß dort $-\delta$ aufgetragen ist.)

Dieses Verhalten erklärt sich folgendermaßen:

Das kontinuierliche Absorptionsgebiet kann man sich bezüglich seines Einflusses auf die Dispersion ersetzt denken durch eine Reihe von Ersatz-oszillatoren, deren Eigenfrequenzen ν_0 bei der Frequenz der Absorptions-

---

[1] R. Ladenburg, *Ztschr. f. Phys.* **4** (1921) 451; A. Smekal, *Die Naturw.* **11** (1923) 873; H. A. Kramers u. W. Heisenberg, *Ztschr. f. Phys.* **31** (1925) 681; H. A. Kramers, *Nature* **113** (1924) 673.

* [The proportionality between $\delta = 1 - n$ and the atomic scattering power has been derived this Vol. p. 174 eq. (2). Ed.]

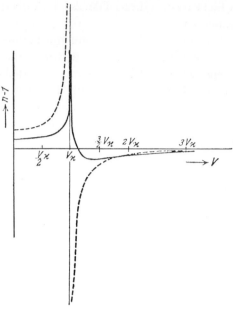

$-\delta = n-1$ als Funktion von ν für 1 Elektron

Fig. 1.

kante ν_0 beginnen und deren Stärke wie $\nu_0{}^{-3}$ abnimmt. Nähern wir uns nun von der langwelligen Seite der Absorptionskante, so wird die Dispersionskurve zunächst negativ ansteigen, aber nicht so stark ansteigen, als ob alle Ersatzoszillatoren an der Stelle der Kante vereint wären, wie dies bei der Linie der Fall ist. Sobald wir aber mit der Frequenz der einfallenden Strahlung die der Absorptionskante überschritten haben, besitzen einige wenige Ersatzoszillatoren schon eine Eigenfrequenz, die kleiner ist als die Frequenz der einfallenden Strahlung; diese liefern einen positiven Anteil zur Dispersion. Der überwiegende Anteil der Ersatzoszillatoren hat aber noch größere Eigenfrequenz als die Frequenz der einfallenden Strahlung. Der starke negative Beitrag dieser härteren Ersatzoszillatoren überwiegt zunächst noch den positiven Anteil der weicheren; in Summa bleibt daher die Dispersionskurve zunächst noch negativ. Sie nähert sich aber nach dem Überschreiten der Absorptionskante wieder der Abszissenachse, um schließlich, wenn der negative Einfluß der härteren Ersatzoszillatoren gerade gleich dem positiven Einfluß der weicheren Ersatzoszillatoren ist, Null zu werden und dann dauernd ins Positive zu gehen.

Bisher haben wir immer nur die von *einer* Elektronensorte hervorgerufenen Dispersionen betrachtet; um die Dispersion des ganzen Atoms zu erhalten, muß man über alle Atomelektronen summieren. Aus Fig. 3 geht hervor, daß die Wirkung der K-Elektronen eines Elementes in der Nähe der Absorptionskante sich deutlich als Anomalie in der Dispersionskurve hervorhebt, obwohl die Zahl der übrigen Elektronen des Atoms die Zahl der K-Elektronen um ein Vielfaches übertrifft. Den Anteil der Streuung setzt man im allgemeinen als unabhängig von der Wellenlänge konstant an, indem man annimmt, daß die Elektronen in den Atomen alle schon so schwingen, als ob die Frequenz der einfallenden Strahlung sehr viel größer wäre als alle Absorptionskanten; dann wäre in der Tat gemäß der Thomsonschen Formel die Streuung unabhängig von der Wellenlänge. Unsere obigen Überlegungen zeigen, daß eben bei Berücksichtigung des feineren Schwingungsmechanismus der Elektronen dies nicht mehr der Fall ist, sondern eine Abhängigkeit des Streukoeffizienten von der Wellenlänge schon bemerkbar wird, obwohl der größte Teil der Elektronen sicher gemäß der Thomsonschen Formel schwingt.

Die Phase der gestreuten Strahlung

Schließlich müssen wir noch auf folgenden oben kurz erwähnten Punkt eingehen. Berechnet man die gestreute Strahlung aus einem elektrischen Moment des Atoms im Sinne der klassischen Theorie, so hat die gestreute Strahlung eine bestimmte Phasendifferenz gegenüber der einfallenden Welle. Bei Berechnung der gestreuten Energie muß man diese Phasendifferenz berücksichtigen.

Bei einer Absorptionslinie ist der Verlauf der Phasendifferenz bekanntlich folgender: auf der langwelligen Seite der Absorptionslinie ist zunächst $\varphi = 0$, steigt erst unmittelbar in der Nähe der Absorptionslinie an und wird in der Mitte der Absorptionslinie gerade $-\pi/2$. Dann wächst φ weiter an und wird schon dicht hinter der Absorptionslinie $-\pi$. Die gestreute Strahlung hat also dann eine Phasendifferenz von 180° gegenüber der einfallenden Strahlung. In unserem Falle liegen die Verhältnisse etwas anders. Der Phasenwinkel steigt mit dem Eintritt in das Absorptionsgebiet an, wird erst erheblich hinter der Absorptionskante $-90°$ und wächst dann langsam weiter bis auf 180°. Der Zustand also, daß die Elektronen mit einer um annähernd 180° gegen die einfallende Strahlung verschobenen Phase schwingen, tritt erst verhältnismäßig weit hinter der Absorptionskante ein *. Diese Verhältnisse werden von Wichtigkeit, wenn

[1] [Graphs of these behaviours are given in paper **78**. Note that in the present paper $\varphi = 0$ corresponds to the phase of the incident beam, in **78** to the phase of the radiation scattered by a free electron, the latter differing $-\pi$ from the former. Ed.]

man die Streuung an Kristallgittern betrachtet und es sich um zwei ineinander gestellte Gitter handelt. Darauf kommen wir weiter unten noch zu sprechen.

ANWENDUNG DER STREUFORMEL AUF KRISTALLINTERFERENZEN

a) *Der Brechungskoeffizient*

Eine Prüfung der oben entwickelten Überlegungen läßt sich bisher am besten an Kristallen ausführen, weil dort die einzigen, bisher vorliegenden Messungen gemacht worden sind und die Intensität der interferenzmäßig gestreuten Strahlung auf ein elektrisches Moment der Kristallatome zurückgeführt wird.

Um unsere Überlegungen auf die Kristallinterferenzen anwenden zu können, brauchen wir in die Formeln, welche nach Ewald die Breite und Intensität der Röntgeninterferenzen bestimmen, für das elektrische Moment des Atoms an Stelle des Ausdrucks (1) den von der quantenmäßigen Dispersionstheorie gegebenen Ausdruck zusetzen. Nun ist, wie man aus der Ewaldschen Theorie weiß, die Breite des Gebietes der Totalreflexion für die Röntgeninterferenzen im wesentlichen durch $n - 1$ gegeben. Es ist also

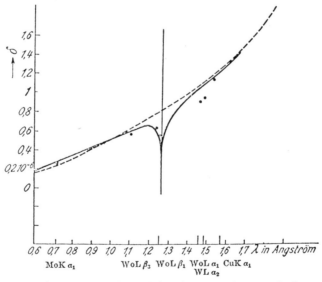

Hier ist δ aufgetragen als Funktion der verwendeten Wellenlänge λ.

Fig. 3.

der Winkelabstand des Schwerpunktes einer Röntgenlinie von dem normalen Braggschen Winkel eine Funktion von $n-1$ und man kann daher aus Messungen dieses Abstandes[1] bzw. aus Messungen der Breite $n-1$ bestimmen und mit unserer Formel vergleichen. In der Fig. 3 ist dieser Vergleich für den Fall der Reflexion an ZnS (111) durchgeführt. Diese Figur zeigt die Dispersionskurve für Zinkblende und zwar stellt die gestrichelte Kurve den Dispersionsanteil der 44 Elektronen dar, deren Eigenfrequenzen neben den Frequenzen der verwendeten Strahlungen vernachlässigt werden können, die sich also im Gebiet der normalen Dispersion befinden. Diese Kurve ist von der Form const/v^2. Die ausgezogene Kurve gibt den berechneten Einfluß der beiden K-Elektronen des Zinks wieder; man sieht, daß in der Nähe der Kante, aber auch *nur* dort, merkliche Abweichungen von dem normalen Verlauf vorliegen. Die schwarzen Punkte sind die experimentell gemessenen Werte[2].

Man sieht aus dem Vergleich der experimentellen Punkte mit der theoretischen Kurve, daß der Typus der letzteren durch die Versuche bestätigt wird, obwohl diese keineswegs ausreichen, um quantitativ den anomalen Verlauf der Dispersionskurve festzulegen.

b) *Die Intensität der Röntgeninterferenzen*

Für den Intensitätsverlauf in Abhängigkeit von der Frequenz der einfallenden Strahlung hat man folgendes Bild zu erwarten. Mit Annäherung an die Kante nimmt die gesamte Intensität ab, weil die K-Elektronen sehr stark schwingen und zwar in entgegengesetzter Phase, wie die übrigen Elektronen; die Intensität steigt mit Überschreiten der Kante dann allmählich wieder an, weil die Phase der K-Elektronen sich immer mehr der der übrigen Elektronen angleicht. Der Intensitätsverlauf ist dann durch eine Kurve gegeben, die der Kurve Fig. 3 sehr ähnlich gebaut ist. Neben den zahlreichen normal streuenden Elektronen ist der Einfluß der beiden K-Elektronen besonders bei schwereren Elementen nicht groß, so daß es nicht leicht sein wird, durch absolute Intensitätsmessungen die Frequenzabhängigkeit des Streukoeffizienten nachzuweisen, um so mehr, als die Absorptionsverhältnisse hier auch noch störend wirken*.

Qualitativ wurde aber das Vorhandensein dieses Effektes dadurch nach-

[1] M. Siegbahn, *Journ. d. phys. et Rad.* **7** (1925) 7; E. Hjalmar, *Ztschr. f. Phys.* **15** (1923) 65; *Ann. d. Phys.* **54** (1917) 519; B. Davis, u. R. v. Nardroff, *Proc. Nat. Ac.* **10** (1924) 60, 384.
[2] W. Ehrenberg u. H. Mark, *Ztschr. f. Phys.* **38** (1926) 129.
* [See, however, this Vol. papers **79–81**. Ed.]

gewiesen, daß bei der Reflexion von Sr-Strahlung an der (111)-Ebene von RbBr die ungeraden Ordnungen auftreten[1], was beweist, daß diese Strahlung von den Rb- bzw. Br-Ionen in verschiedener Weise gestreut wird.

77. Es wird die Kallmann-Marksche Dispersionformel für Röntgenstrahlen im Sinne einer genaueren Berücksichtigung der Oszillatorenverteilung an der *K*-Kante verbessert und die neue Formel mit den Dispersionsmessungen von A. Larsson verglichen. Außerdem wird die Zahl der Dispersionselektronen der *K*- und *L*-Schale für einige Elemente berechnet. Die Ergebnisse sind in befriedigender Übereinstimmung mit der Erfahrung.

Bekanntlich ist es möglich, die Dispersionserscheinungen von Licht und Röntgenstrahlen quantentheoretisch in strenger formaler Analogie zur klassischen Optik zu behandeln[2]. Von diesem Gesichtspunkt ausgehend haben H. Kallmann und H. Mark[3] auf Grund klassischer Überlegungen eine Dispersionsformel für den anomalen Verlauf des Brechungsexponenten von Röntgenstrahlen in der Nähe einer Absorptionskante aufgestellt, welche die experimentellen Ergebnisse, insbesondere diejenigen von A. Larsson[4] über die anomale Dispersion in der Nähe der *K*-Absorptionskante jedenfalls qualitativ richtig wiedergibt. Bei einer genaueren Diskussion der experimentellen Daten scheinen sich jedoch systematische Abweichungen von der Kallmann-Markschen Formel zu ergeben.

Anderseits haben Kallmann und Mark die Ableitung ihrer Formel auf zwei spezielle Voraussetzungen gestützt, welche nur einer ziemlich groben Annäherung an die wirklichen Verhältnisse entsprechen. Erstens nehmen die Autoren (im Anschluß an Kramers) an, daß die Verteilungsdichte der an eine Kantenfrequenz v_k anschließenden Oszillatoren ein Gesetz von der Form

$$\frac{df}{dv_j} = \begin{cases} C/v_j{}^3 \text{ fur } v \geqq v_k \\ 0 \text{ für } v < v_k \end{cases} \tag{1}$$

(v_j Oszillatorenfrequenz) befolgt. Zweitens wird die Konstante C bei dieser Frequenzabhängigkeit so bestimmt, daß die Gesamtzahl der Oszillatoren pro Elektron des Atoms 1 wird, so daß also das vollständige Verteilungs-

[1] H. Mark u. L. Szilard, *Ztschr. f. Phys.* **33** (1925) 688.
[2] H. A. Kramers, *Nature* **113** (1924) 673; H. A. Kramers u. W. Heisenberg, *Ztschr. f. Phys.* **31** (1925) 681; E. Schrödinger, *Ann. d. Phys.* **81** (1926) 109; P. A. M. Dirac, *Proc. Roy. Soc. London* (A) **114** (1927) 710.
[3] H. Kallmann u. H. Mark, *Ann. d. Phys.* **82** (1927) 585 [this Vol. p. 326]; *Naturwissensch.* **14** (1926) 649.
[4] A. Larsson, Experimentelle Untersuchungen über die Dispersion der Röntgenstrahlen. Dissertation Uppsala 1929.

gesetz lautet:

$$\frac{df}{dv_j} = \begin{cases} 2v_k{}^2/v_j{}^3 \text{ für } v \geqq v_k \\ 0 \text{ für } v < v_k \end{cases}. \tag{1a}$$

Diese Normierung der Oszillatorenstärken folgt jedoch nicht, wie man vermuten könnte, aus dem Thomas-Kuhnschen Summensatz[1], da diese nur verlangt, daß die Gesamtzahl der Oszillatoren für alle Übergang eines Atoms in mögliche Anregungszustände gleich der Gesamtelektronenzahl Z ist. In der Tat muß z.B. die 'Zahl der Dispersionselektronen' der K-Schale kleiner als 2 sein, da Übergänge eines Elektrons der K-Schale nach höheren besetzten Schalen wegen des Paulischen Prinzips ausgeschlossen sind.

Die erwähnten Voraussetzungen der Kallmann-Markschen Ableitung lassen sich indessen durch eine exaktere Berücksichtigung des Oszillatorenverteilungsgesetzes korrigieren bzw. schärfer präzisieren[2]. Wir führen im folgenden die hierzu erforderlichen Rechungen unter Bezugnahme auf die Sugiurasche[3] Berechnung der Oszillatorenstärken für wasserstoffähnliche Atome, jedoch unter geeigneter Berücksichtigung der Abschirmung und bei Vernachlässigung der natürlichen Linienbreite der Röntgenlinien für die K- und L-Kante durch, wobei sich, was die K-Kante betrifft, für welche eindeutige quantitative Meßergebnisse vorliegen, eine befriedigende Übereinstimmung mit der Erfahrung ergibt.

Fig. 1 zeigt den Verlauf der Dispersion in der Nähe der K-Kante für Ca und Si im Vergleich mit der Kallmann-Markschen Kurve. Die eingetragenen Meßpunkte entsprechen den sorgfältigen experimentellen Bestimmungen des Brechungsexponenten von Kalkspat (Spiegelungsmethode) und Quarz (Prismenmethode) durch A. Larsson[4]. Die Meßpunkte schließen sich den theoretischen Kurven so gut an, als es bei der Streuung der Meßergebnisse untereinander erwartet werden kann und liegen auf der kurzwelligen Seite der Kante (mit einer Ausnahme) durchweg unterhalb, auf der langwelligen Seite durchweg oberhalb der Kallmann-Markschen Kurve (der qualitative Verlauf der Kurven auf der langwelligen Seite beruht

[1] W. Kuhn, *Ztschr. f. Phys.* **33** (1925) 408; L. H. Thomas u. F. Reiche ebenda **34** (1925) 510.

[2] Kallmann und Mark weisen selbst auf die Möglichkeit einer Verbesserung ihrer Formel gemäß einer geeigneteren Dichteverteilung der Oszillatoren hin (*Naturwissensch., l. c.*, Schlußbemerkung).

[3] Y. Sugiura, *Journ. de phys. et le Radium* **8** (1927) 113; s. auch J. Stobbe, *Ann. d. Phys.* **7** (1930) 661.

[4] A. Larsson, *l. c.* Die in Fig. 1 eingezeichneten Meßpunkte sind der Fig. 42 der Larssonschen Arbeit entnommen. Die δ/λ^2-Werte von Larsson ($\delta = 1 - n_0$) haben wir auf Elektronenzahlen umgerechnet.

333

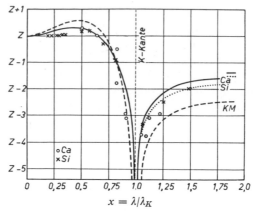

$$x = \lambda/\lambda_K$$

Fig. 1. Verlauf der Dispersionskurvean de r K-Kante. ——— Theoretische Kurve für Ca, — — — theoretische Kurve für Si (auf der kurzwelligen Seite der Kante fällt die Si-Kurve mit der Ca-Kurve praktisch zusammen), — — — Kallmann-Marksche Kurve. Die Lagen der Kanten von Ca und Si sind aufeinander reduziert eingezeichnet: Abszisse jeweils $\lambda/\lambda_{\text{Kante}}$. Ordinate: $(1-n_0)2\pi mc^2/Ne^2\lambda^2$*. Die Meßpunkte (× und ○) nach A. Larsson.

übrigens im wesentlichen auf der exakteren Bestimmung der Zahl der Dispersionselektronen). Insbesondere ist die Lage der Si-Punkte, die unter sich eine geringere Streung aufweisen, in befriedigender Übereinstimmung mit der theoretischen Erwartung. Qualitativ ähnliche Verhältnisse wie Larsson findet H. Kiessig[1] an der K-Kante von Ni (Totalreflexion von Röntgenstrahlen an Nickelspiegel).

Eine zweite Möglichkeit, die Formeln zu prüfen, besteht in der Messung von Streuintensitäten an Kristallinterferenzen. Die Meßergebnisse von Glocker und Schäfer[2] an der K-Kante von Eisen und Chrom, von Bradley und Hope[3] an Eisen sowie von Rusterholz[4] an Kupfer sind jedenfalls in qualitativer Übereinstimmung mit der Theorie.

---

* [The ordinate represents the atomic scattering power for $\theta = 0$, as seen from this Vol. p. 174 eq. (2).]

[1] H. Kiessig, *Ann. d. Phys.* **10** (1931) 715.

[2] R. Glocker u. K. Schäfer, *Ztschr. f. Phys.* **73** (1931) 289. Die von Glocker und Schäfer in dieser Arbeit angegebenen ΔF-Werte für Eisen sind auf der kurzwelligen Seite der K-Kante viel zu groß, schließen sich aber nach neueren Messungen der theoretischen Dispersionskurve gut an (vgl. eine demnächst in *Ztschr. f. Phys.* erscheinende Arbeit von Glocker und Schäfer).

[3] J. A. Bradley u. R. A. H. Hope, *Proc. Roy. Soc. London* (A) **136** (1932) 272.

[4] A. Rusterholz, *Ztschr. f. Phys.* **82** (1933) 538. Die nur auf der langwelligen Seite ausgeführten Messungen entsprechen etwa $n_K = 1{,}3$, in Übereinstimmung mit dem theoretischen Wert.

78 *. Wir betrachten zuerst den einfachen Fall, dass es nur eine einzige Art Resonatoren der Eigenfrequenz ω_0 gibt. Der Verlauf der beiden Grössen f' und f'', wenn $f = f' + if''$ gesetzt wird, ist bei Annahme einer einzigen Frequenz ω_0 in der Figur 1 dargestellt.

In einer einheitlichen Theorie der Dispersion, Absorption und Streuung nach dem Kramersschen Vorgang[1] hat man aber das ganze Gebiet der

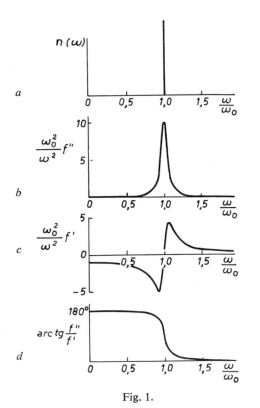

[a The frequency distribution of the oscillator.]

b und c Verlauf von $(\omega_0{}^2/\omega^2)f''$ und $(\omega_0{}^2/\omega^2)f'$ bei Eigenfrequenz ω_0 und Dämpfungsverhältniss $\kappa/\omega_0 = 0{,}1$.

[d Phase of the scattered wave on both sides of ω_0.]

Fig. 1.

* [From this paper figures 1 b, c and 2 b, c have been selected in order to illustrate the difference in resonance scattering by an electron with a single proper frequency and a continuum of frequencies, resp. The author considers the dispersion and so the ordinates of his curves, after being renamed according to note* this Vol. p. 327, contain, besides f, the additional factor $\omega_0{}^2/\omega^2$ and $\omega_R{}^2/\omega^2$, resp. This factor has but little influence in the region of resonance ($\omega/\omega_0 \approx 1$); it cancels in the quotient of the ordinates, which determines the phase of the scattered wave, fig. d, according to $\operatorname{tg}\varphi = f''/f'$. Here f denotes the amplitude scattered by the bound electron relative to that scattered by a free electron. The figures 1 a and 1 d have been inserted in order to complete the analogy with the curves of fig. 2. Ed.]

[1] H. A. Kramers, *Nature* **113** (1924) 673.

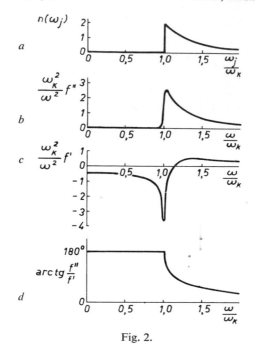

$n(\omega_j)$

a a Das Verteilungsgesetz der Ersatzresonatoren eines K-Elektrons.

$\dfrac{\omega_K^2}{\omega^2}f''$

b b und c Verlauf von f'' und f' bei einer Absorptionskanten mit Eigenfrequenz ω_K und Dämpfungsverhältnis $\kappa/\omega_K = 0{,}01$.

$\dfrac{\omega_K^2}{\omega^2}f'$

c

$\text{arc tg}\,\dfrac{f''}{f'}$

d [d Phasenverschiebung der K-Streuwelle an beiden Seiten der K-Kante (this Vol. p. 365, Fig. 11)].

Fig. 2.

Selektieven Absorption jenseits der Absorptionskanten kontinuierlich mit 'Ersatzoszillatoren' zu besetzen.

Die Funktionen f' und f'' sind zusammen mit der Verteilungsfunktion der K-Resonatoren in der Figur 2 graphisch dargestellt. Man kann die Kurven auffassen als entstanden durch Überlagerung von Kurven vom Typus der Figur 1.

ANOMALOUS f-FACTOR:
MEASUREMENT AND APPLICATION

79. The X-Ray Scattering Powers of Nickel and Oxygen in Nickel Oxide, by R. W. G. WYCKOFF (1930)

▄▄

80. The Atomic Scattering Powers of Nickel, Copper and Iron for Various Wavelengths, by R. W. G. WYCKOFF (1930)

▄▄

81. The Crystal Structure of the Heusler Alloys, by A. J. BRADLEY and J. W. RODGERS (1934)

▄▄

79.   *Abstract*

Atomic F-curves for the nickel and oxygen atoms in NiO have been obtained from measurements of the intensities of the principal powder reflections of molybdenum, copper and nickel $K\alpha$ radiations. Though the scattering power of oxygen remains nearly constant with respect to NaCl for these wave-lengths, that of nickel shows important variations.

This paper forms part of a series of studies of the dependence of the diffracting power of an atom upon the wave-length of the x-rays being scattered. Accurate measurement[1] has shown that with wave-lengths as near together as the $K\alpha$ lines of molybdenum and rhodium the F-values of NaCl are equal for the same $(\sin \theta)/\lambda$. There is likewise some indication[2] that the atoms in this crystal do not have very different scattering powers for copper radiation. Recent comparisons of NaCl and metallic silicon[3] prove that the ratio of their diffracting powers is nearly the same for molybdenum and for copper $K\alpha$ x-rays. All of these observations are with radiations far removed in frequency from any critical values for the diffracting atoms.

Such a parallelism as that prevailing between NaCl and silicon no longer seems to hold if the comparisons involve metallic copper and iron reflecting molybdenum and copper rays. The experiments already made[4] with these metals indicate that their scattering powers decrease more rapidly with increasing wave-length than do those of the atoms of NaCl. This con-

[1] R. W. James and E. M. Firth, *Proc. Roy. Soc.* **A117** (1927) 62.
[2] E. Wagner and H. Kulenkampff, *Ann. d. Physik* **68** (1922) 369.
[3] R. W. G. Wyckoff, *Zeit. f. Krist.* (1930) in press.
[4] A. H. Armstrong, *Phys. Rev.* **34** (1929) 931.

clusion is dependent upon the essential correctness of measured absorption coefficients.

Observations upon NiO avoid such an uncertainty by containing within themselves a comparison of the scattering powers of two atoms—nickel and oxygen. These data consist of determinations of the F-curves of nickel and oxygen using molybdenum, copper and nickel $K\alpha$ radiation. The measurements upon which they are based are spectrometer studies of the intensities of the principal x-ray reflections of powdered NiO. The methods used in obtaining these intensities[1] and reducing them to atomic scattering powers have been described.

Two different samples of chemically pure green NiO gave results which were identical within the limit of experimental error. In order to suppress the effects of extinction both crystal powders were ground thoroughly in an agate mortar and passed through a 325 mesh per linear inch sieve before being formed into a cake.

The molybdenum rays were rendered essentially monochromatic with a ZrO_2 screen. No attempt was made to filter the x-rays emitted by the copper and nickel target tubes but calculation showed that with the resolution used none of the measured $K\alpha$ spectra was contaminated by other reflections.

The crystal structure of NiO is identical with that of NaCl. Reflections with odd indices therefore represent differences between the contributions of nickel and oxygen atoms, those with even indices (all even order spectra)

Table I. The relative intensities of powder reflections of nickel oxide.

Indices	Intensities for $K\alpha$ wave-length of		
	Molybdenum	Copper	Nickel
111	111.8	112.4	129.7
200	159.4	196.1	207.3
220	[100]	[100]	[100]
113	48.9	36.4	42.2
222	29.1	26.4	28.3
400	13.4	10.7	—
133	19.1	—	—
240	28.8	—	—
224	20.5	—	—
333,115	12.5	—	—

[1] A. H. Compton, *X-rays and Electrons* (New York, 1926) Chap. V; R. W. G. Wyckoff and A. H. Armstrong, *Zeit. f. Krist.* **72** (1929) 319.

are due to the cooperation of these two atoms. The relative intensities of the observed reflections for $\text{Ni}\,K\alpha$, $\text{Cu}\,K\alpha$ and $\text{Mo}\,K\alpha$ rays are shown in Table I.

The absolute F-values for molybdenum radiation have been found by comparing the (200) reflection of NiO with (220) of NaCl. A mean of several determinations using both samples of NiO gave $(200)\text{NiO}:(220)\text{NaCl} = = 49.6 : 100$. The apparent accuracy of this ratio is better than 5 percent. The mass absorption coefficient of NiO according to the experiments of

Table II. The F-values of powder reflections of nickel oxide.

Indices	$\sin\theta/\lambda$	$F(\text{Mo }K\alpha)$	$F(\text{Cu }K\alpha)$	$F(\text{Ni }K\alpha)$
111	0.2076	14.13	11.41	13.01
200	.2398	22.60	20.56	22.52
220	.3391	18.28	15.83	16.88
113	.3976	10.76	8.13	9.16
222	.4153	15.12	12.52	13.43
400	.4796	13.65	10.12	—
133	.5223	9.22	—	—
240	.5359	11.65	—	—
224	.5871	10.96	—	—
333,115	.6229	7.96	—	—

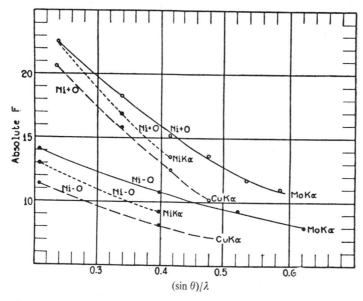

Fig. 1. The reflection F-values observed from NiO using molybdenum, copper and nickel $K\alpha$ radiations.

Windgardh[1] is $\mu/\rho = 37.93$. If Allen's[2] value for nickel is used, μ/ρ becomes 37.21. The absorption coefficient of NaCl as provided by Windgardh's data is $\mu = 18.21 (\rho = 2.16)$. Of the other quantities[3] needed to calculate absolute F's, ρ has been taken as 6.75, $a_0(\text{NiO}) = 4.17\text{Å}$, $a_0(\text{NaCl}) = 5.628\text{Å}$, $F(220, \text{NaCl}) = 15.62$. Introduction of these values into the customary expressions leads to the reflection F's recorded in Table II and Fig. 1. Points on the smooth F-curves drawn through them, when separated by addition and subtraction into atomic F-values for nickel and oxygen, give the numbers listed in Tables III and IV and plotted in Fig. 2.

In order to place the F-curves for copper and nickel radiation upon an 'absolute' scale for comparison with those for molybdenum x-rays, it has been assumed that $F(220, \text{NaCl}) = 15.62$ for all three radiations. The absorption coefficients for NiO as calculated by Jönsson's formula[4] are $\mu = 276.8$ for $\text{Cu}K\alpha$ and $\mu = 345.1$ for $\text{Ni}K\alpha$. They are in good agreement with existing experimental values. Absorption coefficients for NaCl obtained in the same way are $\mu = 161.2$ for $\text{Cu}K\alpha$ and $\mu = 196.2$ for $\text{Ni}K\alpha$. Measurements of the relative intensities of (220) NaCl and (220) NiO have led to the ratios (220) NiO : (220) NaCl = 100 : 57.5 for $\text{Cu}K\alpha$

Table III. Atomic F-values of oxygen in nickel oxide.

$(\sin\theta)/\lambda$	$F(\text{Mo } K\alpha)$	$F(\text{Cu } K\alpha)$	$F(\text{Ni } K\alpha)$
0.240	4.55	4.87	5.23
.270	4.14	4.42	4.62
.300	3.77	3.96	4.06
.330	3.42	3.52	3.52
.360	3.05	3.10	3.05
.390	2.72	2.67	2.58
.420	2.39	2.27	2.30
.450	2.09	(1.87)	—
.480	1.81	(1.53)	—
.510	1.57	—	—
.540	1.35	—	—
.570	1.22	—	—
.600	1.15	—	—

Note: Values in parentheses in this and the following table are obtained by extrapolating the Ni–O curve of fig. 1.

[1] K. A. Windgardh, *Zeits. f. Physik* **8** (1922) 363.
[2] S. J. M. Allen, *Phys. Rev.* **28** (1926) 907.
[3] Internat. Critical Tables (New York, 1926) Vol. I p. 343; R. W. James and E. M. Firth, *op. cit.*
[4] E. Jönsson, Uppsala Univers. Årsskrift (1928).

Table IV. Atomic F-values of nickel in nickel oxide.

$(\sin \theta)/\lambda$	$F(Mo\ K\alpha)$	$F(Cu\ K\alpha)$	$F(Ni\ K\alpha)$
0.240	17.95	15.62	17.37
.270	16.94	14.55	16.07
.300	16.03	13.57	14.87
.330	15.16	12.62	13.78
.360	14.33	11.72	12.81
.390	13.54	10.88	11.90
.420	12.79	10.04	11.37
.450	12.09	(9.25)	—
.480	11.41	(8.55)	—
.510	10.81	—	—
.540	10.25	—	—
.570	9.76	—	—
.600	9.39	—	—

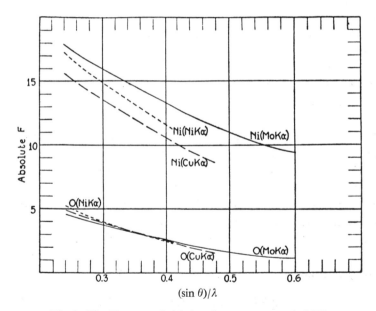

Fig. 2. The F-curves of nickel and oxygen atoms in NiO.

and (220) NiO : (220) NaCl = 100 : 51.8 for Ni $K\alpha$. The reflection F's calculated from these data are recorded in Table II and plotted in Fig. 1. The atomic F's derived from them are listed in Tables III and IV and shown graphically in Fig. 2.

341

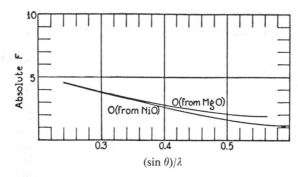

Fig. 3. A comparison of the oxygen F-curves for Mo $K\alpha$ rays as measured in MgO and NiO.

A check upon the accuracy of the measurements of this paper can be had by comparing the oxygen F-curves for Mo $K\alpha$ from NiO and[1] MgO. Though it is scarcely to be expected that they should be identical, these two curves ought to lie close to one another (Fig. 3).

The most significant feature of these results is the fact that though the oxygen F-curves are nearly identical for the three radiations—or, more accurately, vary in the same manner as does NaCl—relatively large differences exist in the curves for the nickel atoms. Since critical wave-lengths of oxygen are farther from the wave-lengths used than are those of NaCl, the observed slight increase in the oxygen F-curves at low angles with increasing wave-lengths is not contrary to expectation. The F-curves of nickel, lower for copper than for molybdenum radiation, agree with existing data upon copper[1] and iron in indicating that for atoms having critical frequencies within the experimental range, coherent scattering decreases with increasing wave-length as this critical range is approached. The greater diffraction of nickel for the nickel than for the copper $K\alpha$ line indicates that this downward trend is broken either some time before or when a wave-length characteristic of the scatterer is reached.

Further experiments are being made with various metals and with several wave-lengths which will bear upon these phenomena.

Rockefeller Institute for Medical Research, New York City

80. The F-values of this paper show clearly the way in which the reflecting power of an atom varies with the wave-length of the x-rays scattered. The phenomena are illustrated by the (200) reflections of nickel as plotted

[1] R. W. G. Wyckoff and A. H. Armstrong, *Zeits. f. Krist.* **72** (1930) 433.

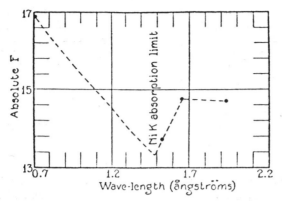

Fig. 3. The dotted curve indicates the variation of the scattering power of nickel with wave-length. The full circles are the measured values of the (200) reflection of metallic nickel.

in Fig. 3. All of the other data of the present paper as well as those from NiO agree with this figure in showing that the scattering power of an atom is at a minimum close to its K critical absorption limit, that it attains a maximum at, or near, its 'resonance' wave-length, but that the reflecting power falls off only slowly on the long wave-length side of this frequency. The photographs made by Mark and Szilard[1] of RbBr using strontium and bromine radiations are obviously an expression of the same variation.

It is hoped through additional experiments to put these scattering powers for long wave-lengths upon an accurate absolute scale.

Rockefeller Institute for Medical Research, New York City

81. Beginning in the year 1898 Heusler discovered a series of ferromagnetic alloys, the most important containing copper, manganese, and aluminium.

In the alloy selected for detailed investigation the proportions of the ingredients did not correspond exactly to the theoretical values for the composition Cu_2MnAl. Analysis of the alloy showed that the approximate composition was Cu 67.5%, Mn 17.5%, Al 15% corresponding to the atomic composition Cu 2.2, Mn 0.65, Al 1.15. The deficit of manganese was therefore made up partly by copper and partly by aluminium.

The ferromagnetic quenched alloy has a unit cell containing 16 atoms, fig. 2. These consist of four sets of atoms (A, B, C, D) each corresponding

---

[1] H. Mark and L. Szilard, *Zeits. f. Physik* **33** (1925) 688 [this Vol. p. 323].

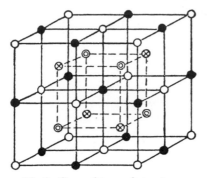

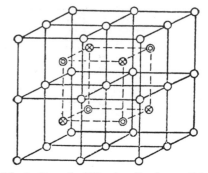

Fig. 2. General type of structure;
○ A, ◎ B, ● C, ⊗ D.

Fig. 3. Quenched Heusler alloy (magnetic);
○ Cu, ◎ Al, ⊗ Mn.

to a face-centred cubic lattice. The superlattice lines are caused by the segregation of the aluminium atoms into one of the four sets of positions (say B). Both Persson[1] and Potter[2] suggest that the ferromagnetism of these alloys is due to the manganese atoms occupying a special position as in fig. 3. It was our object to test this hypothesis. The question is whether the manganese atoms are mixed up at random with the copper atoms or whether they keep to their own positions. The difference between the scattering powers of copper and manganese for X-rays is so slight that this might at first sight appear to be a matter of some difficulty, but, in fact, the problem has been solved by means of accurate photometer measurements of powder photographs taken with X-rays of different wave-lengths, making use of the anomalies in atomic scattering factor which occur when the frequency of the radiation is close to the characteristic absorption frequency of the element.

It has been shown in a number of experimental investigations that the atomic scattering factor (f) of an element for X-rays depends upon the wave-length of the radiation, or to put the matter more precisely, the atomic scattering factor of an element is depressed by the use of radiation whose frequency lies close to the critical K absorption frequency of the scattering element.

In fig. 4 the depressions in the observed f values for iron are plotted against the values of λ/λ_K, λ being the wave-length of the radiations used (Mo, Cu, Co, Fe, Cr characteristic K_α radiations), and λ_K the wave-length of the K absorption edge of iron. The values for molybdenum radiation are taken as zero. In this figure the values of the depression at

[1] *Z. Physik*, **57** (1929) 115.
[2] *Proc. Phys. Soc.*, London, **41** (1929) 135.

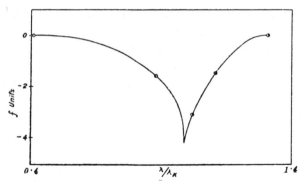

Fig. 4. Depression of f curves in the region of the K absorption edge. ⊙ Points from experiments on FeAl (Bradley and Hope) giving the difference between the normal f values and the values found near the absorption edge.

Table V. Depression in f Curve, due to Anomalous Dispersion.

Scattering elements	λ_K	Zinc K_α radiation $\lambda = 1.434$	Copper K_α radiation $\lambda = 1.539$	Iron K_α radiation $\lambda = 1.934$
Al 13	7.936	0	0	0
Mn 25	1.892	1.0	1.0	3
Cu 29	1.377	2.5	1.5	0

some distance from the absorption edge approach zero, and the biggest values of the depression are in the immediate neighbourhood of the K edge. Plotted as a function of λ/λ_K, theory indicates that the values represented on this curve should be universal. They represent the amounts to be subtracted from the normal f values where the frequency of the radiation is comparable with the critical absorption frequency.

Table V contains the necessary data for the Heusler alloy.

It is now possible to understand the differences in the powder photographs taken with zinc, copper, and iron radiations. As Table V shows, the atomic scattering factor of manganese with iron radiation is three units less than normal, whereas that of copper with iron radiation is practically normal. Hence the difference in scattering power between copper and manganese is *three units greater* than normal. On the other hand, with zinc radiation the scattering power of copper is depressed more than that of manganese, so that the difference in scattering power between copper and manganese is now *1.5 units less* than normal. Thus iron radiation emphasizes the difference in scattering power between copper and

345

manganese, whereas zinc radiation minimizes the difference. This fact naturally leads to differences in the intensities of the weaker reflections, where copper and manganese work in opposite directions. As we shall see later, the figures given in Table V provide not merely a qualitative explanation, but ultimately give a perfect quantitative explanation of all the observed intensities (Table VII).

Before comparing the observed intensities with the calculated values for the most probable arrangement, we shall first give calculations for three different arrangements of manganese atoms with the ideal composition Cu_2MnAl. It will be seen that the differences between the intensities of the superlattice lines in the three cases are so large that it is possible to be quite sure of the ultimate solution.

The three arrangements considered first are:—

(i) Mn in D, Cu in A and C, Al in B.
(ii) Mn and Cu at random in A, C, and D, Al in B.
(iii) Mn in A, Cu in C and D, Al in B.

Table VI. Comparison of Observed and Calculated Intensities for Three Different Structures.

Line		Iron K_α radiation $\lambda = 1.934$				Copper K_α radiation $\lambda = 1.539$			
Σh^2	hkl	Observed with temperature correction	Calculated			Observed with temperature correction	Calculated		
			i	ii	iii		i	ii	iii
3	111	14	10	27	48.5	33	28	43	59
4	200	36	49	14	5	39.5	51	23	14
8	220	340	354	354	354	600	593	593	593
11	311	4.5	2	10	22	11	9.5	17	26
12	222	9.5	12	3	0.5	8	12	5	3
16	400	57	56	56	56	88	90	90	90
19	331	1.5	1	4	9.5	4	3.5	6	8.5
20	420	11.5	17	4	0.5	10	12	5	2.5
24	422	156	148	148	148	173	167	167	167
27	511 333	2	1	4.5	11	2.5	3	4	5.5
32	440	97	95	95	95	51	54	54	54
35	531	3.5	2.5	12.5	30	3.5	3.5	4	5.5
36	600 442	29	46	10	2	4.5	5	2.5	2

82. Hemihedry of Zincblende and X-Ray Reflexion S. NISHIKAWA and K. MATUKAWA (1928)

▬

83. D. COSTER, K. S. KNOL and J. A. PRINS (1930)

▬

82. It is known as Friedel's law[1] that the hemihedrism due to the lack of centre of symmetry of a crystal lattice cannot be revealed by the X-ray diffraction method. The law is based on the assumption that the phase change upon reflexion of X-rays is the same for all kinds of atoms. Thus, for instance, a zincblende crystal gives rise to a Laue pattern of holohedral symmetry. The law, however, may not be conformable to the case in which the radiation is of a wave-length very close to that of the critical absorption of some atoms composing the crystal, in consequence of the characteristic phase lag accompanying the selective absorption due to the atoms.

The present experiment was carried out in order to detect, if possible, any difference in the intensity of reflexion from a pair of hemihedral planes, (111) and ($\overline{1}\overline{1}\overline{1}$), of zincblende, using the tungsten L radiation, of which the spectral lines are distributed over a range across the K critical absorption limit of zinc atoms.

The specimens were taken from transparent brownish crystals from Ani, Japan, and of these a number of plates parallel to (111) plane were made, both surfaces of the plate being polished under the same condition as far as possible. Employing each surface of the plate as the reflecting plane, spectra were obtained by means of an X-ray spectrograph of Müller's type with a metal tube of tungsten target.

Among the lines of the tungsten L series, the β components stand close to the K absorption limit of zinc, which, in fact, lies between β_1 and β_4. Two strong components, β_1 and β_2, of the shorter wave-length suffered the selective absorption from the crystal atoms and their apparent intensities on the photogram were not much different from the intensity of the weak component, β_4, so that they could be conveniently compared with the latter. With a breadth of the slit of about 0.05 mm and an exposure of 20—30 milliampere hours at 30 kV, these lines were well separated and gave a blackening on the plate favourable for the photometric measurement.

By means of a Moll's microphotometer the intensities of the lines were

[1] G. Friedel, *C. R.* **157** (1913) 1533 [this Vol. p. 95].

recorded and it was found that the relative intensities of the above three lines were different in two photograms corresponding respectively to (111) and ($\overline{1}\overline{1}\overline{1}$) reflexions. If it is assumed that the intensity of the β_4 line is the same for both the reflexions, the β_1 and β_2 lines are reflected more strongly from the ($\overline{1}\overline{1}\overline{1}$) plane than from the (111).

It must be noted that the relative intensity of the lines depends to some extent on the smoothness of the polished surface. The surface condition affects the extinction effect of the reflecting plane and accordingly the intensity of the reflected rays. As the planes in consideration have a polarity, the actual states of the surface with respect to the extinction effect may not be equal in the opposite faces, although they are carefully polished so as to give the same appearance. Thus, the apparent difference in the relative intensities of the spectral lines may be accounted for as due to the different extinction effects. Nevertheless, a difference in the definite sense above stated was always retained when apparent states of the surface were slightly varied and this would afford a means of distinguishing between the positive and negative faces.

In order to be free from such an ambiguity caused by the surface condition, the method of rotating crystal was tried using a cleavage face (110) as the reflector and one of the principal axes as the axis of rotation. In this case, the spectra reflected by (111) and ($\overline{1}\overline{1}\overline{1}$) planes appear symmetrically with respect to the principal spectrum due to ($hk0$) planes, and they are originated in one and the same surface by the same pencil of incident rays. If, the absorption and other factors, being the same for both planes, the above difference in the relative intensities still persists in this case, then it may be pretty sure that we may assign the difference to an effect of phase retardation. The experiment is still in progress, but so far as qualitatively tested, the same difference seems to exist. A further discussion will be postponed until some more quantitative results are obtained.

Institute of Physical and Chemical Research, Tokyo

83. In § 1 wird gezeigt, daß—falls man zwei Linien beiderseits der Zink-K-Kante miteinander vergleicht—man einen meßbaren Unterschied in deren Intensitätsverhältnis für Reflexionen an den beiden verschiedenen (111)-Flächen der Zinkblende erwarten kann. Dieser Unterschied hängt zusammen mit dem polaren Charakter der ZnS und wird verursacht durch die Tatsache, daß die Phasendifferenz zwischen Primärwelle und Streuwelle für Streuung an Zink anders ist als für Streuung an Schwefel. In § 2 werden Meßresultate gebracht, welche den in § 1 erwähnten Effekt sicherstellen. Den ZnS-Kristall kann man sich aufgebaut denken aus Doppelschichten in der (111)-Richtung, bestehend aus je einer Zn-Netzebene und einer S-Netzebene in einer Distanz von einem Viertel der Gitterkonstante. Es wird nun an natürlichen Kristallflächen gezeigt, daß die glänzende, gut entwickelte (111)-Fläche die S-Atome der Doppelschichten außen hat, während die matte, weniger gut entwickelte Fläche die Zn-Atome außen hat. In § 3 werden die Resultate piezoelektrischer Untersuchungen gegeben. Bei Druck senkrecht zu den (111)-Flächen wird die glänzende Fläche (Schwefel außen) *positiv*. In § 4 wird das Zahlenmaterial von § 2 eingehend diskutiert. Es zeigt sich, daß es nötigt ist anzunehmen, daß nicht nur die Amplitude, sondern auch die Phase der von Atomen gestreuten Röntgenwellen eine Funktion des Ablenkungswinkels sei. Es wird die Abhängigkeit der Phase bei Streuung an Zink von Linien in der Nähe der Zink-K-Kante abgeschätzt. Diese Abschätzung wird in qualitativer Übereinstimmung mit der Erfahrung gefunden.

§ 1. *Einleitung*

Gelegentlich einer näheren Diskussion über die Gültigkeit des Friedelschen Satzes von der Symmetrie der Röntgeninterferenzen hat schon Ewald [1] die Behauptung ausgesprochen, daß dieser Satz nicht mehr zu gelten braucht, wenn man die individuellen Phasenunterschiede zwischen den an den verschiedenen Atomsorten gestreuten Sekundärwellen mit der Primärwelle in Betracht zieht.

Diese Phasenunterschiede lassen sich nun für eine bestimmte Atomart in halbklassischer Weise leicht abschätzen. Wenn n der (im allgemeinen komplexe) Brechungsquotient einer nur aus der betrachteten Atomart aufgebauten Substanz ist, E die elektrische Feldstärke, D die dielektrische Verschiebung, P die elektrische Polarisation darstellt, so gilt die bekannte Beziehung:

$$n^2 = D/E = 1 + 4\pi P/E$$

oder

$$n^2 - 1 = 4\pi P/E. \tag{1}$$

Wir können nun ganz allgemein schreiben:

$$n = 1 - \alpha - i\beta, \tag{2}$$

wo α und β im Röntgengebiet positive Größen klein gegen Eins sind, β ist der Absorptionskoeffizient auf eine Strecke $\lambda/4\pi$, $1 - \alpha$ ist der (reelle) Brechungsquotient, der im Röntgengebiet bekanntlich kleiner als Eins

---

[1] P. P. Ewald und C. Hermann, *Zeitschr. f. Krist.* **65** (1927) 251. Ein 'Beweis', den Ewald anfänglich für die Richtigkeit des Friedelschen Satzes gegeben hat (*Physica* **5** (1925) 363), wurde später von ihm, durch eine Bemerkung der Herren N. H. Kolkmeyer, A. Karssen und J. M. Bijvoet dazu veranlaßt, widerrufen (*Physica* **6** (1926) 336).

ist. Aus (1) und (2) läßt sich folgern:

$$4\pi P = -2(\alpha + i\beta)E. \tag{3}$$

Die Phase der gestreuten Welle wird von der Phase der Polarisation bestimmt, der relative Phasenunterschied zwischen Streuwelle und Primärwelle wird also gemessen durch arc tg (β/α). Es läßt sich leicht abschätzen, daß die Größe β/α im allgemeinen nicht mehr als einige Hundertstel beträgt. Wenn man aber mit der Wellenlänge der gestreuten Welle eine Absorptionskante eines streuenden Elementes in der Richtung nach kurzen Wellen passiert, wird—abgesehen von der unmittelbaren Nähe der Kante— die Größe α sich wenig ändern, während die Größe β einen Sprung erfährt, welche z.B. bei der K-Kante etwa einen Faktor 8 beträgt. Man hat also die größte Wahrscheinlichkeit, einen Einfluß der Phasendifferenz in der Nähe einer Absorptionskante eines der im Kristall befindlichen Elemente zu beobachten.

Wir haben deshalb die relative Intensität untersucht von Linien beiderseits der K-Kante des Zinks, welche von der (111)-Fläche der Zinkblende reflektiert werden [1]. Die Zinkblende ist ein polarer Kristall, die (111)-Netzebenen sind abwechselnd nur von Schwefel- oder von Zinkatomen besetzt, eine Schwefelnetzebene teilt den Abstand zweier sukzessiver Zinknetzebenen im Verhältnis 1 : 3. Als reflektierte Linien wurden zuerst die $L\alpha_1$- und $L\alpha_2$-Linien des Goldes benutzt. Die K-Kante des Zinks liegt bei 1281,0 X-E., die $L\alpha_1$-Linie bei 1273,77, die $L\alpha_2$-Linie bei 1285,02 X-E.

Für die Phasenverschiebungen findet man mit Hilfe der β [2] und α [3] Werte die in Tabelle 3 zusammengestellten Werte [4].

---

[1] Schon vor einiger Zeit ist eine analoge Untersuchung von S. Nishikawa und K. Matukawa (*Proceedings Imperial Academy of Tokyo* 4 (1928), 96)* gemacht worden. Ihre Resultate sind mit unseren weiter unten zu besprechenden insoweit qualitativ im Einklang, daß sie ein anderes Intensitätsverhältnis für beiderseits der K-Kante des Zinks liegende Wolframlinien finden, wenn sie das eine Mal an der (111)-Fläche, das andere Mal an der $(\overline{1}\overline{1}\overline{1})$-Fläche der Zinkblende reflektiert werden. Eine theoretische Diskussion aber fehlt bei ihnen ganz. Weiter ist der Einfluß der äußeren reflektierenden Oberfläche des Kristalls nicht eliminiert worden, da sie keine höheren Ordnungen untersuchen, so daß sie nicht imstande waren, ein quantitatives Resultat zu gewinnen. Weder die Reflexion an natürlichen Oktaederflächen noch der Zusammenhang mit dem piezoelektrischen Effekt wurde von ihnen untersucht.

[2] A. Jönsson, Dissertation Upsala 1928.

[3] Siehe z.B. J. A. Prins, *Zeitschr. f. Phys.* 47 (1928) 479.

[4] J. A. Prins, *l.c.*

* [This Vol. p. 349]

Tabelle 3. Phasenverschiebungen

Wellenlängen	Zink		Schwefel	
	β/α	arc tg(β/α)	β/α	arc tg(β/α)
1273,77	0,21	12°	0,022	1°20′
1285,02	0,025	1°30′	0,022	1°20′

Man kann also annehmen, daß für die Wellenlänge 1285,02 X-E. Zn und S in Phase streuen, während für die Wellenlänge 1273,77 Zn relativ zu S mit einem Phasenvorsprung von 10°30′ streut.

Die vorliegende Untersuchung beschäftigt sich nun mit dem Einfluß dieses Phasensprunges auf die Kristallreflexionen des ZnS-Kristalls. Hierbei muß man jedoch noch die Möglichkeit einer Komplikation ins Auge fassen: Die gerade berechnete Phasenverschiebung bezieht sich auf die Streuwelle mit Ablenkungswinkel Null. Die Ablenkungswinkel bei den Kristallreflexionen sind jedoch größer als Null, und deshalb braucht die Phasenverschiebung hierfür nicht notwendig genau dieselbe zu sein. Tatsächlich ergeben unsere Messungen und in Einklang damit die in § 4 angestellten Betrachtungen eine etwas größere Phasenverschiebung für die Kristallreflexionen (namentlich höherer Ordnung) als die für den Ablenkungswinkel Null berechnete. Wir werden jedoch hier erst noch einmal mit dem letzten Wert rechnen.

Bei der Reflexion A in erster Ordnung an der (111)-Fläche (siehe Fig. 1) wird, abgesehen von eventuellen Phasensprüngen bei der Zerstreuung, die von den Zn-Atomen gestreute Welle 90° in Phase vorgehen gegenüber der von S-Atomen gestreuten Welle, bei der Reflexion B ist es gerade umgekehrt. Setzt man nun auch die Phasensprünge bei der Zerstreuung in Rechnung, so ergibt sich bei der Reflexion A ein totaler Phasenunterschied von 100°30′ und bei Reflexion B einer von 79°30′. Man sieht sofort ein, daß dadurch

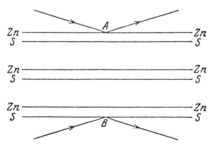

Fig. 1. Reflexion an den beiden Oktaederflächen (A und B) der Zinkblende.

353

die Reflexion A eine schwächere $L\alpha_1$ liefern wird als die Reflexion B. Da ein solcher Einfluß bei der $L\alpha_2$ nicht zu erwarten ist, oder jedenfalls viel kleiner ausfallen muß, wird also die relative Intensität beider Linien ein ausgezeichnetes Maß für einen derartigen Effekt liefern. Will man auch die Größe des Effektes abschätzen, so hat man den Einfluß des genannten Phasenunterschiedes auf den Strukturfaktor zu bestimmen. Wir nehmen hier an, daß das Streuvermögen des Zn-Atoms zweimal so groß ist als dasjenige des S-Atoms. Für das Verhältnis des Strukturfaktors bei der Reflexion B bzw. A (Fig. 1) unter Benutzung von der $L\alpha_1$-Strahlung des Goldes findet man nun:

$$S_B/S_A = \sqrt{\{(5 + 4 \sin 10°30')/(5 - 4 \sin 10°30')\}} = 1,15$$

während dasselbe Verhältnis bei Benutzung der $L\alpha_2$-Linie 1 beträgt.

Bei der experimentellen Prüfung dieser abgeschätzten Zahlen stößt man auf die Schwierigkeit, daß der Einfluß des Absorptionskoeffizienten auf die reflektierte Intensität ein anderer ist, je nachdem ein idealer Kristall oder ein Mosaikkristall nach Darwin vorliegt. Im letzten Falle wird die Eindringungstiefe der Strahlung durch den makroskopischen Absorptionskoeffizienten bestimmt und da dieser für beide Seiten des Kristalls denselben Wert hat, ergibt sich in bekannter Weise, daß die an beiden Seiten reflektierten Intensitäten I_A bzw. I_B für eine bestimmte Wellenlänge sich verhalten wie die Quadrate der Strukturfaktoren. Wenn man verschiedene Wellenlängen vergleicht, ist zu berücksichtigen, daß die Intensitäten sich *ceteris paribus* umgekehrt wie die Absorptionskoeffizienten verhalten. Dieser erleidet nun im vorliegenden Falle an der Zn-K-Kante einen Sprung im Verhältnis 5,8 (für reines Zink 7,8).

Für den Fall eines idealen Kristalls könnte man meinen, daß die Intensitäten sich verhielten wie die Strukturamplituden, weil dies bei Vernachlässigung der Absorption allgemein gilt. Im vorliegenden Falle jedoch spielt die Absorption eine wesentliche Rolle und weil sich über deren Einfluß in der Literatur nur spärliche Bemerkungen finden, die uns übrigens nicht ganz zutreffend scheinen, ist hierüber von dem einen von uns eine nähere Betrachtung angestellt, die demnächst in dieser Zeitschrift erscheinen wird. Hierbei stellt sich heraus, daß merkwürdigerweise auch in diesem Falle eines idealen Kristalls genau wie oben für den Mosaikkristall gilt:

$$I_A/I_B = S_A{}^2/S_B{}^2.$$

Für den Sprung im Reflexionsvermögen an der Zn-K-Kante ergibt sich natürlich für den idealen Kristall ein viel geringerer Wert als der obige (5,8), nämlich etwa 1,5.

354

In Wirklichkeit wird man es meistens wohl mit einem Zwischenfall dieser beiden Grenzfälle zu tun haben, so daß sich über den Einfluß der Absorption auf die Intensität der reflektierten Strahlung *a priori* nicht viel aussagen läßt. Es könnte zufälligerweise sein, daß die beiden zu untersuchenden (111)-Flächen einen verschiedenen Grad von Idealität zeigten; diesen Effekt würde man von dem gesuchten Effekt, ohne weiteres nicht trennen können.

Eine andere Schwierigkeit wird durch die Beschaffenheit der äußeren Oberfläche des Kristalls verursacht[1]. Wie groß dieser Einfluß sein kann, zeigte sich, als wir an derselben (111)-Fläche desselben Kristallstückes die zwei Goldlinien aufnahmen, einmal als die Fläche flachgeschliffen aber noch nicht poliert war, das andere Mal nach dem Polieren. Das erstemal war die $L\alpha_1$-Linie relativ zu der $L\alpha_2$-Linie viel schwächer als im zweiten Falle. Es scheint also, daß im ersten Falle an der Oberfläche des Kristalles sich ganz desorientierte Mikrokriställchen befinden, die nur zu der Absorption und nicht zu der Braggschen Reflexion beitragen.

Wir haben uns nun von diesen störenden Einflüssen frei gemacht, indem wir die relativen Intensitäten der beiden Au-$L\alpha_1$Linien bei der (111)-Reflexion an Zinkblende in den verschiedenen Ordnungen miteinander verglichen haben. Wie oben auseinandergesetzt wurde, hat man in der ersten Ordnung bei der Reflexion *A* (siehe Fig. 1) eine schwächere $L\alpha_1$-Linie zu erwarten als bei der Reflexion *B*. Man sieht nun leicht ein, daß in der zweiten Ordnung, wo bei Vernachlässigung des Phasensprunges ein Phasenunterschied von 180° zwischen den von Zink- und Schwefelatomen gestreuten Wellen bestehen würde, gar kein Unterschied zwischen *A* und *B* zu erwarten ist, während in dritter Ordnung die Sache gerade umgekehrt liegt als in der ersten Ordnung, und Reflexion *B* die schwächere $L\alpha_1$-Linie liefern würde.

§ 2. *I. Teil*: *Messungen mittels Au-Lα-Strahlung an angeschliffenen und polierten Begrenzungsebenen*

Wir haben deshalb das Intensitätsverhältnis der erwähnten Goldlinien in verschiedenen Ordnungen untersucht. Wir benutzten für die Intensitätsmessungen die photographische Methode. Wir überzeugten uns erst davon, daß die Linien über eine Höhe von etwa 15 mm homogen geschwärzt

---

[1] Diese Schwierigkeit ist auch von Nishikawa and Matukawa in ihren Untersuchungen in starker Weise empfunden worden.

waren. Wenn dies nicht der Fall war, konnte dies immer durch eine Ver-
legung oder Verkleinerung des Brennfleckes nach einigem Ausprobieren
erreicht werden.

Die Schwärzungsskale wurde auf der Platte mittels eines rotierenden
Sektors angebracht. Ein homogener Teil der Linien wurde dabei in vier
Felder von je 3 mm Höhe verteilt mit Belichtungszeiten von bzw. 100,
75, 50 und 25%. Bekanntlich ist diese Methode im bezüglichen Röntgengebiet einwandfrei, da der Exponent p des Schwarzschildschen Gesetzes:
$S = f(it^p)$ mit großer Annäherung 1 beträgt [1].

Es wurden drei künstlich aus größeren Stücken geschnittene Kristallplättchen [2] von etwa 3 mm Dicke mit polierten parallelen (111)-Flächen
als Begrenzungsebenen benutzt. Bekanntlich zeigt die Zinkblende häufig
Zwillingsbildung, die Zwillingsachse steht senkrecht auf einer der (111)-
Flächen. Falls diese Fläche nicht mit der reflektierenden Begrenzungs-
fläche identisch wäre, würden dadurch Anomalien in der Reflexion eintreten. Um dies näher zu untersuchen, wurden die Kristalle nacheinander
auf einen Kreuzschlitten in dem Spektrographen montiert. Sie konnten
auf diese Weise mit verschiedenen Teilen ihrer Vorderfläche in die Spektro-
graphenachse einjustiert werden. Es wurden so dann jedesmal Aufnahmen
mit stillestehendem Kristall gemacht.

Bei zwei dieser Kristallplättchen (I und II) hatten die (111)-Begrenzungs-
ebenen etwa 2 cm² Oberfläche. Insoweit es die Intensität der Röntgen-
strahlenreflexion betrifft, benahmen diese sich als ganz homogen. Auch
zeigten sie keine Lamellenbildung, wie man dies oft bei der Zinkblende
beobachtet. Nur in der Färbung (gelb mit nicht sehr scharf begrenzten
braungelben Partien) waren sie inhomogen. Weiter wurde noch ein größeres,
braungelbes Plättchen (III) von etwa 4 cm² Oberfläche untersucht. Dies
Plättchen war nur in der Mitte homogen bezüglich der Reflexion. Es
zeigte deutlich ein Streifung, welche mit Inhomogenitäten in der Reflexion
zusammenzuhängen schien. Es wurde sowohl bei den Röntgenmessungen
als bei den piezoelektrischen Untersuchungen (§ 3) nur der homogene
mittlere Teil benutzt. Obzwar also bei diesem Kristall III wegen der oben
besprochenen Inhomogenitäten Unsicherkeiten überbleiben, sind die erhaltenen Resultate hier doch vollständigkeitshalber mitgeteilt.

Bei den definitiven Messungen wurde ein Bündel Röntgenstrahlen von
etwa 1° Öffnungswinkel abgeblendet. Der Kristall wurde während der
Belichtung über einen Winkel von etwa 1°40′ mit Hilfe einer Mikrometer-
schraube nach gleichen Zeitintervallen um Schritte von etwa drei Bogen-

---

[1] A. Bouwers, Dissertation Utrecht 1924.
[2] Bezogen von der Firma Steeg und Reuter.

356

minuten hin und her gedreht. Der Vorteil dieser Drehung ist, daß man sich frei gemacht hat von Inhomogenitäten im Antikathodenfokus und von Abweichungen des Reflexionsvermögens der Kristalloberfläche. Ein Nachteil ist, daß man etwas mehr Schwärzung in dem kontinuierlichen Untergrund bekommt wegen diffuser Streuung und Fluoreszenzerregung des Kristalles. Besonders in zweiter Ordnung der Goldlinien wirkte dieses sehr störend, da in diesem Falle auch das normal in dritter Ordnung reflektierte kontinuierliche Röntgenlicht des Wellenlängengebietes von etwa 850 X-E. viel Schwärzung verursacht. Die dritte Ordnung bei der (111)-Reflexion der Zinkblende ist nämlich noch etwas stärker als die zweite Ordnung. Im bezüglichen Gebiete wirkt sie überdies stärker auf die photographische Platte ein, da sie jenseits der K-Kante des Broms der photographischen Platte liegt. Betreibt man die Röntgenröhre mit so niedriger Spannung, daß die dritte Ordnung fehlt, so wird auch die zweite Ordnung so schwach, daß man zu lange Expositionszeiten braucht und die kontinuierliche Strahlung erster Ordnung sich wieder sehr störend bemerkbar macht.

Obwohl die Platten der zweiten Ordnung nirgends mit unseren theoretischen Aussagen in Streit waren, wurden sie doch weiter nicht berücksichtigt, weil man wegen der oben skizzierten Ursachen keine sicheren Schlüsse aus ihnen ziehen kann. Glücklicherweise stand es besser mit der dritten Ordnung. Auch hier war ein starker Untergrund anwesend, für welchen aber in befriedigender Weise korrigiert werden konnte. In den Fig. 2, 3, 4 und 5 geben wir die mit dem Mollschen Apparat aufgenommenen Photometerkurven einiger mit Kristall I erhaltener Platten; die Fig. 2 und 3 sind die ersten Ordnungen an zwei Flächen, die wir ganz willkürlich bzw. Vorder- und Hinterseite nennen wollen. Fig. 4 ist die dritte Ordnung der Vorderseite. Fig. 5 diejenige der Hinterseite. Wie man sieht, liegen die Intensitätsverhältnisse der $L\alpha_1$- und $L\alpha_2$-Linien, gerade wie man nach dem Vorhergehenden erwarten möchte, in der dritten Ordnung umgekehrt als in der ersten Ordnung. Weiter kann man schließen, daß die 'Vorderseite' mit der Fläche B der Fig. 1 identisch ist.

Was nun die quantitative Verwertung der Photometerkurven betrifft: In jeder Figur sind die vier Felder von 25, 50, 75 und 100% und überdies ein unbelichteter Teil der Platte registriert. Es wurde nun graphisch eine Schwärzungskurve in folgender Weise ermittelt: Wie gesagt, rührt die Totalschwärzung wegen Streuung und Fluoreszenz von verschiedenen Wellenlängen her, ganz weiche Röntgenstrahlen sind aber wegen Absorption in der Luft und in der Aluminiumfolie, welche die Röntgenröhre abschließt, ausgeschlossen. Es wurde nun angenommen, daß für die Wellenlängen, welche hier in Frage kommen, dasselbe Schwärzungsgesetz gilt. Diese

357

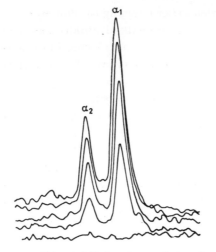

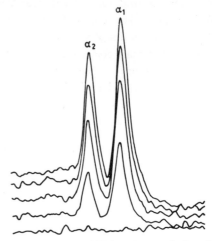

Fig. 2. Die Goldlinien $L\alpha_1$ und $L\alpha_2$ in *erster* Ordnung an der Oktaederfläche der Zinkblende (*Vorderseite*) reflektiert.

Fig. 3. Die Goldlinien $L\alpha_1$ und $L\alpha_2$ in *erster* Ordnung an der Oktaederfläche der Zinkblende (*Hinterseite*) reflektiert.

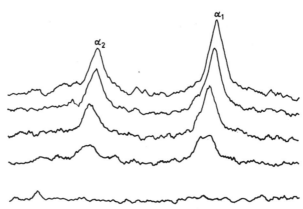

Fig. 4. Die Goldlinien $L\alpha_1$ und $L\alpha_2$ in *dritter* Ordnung an der Oktaederfläche der Zinkblende (*Vorderseite*) reflektiert.

Annahme ist nach den Untersuchungen von Bouwers [1] wohl berechtigt. Eine Beeinflussung in qualitativer Hinsicht ist dadurch jedenfalls nicht zu befürchten. Es wurde nun die Größe $U_0 - U$ (U_0 ist der Galvanometer-

---

[1] A. Bouwers, Dissertation *l.c.* Bouwers benutzt das Schwärzungsgesetz $Z = C\log(1 + It/a)$ wo Z die Schwärzung, I die Intensität der Strahlung und t die Zeit ist. C und a sind Konstanten. Nach Bouwers ist C weitgehend von der Wellenlänge unabhängig. Dies genügt zur Berechtigung unseres oben skizzierten Verfahrens.

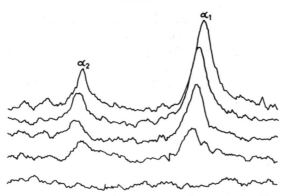

Fig. 5. Die Goldlinien $L\alpha_1$ und $L\alpha_2$ in *dritter* Ordnung an der Oktaederfläche der Zinkblende (*Hinterseite*) reflektiert.

ausschlag beim Photometrieren im unbelichteten Gebiet, U derjenige in einem der respektiven Felder jeweils an der Stelle der $Au\,L\alpha_1$-Linie) als Funktion der totalen Strahlungsintensität (in %) graphisch dargestellt. Mit Hilfe der erhaltenen Kurve konnte die Intensität der $L\alpha_2$ und diejenige des kontinuierlichen Hintergrundes rechts und links der beiden Linien bestimmt werden; diese letzte wurde in Minderung gebracht, um die wahre Linienintensität zu erhalten.

Tabelle 4. Die Bestimmung des Verhältnisses des Reflexionsvermögens für die Linien $Au\,L\alpha_1$ und $Au\,L\alpha_2$ aus den Fig. 2, 3, 4 und 5.

	$Au\,L\alpha_1$ %	$Au\,L\alpha_2$ %	$I\alpha_1/I\alpha_2$	$R\alpha_1/R\alpha_2$
Fig. 2, Vorderseite 1. Ordnung	93	25	3,72	0,41
Fig. 3, Hinterseite 1. ,,	92	54	1,70	0,19
Fig. 4, Vorderseite 3. ,,	54,5	29	1,88	0,21
Fig. 5, Hinterseite 3. ,,	67	23	2,91	0,32

Die Tabelle 4 gibt als ein Beispiel die quantitative Verwertung der Kurven 2, 3, 4 und 5. In der zweiten Spalte steht die Intensität der $L\alpha_1$ in Prozenten von der Totalintensität an derselben Stelle, in der dritten Spalte steht die Intensität der $L\alpha_2$ relativ zur Totalintensität bei der $L\alpha_1$, die vierte Spalte gibt das Intensitätsverhältnis der $L\alpha_1$ und $L\alpha_2$, während die fünfte Spalte das Verhältnis des Reflexionsvermögens des ZnS-Kristalles für die zwei Strahlungsarten gibt. Da sich die wirklichen Intensitäten der zwei $L\alpha$-Linien wie 9 : 1 verhalten[1], werden die Zahlen der letzten Spalte

---

[1] Dies Intensitätsverhältnis wurde von uns mit einem Kalkspatkristall experimentell bestimmt. Es ist in Übereinstimmung mit den Werten von anderen Forschern für die $L\alpha$-Linien des W. gefunden.

durch eine Division durch 9 aus denen der vierten Spalte abgeleitet. Sowohl aus der Tabelle 4 wie aus den Photometerkurven kann man ersehen, daß besonders in der dritten Ordnung die Korrektion wegen des kontinuierlichen Untergrundes ziemlich groß ist.

Es wurden nun von jedem der drei Kristalle von beiden (111)-Flächen mindestens drei Aufnahmen gemacht, welche in derselben Weise verwertet wurden. Die erhaltenen Mittelwerte für das Verhältnis des Reflexionsvermögens für die beiden Goldlinien gibt die Tabelle 5.

Tabelle 5. Das Verhältnis des Reflexionsvermögens an den (111)-Flächen der Zinkblende für die Linien Au $L\alpha_1$ und $L\alpha_2$.

Kristall	I	II	III
Vorderseite 1. Ordnung	0,40	0,29	0,29
Hinterseite 1. „	0,20	0,30	0,28
Vorderseite 3. „	0,21	0,17	0,20
Hinterseite 3. „	0,31	0,37	0,39

Wie oben erwähnt, wurde vom Kristall I willkürlich eine Seite als Vorderseite bezeichnet. Von den Kristallen II und III wurden die damit piezoelektrisch gleichwertigen Seiten so genannt. Die experimentell bestimmten Werte weichen in der Regel weniger als 5% von den Mittelwerten der Tabelle 5 ab.

Aus der Tabelle 5 schließen wir, daß auch für die Kristalle II und III die Vorderseite als Seite B der Fig. 1 zu bezeichnen ist. Wegen der oben besprochenen Inhomogenitäten des Kristalles III wollen wir den für diesen Kristall erhaltenen Werten keinen sehr großen Wert beilegen. Was aber die Kristalle I und II betrifft, so sehen wir, daß für Kristall I der Unterschied in erster Ordnung am größten ist, während dies bei Kristall II in dritter Ordnung der Fall ist (die erste Ordnung gibt hier innerhalb der Fehlergrenze zusammenfallende Werte). Wir schreiben dies der verschiedenen Beschaffenheit der äußeren Oberfläche zu (vgl. § 1).

§ 2. II. Teil. Messungen mittels Wolframstrahlung an natürlichen (111)-Begrenzungsebenen

Es wurden weiter noch die natürlichen (111)-Begrenzungsebenen der Zinkblende untersucht. Die natürlichen Oktaederflächen der Zinkblende verteilen sich auf zwei verschiedenartige Tetraeder. Das eine Tetraeder hat im allgemeinen gut entwickelte, glänzende, das andere weniger gut entwickelte, matte Flächen. Es war nun interessant zu wissen, welche dieser

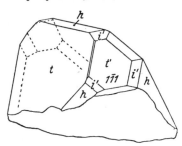

Fig. 6. Zinkblendekristall von tetraedrischem Habitus, von dem das Reflexionsvermögen
der Flächen (1Ī1) und (Ī1Ī) untersucht wurde.

beiden Flächen als *A*, welche als *B* der Fig. 1 angesprochen werden muß.

Der Kristall wurde in einem Drehkristallspektrographen montiert und
mit zwei parallelen Tetraederflächen nacheinander ((1Ī1) von *t'* und (Ī1Ī)
von *t*) in die Drehungsachse einjustiert. Die Fläche (1Ī1) ist etwa 4 mm² groß,
(Ī1Ī) etwa 12 mm²; sie wurden nicht poliert, sondern lediglich mit Alkohol
gereinigt. Der Kristall wurde gleichmäßig über einen Winkelbereich von
etwa 4° mit der Zn-Kante in der Mitte gedreht. Das einfallende Röntgen-
bündel war so abgeblendet, daß von beiden Flächen ein gleich großer Teil
getroffen wurde. Immer wurden je zwei oder mehr Aufnahmen, die eine
von der matten Fläche, die andere von der glänzenden, genau gleich exponiert und *zusammen entwickelt*. Es wurden ungefähr 10 Paar Aufnahmen
in erster Ordnung und ebensoviele in dritter Ordnung gemacht.

Schon eine erste Betrachtung dieser Kurven zeigt, daß an der kurzwelligen Seite der Zink-*K*-Kante in erster Ordnung die matte Fläche
relativ schwächer reflektiert als die glänzende Fläche, während es in dritter

Tabelle 7. Verhältnis des Reflexionsvermögens *R* kurzw./*R* langw. in dritter Ordnung.

	Aus $L\beta_1$ und $L\beta_4$		Aus $L\beta_3$ und $L\beta_4$		Aus $L\beta_2$ und $L\beta_4$	
	matt	glänzend	matt	glänzend	matt	glänzend
	0,33	0,16	0,40	0,28	0,40	0,25
	30	15	45	26	35	24
	31	18	40	34	27	24
	32	16	56	30	25	18
	35	16	54	31	37	28
Im Mittel matt/glänzend	2,0		!,58		1,40	

Ordnung gerade umgekehrt liegt. Hieraus ist zu schließen, daß die matte Fläche mit Seite A, die glänzende Fläche mit Seite B der Fig. 1 zu identifizieren ist. (...)

In der Tabelle 7 steht das Verhältnis R kurzw./R langw., aus fünf verschiedenen Plattenpaaren bestimmt, einmal unter Benutzung der Wolfram Linien $L\beta_1$ und $L\beta_4$, einmal mit $L\beta_3$ und $L\beta_4$ und einmal mit $L\beta_2$ und $L\beta_4$. [for wavelengths see Tab. 9. Ed.] Obendrein sind in der unteren Zeile die Verhältnisse des Mittelwertes von R kurzw./R langw. für die matte zu dem für die glänzende Fläche angegeben. Die Differenz zwischen der matten und der glänzenden Fläche (d.h. der Flächen A und B der Fig. 1) scheint ziemlich stark abzunehmen, wenn man an der kurzwelligen Seite der Zn-Kante kürzere Wellenlängen benutzt. Wir kommen auf diesen Sachverhalt in § 4 zurück.

§ 4. *Nähere theoretische Diskussion der Ergebnisse*

Zum Schluß wollen wir etwas näher auf die Zahlen der Tabellen 4, 5, und 7 eingehen. Obwohl die Anzahl von uns untersuchter Kristallindividuen (im Total 4) zu klein ist, um zu versuchen, durch eine Art Mittelwertbildung Resultate zu gewinnen, die von dem besonderen Zustand der (111)-Begrenzungsebenen unabhängig ist, glauben wir doch schließen zu können:

1. daß der Unterschied im Reflexionsvermögen der beiden (111)-Flächen im Mittel etwas größer ist als nach der einfachen Theorie des § 1 zu erwarten war;

2. daß im Mittel dieser Effekt in der dritten Ordnung etwas stärker ausgesprochen zu sein scheint als in der ersten Ordnung.

Was das Letzte anbelangt, so würde man nach den theoretischen Betrachtungen des § 1 eher das Umgekehrte erwartet haben. Ist doch die Amplitude der von den Zinkatomen oder von den Schwefelatomen allein gestreuten Wellen mit dem Atomfaktor des bezüglichen Elementes proportional. Der Atomfaktor des Schwefels nimmt mit größeren Streuwinkeln schneller ab als derjenige des Zinks, so daß der Einfluß des Schwefels gegenüber demjenigen des Zinks immer mehr zurücktritt. Da eben das Zusammenwirken beider Atomsorten den behandelten Effekt ergab, würde man erwarten, daß dieser—gerade umgekehrt als tatsächlich der Fall ist—in erster Ordnung am deutlichsten zutage treten würde.

Es kommt uns vor, daß beide hier genannten Eigentümlichkeiten damit zusammenhängen, daß die in § 1 gegebene theoretische Diskussion des fraglichen Effektes noch einer Erweiterung bedarf. Wir haben dort angenommen, daß die Phasenverschiebung der Streuwelle in allen Richtungen dieselbe ist. Dem ist nicht mehr so, wenn wir z.B. annehmen, daß jede Elektronenschale mit ihrem eigenen Atomfaktor und ihrer eigenen Phasenverschiebung streut. Für unseren Zweck genügt es, allein die K-Elektronen des Zinks mit ihren eigenen α_K und β_K separat zu nehmen und alle übrigen Elektronen dieses Atoms zusammenzufassen, während eine solche Trennung beim Schwefel unnötig ist. Aus der unten folgenden Rechnung ergibt sich, daß dadurch besonders für Linien in der unmittelbaren Nähe der Zink-K-Kante wie die Linie Au$L\alpha_1$ der Effekt größer ausfällt, als aus der theoretischen Auffassung des § 1 folgen würde. Man sieht nun auch leicht ein, daß die zweite obengenannte Eigentümlichkeit, nämlich daß der gesuchte Effekt in der dritten Ordnung etwas stärker auftritt als in der ersten Ordnung, sich in derselben Weise erklären läßt. Es nimmt doch der Atomfaktor bei größerem Streuwinkel ziemlich stark ab, der Beitrag der K-Elektronen zu dem Atomfaktor ist aber wegen der geringen räumlichen Ausbreitung der K-Schale viel weniger vom Streuwinkel abhängig. In dritter Ordnung haben dadurch beim Zink die K-Elektronen auf das totale Streuvermögen des Atoms einen relativ viel größeren Einfluß. Da gerade sie für den von uns gesuchten Effekt verantwortlich sind, darf es also nicht wundern, wenn der Effekt in dritter Ordnung stärker ausgesprochen ist als in erster Ordnung.

Wir werden deshalb jetzt die Rechnung von § 1 noch einmal durchführen unter der Annahme, daß die K-Elektronen des Zinks separat zu behandeln sind. Die Ergebnisse sind dann etwas verschieden von denen des § 1 und stimmen, wie wir sehen werden, besser mit den experimentellen Zahlen.

Den Ausgangspunkt der Betrachtungen von § 1 bildete die Formel (3):

$$4\pi P = -2(\alpha + i\beta)E.$$

Anstatt der dort angegebenen Werte von α und β, die sich auf den Ablenkungswinkel Null beziehen, haben wir jetzt die analogen Größen für die endlichen Ablenkungswinkel der Kristallreflexionen erster und dritter Ordnung zu berechnen, welche a und b genannt seien, so daß jetzt maßgebend ist eine 'Polarisation' P, gegeben durch:

$$4\pi P = -2(a + ib)E,$$

wo a und b im allgemeinen Funktionen des Ablenkungswinkels sind. Um Anschluß an die übliche Bezeichnungsweise zu bekommen, werden wir nicht mit a und b rechnen, sondern mit dem sogenannten Atomfaktor F, der angibt, wie sich $a + ib$ verhält zu dem Betrag, den ein einzelnes freies Elektron pro Atom liefern würde. Der Atomfaktor würde bei Vernach-

363

lässigung der Eigenfrequenzen und der Wegunterschiede im Atom einfach die Zahl der Elektronen sein. In unserem Falle ist er jedoch eine komplexe Zahl $F' + iF''$, die wir jetzt berechnen werden.

Für Zink haben wir dabei, wie oben angeführt wurde, die K-Elektronen separat zu betrachten, während es genügt, alle übrigen Elektronen zusammenzufassen. Wir schreiben dementsprechend für Zink:

$$F' = F_K' + F_R' \text{ und } F'' = F_K'' + F_R'',$$

wo der Buchstabe K sich auf die K-Elektronen und der Buchstabe R sich auf die übrigen Elektronen bezieht. Fur die Berechnung der F_K' wurde die folgende Formel benutzt:

$$F_K' = n_K\{1 + (\ln |x^2 - 1|)/x^2\}, \qquad (4)[1]$$

wo n_K die Anzahl der K-Elektronen im Atom bedeutet, während $x = \lambda_K/\lambda$ (λ_K = Wellenlänge der Zink-K-Kante, λ ist die bei der Reflexion benutzte Wellenlänge). Für n_K wurde der Wert 1,3 angenommen, da man mit diesem den richtigen Wert für den Absorptionskoeffizienten bekommt[2]. Es wurde also angenommen, daß F_K' sowohl in dritter als in erster Ordnung den in Formel (4) gegebenen Wert hat. Weiter[1] ist:

$$F_K''/F_K' = \beta_K/\alpha_K = \pi/(x^2 + \ln |x^2 - 1|), \qquad (5)$$

wo x dieselbe Bedeutung wie oben hat. Der arc tg des Ausdrucks (5) ergibt die Phasenverschiebung der K-Streuwelle gegenüber der Primärwelle. Diese Funktion ist graphisch dargestellt in Fig. 11.

Bei der Berechnung von F_R' wurde in folgender Weise vorgegangen: Von Bragg und West[3] sind die Atomfaktoren für zehn Elemente von Sauerstoff bis Eisen berechnet. Wir haben für Zn ihre Werte extrapoliert und finden für die erste Ordnung der (111)-Fläche der Zinkblende (($\sin \theta$)/λ = = 0,16) bzw. dritte Ordnung (($\sin \theta$)/λ = 0,485) die Werte 22 bzw. 13,3. Weder bei der Berechnung der Atomfaktoren von Bragg und West noch bei der experimentellen Prüfung, wo ziemlich harte Strahlung (Rh$K\alpha$) benutzt wurde, hat man sich beschäftigt mit den besonderen Umständen, welche in der Nähe einer Absorptionskante des abbeugenden Elementes auftreten. Wir können deshalb annehmen, daß obenstehende Zahlen auch für Linien in der Nähe der K-Kante des Zinks gelten, insoweit es nicht die K-Elektronen betrifft. Für die K-Elektronen wollen wir 1,3 in Abzug

---

[1] J. A. Prins, *Zeitschr. f. Phys.* **47** (1928) 479.

[2] Vgl. J. A. Prins, *l.c.*; S. J. M. Allen, *Phys. Rev.* **28** (1926) 907; R. A. Houstoun, *Phil. Mag.* **2** (1926) 512; R. de L. Kronig, *Journ. Opt. Soc. Amer.* **12** (1926) 547; F. K. Richtmyer, *Phil. Mag.* **4** (1927) 1296.

[3] W. L. Bragg und J. West, *Zeitschr. f. Krist.* **69** (1929) 118.

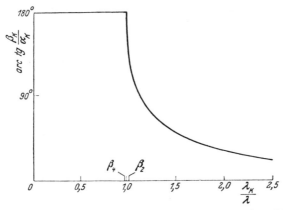

Fig. 11. Phasenverschiebung der *K*-Streuwelle an beiden Seiten der *K*-Kante. Die zwei angegebenen Linien (WLβ_4 und β_2) grenzen das im vorhergehenden untersuchte Spektralgebiet ab.

bringen und nehmen deshalb $F_R' = 20,7$ in erster Ordnung und $F_R' = 12,0$ in dritter Ordnung.

Was F_R'' für Zink anbelangt, läßt diese sich aus dem Absorptionskoeffizienten für Ablenkungswinkel Null zu 0.6 berechnen. Es wurde angenommen, daß diese Größe im selben Maße wie F_R' vom Abbeugungswinkel abhängt. Für die erste Ordnung finden wir also $F_R'' = 20,7 \cdot 0,6/28 = 0,4$, für die dritte Ordnung $F_R'' = 12,0 \cdot 0,6/28 = 0,3$. Übrigens haben diese kleinen Zahlen auf das Endresultat einen geringen Einfluß. Wir kommen in dieser Weise zu Tabelle 8.

Für Schwefel haben wir aus der oben zitierten Tabelle von Bragg und West die Werte $|F| = 12$ in erster Ordnung und $|F| = 6$ in dritter Ordnung interpoliert. Für arc tg (F''/F') = arc tg (β/α) berechnet sich, wie in § 1 ausgeführt wurde, 1°20'.

Tabelle 8. *F*-Werte für Zink.

Linie	F_K'	F_K''	arctg $\dfrac{F_K''}{F_K'}$	1. Ordnung			3. Ordnung		
				F'	F''	arctg $\dfrac{F''}{F'}$	F'	F''	arctg $\dfrac{F''}{F'}$
W-$L\beta_4$	1298,8	$-3,5$	0	180°	17,2	0,4	1°20'	8,5	0,3	2°
Au-$L\alpha_2$	1285,02	$-5,3$	0	180°	15,4	0,4	1°30'	6,7	0,3	3°30'
W-$L\beta_1$	1279,2	$-6,1$	4,1	146°	14,6	4,5	17°20'	5,9	4,4	36°40'
Au-$L\alpha_1$	1273,77	$-4,3$	4,1	136°	16,4	4,5	15°20'	7,7	4,4	29°40'
W-$L\beta_3$	1259,9	$-3,0$	4,0	127°	17,7	4,4	14° 0'	9,0	4,3	25°30'
W-$L\beta_2$	1242,0	$-2,1$	3,8	118°	18,6	4,2	12°40'	9,9	4,1	22°30'

365

Wir haben nun noch den Strukturfaktor für Reflexionen in erster und dritter Ordnung an der Oktaederfläche der Zinkblende zu berechnen. Wir nennen den Absolutwert $|F|$ für Zink F_{Zn}, für Schwefel F_S und den Strukturfaktor des ZnS für Reflexionen an der (111)-Fläche F_{ZnS}. Wir haben jetzt die Größen F_{Zn} und F_S mit Berücksichtigung der gegenseitigen Phasendifferenz zusammenzusetzen. Diese Phasendifferenz setzt sich zusammen aus der Differenz φ, der eben berechneten arc tg F''/F' für Zn und S und der geometrischen Phasendifferenz, die in erster und dritter Ordnung (siehe § 1) $\pm 90°$ beträgt. Deshalb gilt:

$$F_{ZnS}^2 = F_{Zn}^2 + F_S^2 \pm 2F_{Zn}F_S \sin \varphi. \tag{6}$$

In der ersten Ordnung gilt das Pluszeichen für die Reflexion B der Fig. 1 und das Minuszeichen für die Reflexion A. In dritter Ordnung liegt die Sache gerade umgekehrt.

Wir wollen den in der Tabelle 9 enthaltenen Zahlen keinen großen Wert beilegen. Wenn z.B. die Lage der Zn-K-Kante relativ zu den Linien Au-$L\alpha_2$ und W-$L\beta_1$ ein wenig anders angenommen wird, würden sich besonders die Werte für diese ganz nahe an der Kante liegenden Linien beträchtlich ändern. Wir meinen aber, daß die Tabelle von verschiedenen experimentell gefundenen Eigentümlichkeiten in ausgezeichneter Weise Rechenschaft gibt. Erstens bekommen wir in Übereinstimmung mit dem Experiment einen größeren Unterschied im Reflexionsvermögen der beiden Oktaederflächen als nach der einfachen Theorie des § 1. Zweitens werden wir auch der Tatsache gerecht, daß dieser Unterschied in dritter Ordnung größer ist als in erster Ordnung.

Eine dritte Eigentümlichkeit, die wir noch nicht erwähnt haben, geht aus der unteren Zeile der Tabelle 7 hervor: es ist die Tatsache, daß der Unterschied zwischen beiden Oktaederflächen so rasch abnimmt, wenn man Linien etwas weiter zu der harten Seite der Zn-Kante zum Vergleich benutzt. Nach den theoretischen Überlegungen des § 1 würde dieser Unterschied nur ganz allmählich kleiner werden müssen. Falls wir aber die K-Elektronen des Zinks, so wie wir es bei der Berechnung der Tabelle 9 gemacht haben, mit ihren eigenen α und β separat nehmen, wird man auch dieser Eigentümlichkeit gerecht, wie aus einem Vergleich von Tabelle 9 mit 7 hervorgeht.

Der ziemlich guten Übereinstimmung zwischen den Zahlen der letzten Spalte der Tabelle 9 und denjenigen der unteren Zeile der Tabelle 7 wollen wir keinen allzugroßen Wert beilegen. Denn wir hätten eher erwartet, daß die *Quadrate* der in der letzten Zeile der Tabelle 9 stehenden Zahlen mit den beobachteten Intensitätsverhältnissen stimmen würden. Vielleicht müssen wir hieraus schließen, daß auch die Rechnung dieses Paragraphen

366

Tabelle 9. Strukturfaktor der Oktaederflächen der ZnS.

Linie		F_{Zn}	F_S	φ	$F_{ZnS}(A)$	$F_{ZnS}(B)$
			1. Ordnung:			$\dfrac{F_{ZnS}(B)}{F_{ZnS}(A)}$
Zn-Kante	1281,0					
W-$L\beta_4$	1298,8	17,2	12	0	21,0	1
Au-$L\alpha_2$	1285,02	15,2	12	0	19,4	1
W-$L\beta_1$	1279,2	15,1	12	16° 0′	16,5	21,7	1,31
Au-$L\alpha_1$	1273,77	16,7	12	14° 0′	17,9	22,9	1,28
W-$L\beta_3$	1259,9	18,2	12	12°40′	19,5	23,9	1,23
W-$L\beta_2$	1242,0	19,0	12	11°20′	20,4	24,4	1,20
			3. Ordnung:			$\dfrac{F_{ZnS}(A)}{F_{ZnS}(B)}$
W-$L\beta_4$	1298,8	8,5	6	0	10,4	1
Au-$L\alpha_2$	1285,02	6,7	6	1°	9,0	1
W-$L\beta_1$	1279,2	7,1	6	35°20′	11,7	6,1	1,92
Au-$L\alpha_1$	1273,77	8,6	6	28°20′	12,6	7,9	1,60
W-$L\beta_3$	1259,9	9,9	6	24°10′	13,5	9,3	1,45
W-$L\beta_2$	1242,0	10,8	6	21°10′	14,0	10,3	1,36

nicht ganz der Wirklichkeit entspricht. Es wäre z.B. durchaus möglich, daß der wirkliche Sachverhalt zwischen den beiden in § 1 und § 4 gegebenen Auffassungen liegt.

Zusammenfassend können wir sagen, daß alle hier besprochenen Eigentümlichkeiten darauf hinweisen, daß nicht nur die Amplitude, sondern auch die Phase der von einem Atom gestreuten Röntgenwelle vom Ablenkungswinkel abhängig ist. Die bei der Berechnung der Tabelle 9 benutzte Methode bringt diese Abhängigkeit jedenfalls qualitativ richtig zum Ausdruck.

Groningen, Natuurkundig Laboratorium der Rijks-Universiteit

367

Index of Names

(Numbers in ordinary print refer to pages, fat numbers to papers—the paper-number is found in the head-line of each left page after the number of the chapter).

Index of Subjects

(Numbers in ordinary print refer to pages, fat numbers to papers—the page-number is found in the head-line of each left page after the number of the chapter).

Absent reflections, 42
absolute intensities
  calculation
    in the dynamical theory, **53**
    in the kinematical theory, **46**, 274
  measurement, 272
absorption coefficient, 63, 277
  see also extinction coefficient
absorption factor, 196
alkalihalides, *see* structure determination
anomalous scattering
  and Friedel's law, 97, 102, **82, 83**
  and structure determination, **81**
  experimental, **75, 79, 80, 83**
  theoretical, **76, 77, 78, 83**
  see also dispersion curve
atomic scattering factor, 8, 9, 63, 75, 78, 214
  calculation of – – –, 186, 281, **62, 63, 64, 65, 66, 67**
  of Li and F in LiF, **52**
  of Na and Cl in NaCl, 279, **61, 62**
  see also anomalous scattering
avenues, **2**, 28, **4, 5**

Barkla's law, 188
boundary conditions, 230, 261
bragg reflection law, 40
  deviation from – – –
    in the dynamical theory, 207, 234, 236, 238
    in the kinematical theory, 171
    in reciprocal lattice, **27**

Cell dimensions
  absolute – –, 6, 7, 70
centre of inversion
  and X-ray intensities, *see* Friedel's law
characteristic spectrum, *see* spectrum
compton-scattering, 300
corpuscular character of X-rays, *see* X-rays
crystal imperfection, 106, 311, 318, 321
  and diffraction intensity, 106, 212, 286, **70, 71, 72, 73, 74a**
  and divergence of reflected beam, 106, 212, 214, **57**
crystal structure determination, *see* structure determination

Debije-factor, *see* temperature factor
dense net-planes and reflection intensity, 35, **37**
  see also Lorentz-factor
deviations from Bragg's law, *see* Bragg's reflection law
diamond
  analysis of powder intensities, 195
  Laue diagram, 12, 19
  reflection intensity, 239
    of (222) reflection, **68**
  temperature factor, *see* temperature factor
dielectric constant, 247, 256
diffracted rays
  origin of – –, *see* X-rays
diffraction intensities, *see* intensity
dispersion curve
  in region of resonance, 330, 333
dispersion surface, 224, 259
  Laue case, 230, 321
  Bragg case, 230, 232
  equation, 259
distribution of electrons
  in Na- and Cl-ions, **62**
see also atomic scattering factor
dynamical theory
  Darwin's – –, **53**, 219, 244
  Ewald's – –, **54, 55, 56**, 244, 252
    basic equation, 252
  Laue's – –, **59**
    basic equation, 251
  Lohr's – –, 247
  Schlapp's – –, **58**

Electron distribution in atom
  see distribution of electrons
'Ersatz' oscillators, 327, **77**, 336
'Excess' scattering, 179, 183
see also atomic scattering factor
extinction, 277, 284, 295, **70, 71, 72, 73**, 320
  coefficient, 286, 305
    measurement, 287, 319
  primary, 310, 315
  secondary, 310, 314

Scattering
    by an atom, *see* atomic scattering factor
    by bound electron, 177
    by free electron, 178, 189
    by valency electrons, **68, 69**
    by a crystal, *see* intensity formulae
schwarzschild's law, 356
self-consistent field, **66**
shape of Laue spots, *see* Laue pattern
sodium chloride, *see* rock-salt
space-lattice, 7, 8
spectrometer, 56, 266
see also intensity measurement
spectrum
    characteristic **15**
    limit of continuous –, **13, 14**
sphere of reflection, **27, 39**
spinel, *see* structure determination
structure, *see* crystal structure
    amplitude, *see* structure factor
    determination of
        alkali halides, 16
        Heusler alloy, **78**
        iron-pyrite, **17, 18**
        magnetite and spinel, **19**
    factor, **32, 33, 34, 35**, 176, 210, 238
    of FeS$_2$ 78, 84
sweep-curve, 106, 289, 318

Temperature factor
    classical derivation for independently
        vibrating atoms, **40, 41, 42**, 176, 210
    experimental determination, **43**, 276
    of diamond, 12, 19, 159, 198
    quantummechanical derivation for elastic
        heat-waves, **44, 45**
thermal motion and crystal diffraction, 12
see further temperature factor
thomson-factor, see polarization factor
total reflection, 209, 219, 233, 237, 238, 244

Wave-length
    order of magnitude, 6, 7
    absolute determination, 70
wave character of X-rays, *see* X-rays

X-rays
    characteristic, **15**
    corpuscular character, 12, 25, 29, 58
    origin of diffracted –, 13, 21, 57
    wave character, 5, 7, 12, 29, 30

Zinc-blende
    Laue pattern, *see* Laue pattern
    sense of polarity of [111], **82, 83**